D1256199

CRYSTALLIZATION

Theory and Practice

ANDREW VAN HOOK

Professor of Chemistry
College of the Holy Cross
Worcester, Mass.

New York
REINHOLD PUBLISHING CORPORATION
Chapman & Hall, Ltd., London

Library of Congress Catalog Card Number 61-17261

Printed in the United States of America

GENERAL INTRODUCTION

American Chemical Society's Series of Chemical Monographs

By arrangement with the Interallied Conference of Pure and Applied Chemistry, which met in London and Brussels in July, 1919, the American Chemical Society was to undertake the production and publication of Scientific and Technologic Monographs on Chemical subjects. At the same time it was agreed that the National Research Council, in cooperation with the American Chemical Society and the American Physical Society, should undertake the production and publication of Critical Tables of Chemical and Physical Constants. The American Chemical Society and the National Research Council mutually agreed to care for these two fields of chemical progress. The American Chemical Society named as Trustees, to make the necessary arrangements of the publication of the Monographs, Charles L. Parsons, secretary of the Society, Washington, D. C.; the late John E. Teeple, then treasurer of the Society, New York; and the late Professor Gellert Alleman of Swarthmore College. The Trustees arranged for the publication of the ACS Series of (a) Scientific and (b) Technological Monographs by the Chemical Catalog Company, Inc. (Reinhold Publishing Corporation, successor) of New York.

The Council of the American Chemical Society, acting through its Committee on National Policy, appointed editors (the present list of whom appears at the close of this sketch) to select authors of competent authority in their respective fields and to consider critically the manuscripts submitted.

The first Monograph of the Series appeared in 1921. After twenty-three years of experience certain modifications of general policy were indicated. In the beginning there still remained from the preceding five decades a distinct though arbitrary differentiation between so-called "pure science" publications and technologic or applied science literature. By 1944 this differentiation was fast becoming nebulous. Research in private enterprise had grown apace and not a little of it was pursued on the frontiers of knowledge. Furthermore, most workers in the sciences were coming to see the artificiality of the separation. The methods of both groups of workers are the same. They employ the same instrumentalities, and frankly recognize that their objectives are common, namely, the search for new knowledge for the service of man. The officers of the Society therefore combined the two editorial Boards in a single Board of twelve representative members.

Also in the beginning of the Series, it seemed expedient to construe rather broadly the definition of a Monograph. Needs of workers had to be recognized. Consequently among the first hundred Monographs appeared works in the form of treatises covering in some instances rather broad areas. Because such necessary works do not now want for publishers, it is considered advisable to hew more strictly to the line of the Monograph character, which means more complete and critical treatment of relatively restricted areas, and, where a broader field needs coverage, to subdivide it into logical subareas. The prodigious expansion of new knowledge makes such a change desirable.

These Monographs are intended to serve two principal purposes: first, to make available to chemists a thorough treatment of a selected area in form usable by persons working in more or less unrelated fields to the end that they may correlate their own work with a larger area of physical science discipline; second, to stimulate further research in the specific field treated. To implement this purpose the authors of Monographs are expected to give extended references to the literature. Where the literature is of such volume that a complete bibliography is impracticable, the authors are expected to append a list of references critically selected on the basis of their relative importance and significance.

ACKNOWLEDGMENTS

The following figures and quotations have been taken from current literature and other sources. The author wishes to thank the separate authors, publishers and sources for permission to reproduce them.

Acta Crystallographica, published by the International Union of Crystallography: Quotation p. 277.

Analytical Chemistry, published by the American Chemical Society; Figures 4-4 and 6-12.

Canadian Journal of Chemistry, published by the National Research Council; Figures 3-20 and 4-20.

Chemical Reviews, published by Williams and Wilkins Co.: Figures 6-41 and 6-42.

Industrial and Engineering Chemistry, published by the American Chemical Society: Quotation p. 20, Figures 2-13, 4-11, 6-11, 6-19, 6-20, 6-21, 6-22, and Tables 6-3 and 6-5.

Journal of Agricultural and Food Chemistry, published by the American Chemical Society: Figures 6-43 and 6-44.

Journal of the American Chemical Society, published by the American Chemical Society: Figures 6-33 and 6-34.

Journal of Chemical Physics, published by the American Institute of Physics: Figures 3-18, 3-19, 3-21 and 4-6.

Journal of the Franklin Institute, published by the Franklin Institute: Figures 6-30 and 6-31.

Journal of Physical Chemistry, published by the American Chemical Society: Figure 4-17.

National Bureau of Standards Journal of Research, published by the U. S. National Bureau of Standards: Figure 4-5 and Table 4-6.

Nature, published by Macmillan and Co., Ltd: Figure 6-2.

Philosophical Magazine, published by Taylor and Francis, Ltd.: Figure 3-15.

Proceedings of the Royal Society, published by the Royal Society: Figure 1-17.

Quarterly Reviews (London), published by the Chemical Society: Quotation p. 103.

Review of Scientific Instruments, published by the American Institute of Physics: Figure 5-7.

Transactions of the American Geophysical Union, published by the American Geophysical Union: Figure 1-4.

Transactions of the Faraday Society, published by the Faraday Society: Figures 3-24, 3-25, 5-12, 6-17, and Quotation p. 274.

Zeitschrift für Elektochemie, published by Verlag Chemie GmbH.: Figure 3-11 and Table 6-10.

American Society for Metals, Symposium on Physical Metallurgy, 1950: Table 3-3.

Bell Telephone Laboratories: Figures 5-8, 6-35 and 6-40.

Boas, W., "Physics of Metals and Alloys," 1947, published by John Wiley & Sons, Inc.: Figure 2-8.

Buflovak Equipment Division, Blaw-Knox Co.: Figure 5-23.

Cambridge Instrument Co., Ltd.: Figures 1-12 and 1-13.

Corning Glass Works: Table 6-11.

Dekeyser, W., and Amelinckx, S., "Les Dislocations et les Croissance des Cristaux," 1955, published by Masson & Cie., Paris: Figure 3-16.

Doremus, R. H., Roberts, B. W., and Turnbull, D., "Growth and Perfection of Crystals," 1958, published by John Wiley & Sons, Inc.: Tables 4-7 and 6-12.

Dorr Co.: Figures 5-17 and 5-18.

General Electric Research Laboratory: Figures 6-37, 6-38, 6-39 and 6-45.

Harshaw Chemical Co.: Figures 6-23, 6-24, 6-25, 6-32 and 6-36.

Honolulu Iron Works Co.: Figure 5-18.

International Salt Co.: Figure 6-15.

Linde Air Products Co.: Figures 6-27, 6-28 and 6-29.

Matz, G., "Die Kristallisation in der Verfahrensrechnik," 1954, published by Springer-Verlag: Table 4-8.

National Aeronautics and Space Administration: Figure 1-13.

Nippon Electric Company Limited: Tables 4-14 and 4-15.

Perry, J. H., "Chemical Engineers' Handbook," 1941, published by McGraw-Hill Book Co.: Quotations pp. 156 and 217, and Table 6-7.

Powers, H. E. C., Tate & Lyle, Ltd.: Figures 5-3 and 6-1.

Struthers-Wells Co.: Figures 5-24, 5-25, 5-26 and 5-27.

Weissberger, A., "Technique of Organic Chemistry," 1952, published by Interscience Publishers, Inc.: Figures 5-1, 5-4 and 5-5.

PREFACE

The beauty of crystals has always fascinated man. While their perfection and form are completely described and catalogued by means of the established laws of classical and X-ray crystallography, the same cannot be said about their generation and growth. Although considerable experimental observation and empirical explanation accumulated during the last part of the nineteenth century and beginning of the twentieth, activity in this field then waned. It was soon revived, however, by interest in the production of large monocrystals. This was especially evident at the "Discussions on Crystal Growth" held by the Faraday Society in 1949 at Bristol. The current state of both theoretical and practical interests is indicated by the symposia, books, and reviews given in the Appendix.

It was originally intended to review the entire subject of crystal growth in considerable detail in the present work. However, the appearance of Buckley's book, as well as that of Matz, rendered this unnecessary, so that the original plan was drastically revised to emphasize recent theories (Chapter 3) and to describe principal crystallization processes (Chapter 5) and industries (Chapter 6). It is believed that the data presented in Chapter 4 represent the variety and form that are available in the scientific literature and it is hoped that the references cited in this chapter, as well as in the others, will serve as a good lead for anyone desiring further information and details. It will be obvious that Chapter 1 was written by a chemist for chemists. Chapter 2 indicates only those basic ideas considered to be important for an effective appreciation of the subsequent chapters.

Many friends have helped me directly or indirectly in the writing of this book. Dr. Stookey has contributed the section on nucleation in glass. Dr. H. Klug and my son W. Alexander have read the manuscript in its entirety, while Messrs. Dunning, Honigmann, Powers, Turnbull, J. VanHook, and Walker have read and corrected separate parts. The Sugar Research Foundation Inc. has supported many of the author's investigations on sugar crystallization which were the original stimulant for considering a more general work.

My daughters, Suzanne and Jane, and others have helped with the onerous job of typing from a longhand manuscript. Many figures and some quotations were copied from current literature and are so indicated. However, I wish to make here a general acknowledgment and to express my gratitude to the many friends who have helped me in so many ways in the preparation of this monograph.

Leicester, Mass.
August, 1961

ANDREW VANHOOK

CONTENTS

Chapter 1

HISTORICAL REVIEW

INTRODUCTION

It is only natural to speculate on the birth and growth of crystals while yet admiring the perfection of the final form as found in nature or fashioned otherwise. While this latter aspect of crystals has evolved into the science of crystallography since the early work of Steno (1669), Rome de l'Isle (1772), and Haüy (1801), the development of the kinetic features has by no means been as steady and exact. As P. R. Rowland[52] expressed it in a remark at the Faraday Society Discussion on crystal growth in 1949, "The subject is still in the alchemical stage." Other workers[37, 136] have expressed a similar opinion (but perhaps not as strongly) in pointing out the need for a complete dynamic theory of crystal growth.

In any event, there is a vast accumulation of observations and empirical explanations regarding the generation and growth of crystals under many circumstances. Much of it is unsuited for theoretical use except in qualitative ways and it seem necessary to the author that much more discriminating information will be required for fuller tests of existing theories and those to come.

The alchemists and early chemists and crystallographers recognized many of the well-known features of the crystallization process.[218] Geber (720–813) mentions the purification of many salts by recrystallization, and Caesalpinus (1600) observed that sugar, saltpeter, alum, and the vitriols separated from solution in typical, easily recognized forms. Biringuccio (1540) gave detailed instructions for the leaching of saltpeter and its purification by recrystallization. He also indicated that the purity of the product depends to a great extent upon the purity of the mother liquor from which it is obtained. Somewhat later, Glauber (1604–1670) made frequent reference to the use of crystallization in the separation and purification of "Glauber's salt" (Sal Mirabile).[152] This salt was later observed to supersaturate very readily and much of the early work on this phenomenon was conducted with it.

Robert Boyle recognized, in 1691, that crystal habit may be modified by the rate of deposition from solution, and at about the same time it was discerned that crystals were frequently more regular and characteristic when their growth was slower, the solvent more fluid, and the substance more soluble. The first recorded recognition of the not uncommon possibility of supercooling water was also noted at this time by Fahrenheit.[70, 252] He was able to chill water 6 to 8°F below the normal freezing point, and noted the release of heat when ice formation ensued. This was confirmed by Joseph Black, in 1761, who reaffirmed the earlier implied requirement of a supercooled or supersaturated condition for the initiation of growth of a solid substance.

It was not long afterward that the first systematic description of the crystallization process appeared. This was the very extensive work of Lowitz,[157, 270] in which he investigated and described most of the now well-known features of supersaturated solutions. Although Lowitz dealt primarily with salt solutions, he recognized the similarity between supersaturation of a solute and supercooling of a liquid. He emphasized the common occurrence of these conditions—situations that are even currently overlooked in spite of frequent notice[52, 53, 166] to the contrary. Lowitz pointed out that the ability to form supersaturated solutions varied considerably with different salts and also depended upon the history and treatment in any particular case. For instance, previous heating of the solution ("curing"), or removal of the first crystals formed, often increased the subsequent degree of supercooling or supersaturation that could be attained. From his experiments on the addition of fragments of different crystals to particular salt solutions, he recognized a specificity of nucleating agents over and above the powerful initiating influence of dust particles. He found that only $NaNO_3$ or $Na_2SO_4 \cdot 10H_2O$ deposited, respectively, from a mixed supersaturated solution upon seeding with the separate salts. The identity of crystallizing salt and nucleating agent was not required in all cases.

This observation, added to those of Rome de l'Isle (1772), Le Blanc (1784), Vauquelin (1797) and others, prepared the way for the generalizations of Mitscherlich[34, 173] in 1819 regarding isomorphism and epitaxy. Lowitz also regarded glasses, strong syrups, and the vitreous products of fused salts as matter in the supercooled or supersaturated condition. This same worker[267] has also been credited with the discovery of the use of carbon for the purification of sugar, saltpeter and other solutions, thereby improving their crystallizing behavior.

Gay-Lussac[90] confirmed and extended many of Lowitz's observations in his studies of the separation of a wide variety of salts (Na_2SO_4, Na_3PO_4, Na_2CO_3, alums, $NaNO_3$, $Ba(OH)_2$, $H_2C_2O_4$, K_2SO_4, NH_4Cl, etc.) and gases from water solutions. He also extended the supercooling of water in bulk to −10 to −12°C. At the same time Schweigger[249] made the significant observations that previous filtration of supersaturated solutions increased the resistance to subsequent crystallization, that a magnetic field had no effect on the extent of supercooling, and, perhaps most significant of all, that a seed or nucleus must be of a certain size in order to initiate crystallization. This first concept of a critical-size nucleus was studied in much detail later on by Wilhelm Ostwald,[188] and it occupies a prominent role in most of the theories of crystal growth.

One of the first of many early papers on the Na_2SO_4–H_2O system was reported by Zis in 1815. He[281] recognized that sodium sulfate aqueous solutions could be supersaturated simultaneously with respect to both the anhydrous and the hydrate salts. This pioneer work was followed by the very intensive investigations of Löwel,[156] and still later by the papers of Goskgnski (1851), Selmi (1851), Dess, and other workers[188] on the same system as well as those of $MgSO_4$, Na_2CO_3 and the alums. The excellence of Löwel's data is indicated in Figure 1-1 where some of his values[75] are compared with more recent ones.[115] The metastable relationships of the two hydrates are evident and Löwel pointed this out by the fact that a solution saturated at 18°C showed a crystal of the heptahydrate rather than the stable decahydrate when cooled to 8 or 9°C. Ostwald credits these observations as basic to the formulation of his Law of Stages. Löwel also appreciated the powerful catalytic effect of the dust of the atmosphere in inducing

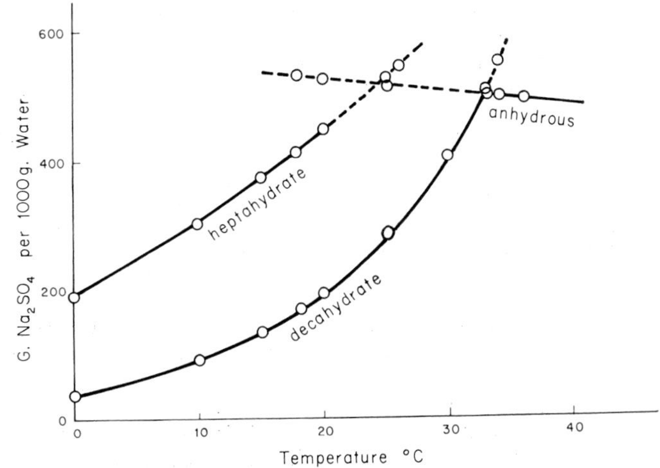

Figure 1-1. Na_2SO_4-H_2O system; illustrating the excellence of Löwel's data.
o and dotted lines—Löwel's values[75]
Full lines—later values[115]

crystallization in many supersaturated solutions, as had Lowitz[157] and also Lieben.[154] These observations were soon confirmed and extended by Violette.[263]

There now ensued a period of very active investigation, stimulated largely by the work of Gernez[91] in Paris. Gernez' early work continued the pattern of qualitative studies of previous investigators, while his later work introduced quantitative measurements into this field. For the first part he repeated much of the previous work on the causes of crystallization of sodium sulfate. Then, from observations on the behavior of over 100 different salts which form supersaturated solutions readily, he compiled a list of 27 groups within which reciprocal crystallization occurs. This original list is given in Table 1-1.

This list of Gernez' stimulated a flood of papers during the last third of the 19th century. Many of these were concerned with the question of what

TABLE 1-1. GERNEZ' LIST OF RECIPROCALLY CRYSTALLIZING SALTS.[91]

1. Acetates of NH_4, Ba, Ca, Co, Mg, Mn, Pb, Na, Sr, Zn, K
2. Nitrates of NH_4, Ag, Ca, Co, Cu, Mn, Sr, U, Zn
3. Nitrites of Pb, K
4. Arsenates of K, Na
5. Benzoates of K, NH_4
6. Borates of NH_4, Na
7. Sodium carbonate
8. Chlorates of Ag, Ba, Na, Sr
9. Chlorides of Sb, Ba, Ca, Cu, Mg, Mn, Fe
10. Nitrates of NH_4, K, Na
11. Sodium chromate and potassium dichromate
12. Formates of Na, Sr
13. Hydrates of Ba, Sr, chloral
14. Thiosulfates of NH_4, Ca, Na
15. Sodium hyposulfate
16. Ammonium molybdate
17. Ammonium oxalate
18. Phosphates of NH_4, Na-NH_4, Na; Na pyrophosphate
19. Potassium phosphate
20. Sodium selenate
21. Sulfates of Co, Cu, Fe, Be, Mg, Ni, Na, Zn; NH_4–Fe, NH_4–Mg, K–Ni, Zn–Mn; $KHSO_4$, NH_4, Th, K, Na, alums of Al, Cr, and Fe
22. Na_2SO_3, NH_4HSO_3
23. K and Na hydrosulfides
24. Sodium sulfoantimonate
25. Tartrates of NH_4, Na, Sb–K, Sb–NH_4, Na–NH_4, Na–K, Na–Tl
26. Citric acid and racemic tartaric acid
27. Mannite, lactose and sucrose*

* The present author has been unable to confirm this particular reciprocity.

salts would start and grow in which solutions, etc. The work of de Boisbaudran,[24] among others, indicated that certain demands of isomorphism of the Mitscherlich type were required for reciprocal nucleation and growth in solution, although many exceptions were noted. Especially disturbing was the fact that sodium formate and sodium valerate, which are almost isomorphous with sodium acetate, do not nucleate and grow in these solutions, or vice versa.

Many polemics started over such confusing observations and while no definite conclusions were reached (nor do we yet know the complete answer to all these questions[193]), it is obvious from many of these early papers that a liberal interpretation of what constitutes isomorphism is necessary (epitaxy, *vide infra*), and that surface energy considerations are most significant in determining the generation and growth of nuclei in supersaturated solutions.

The second phase of Gernez' work dealt with the linear rates of growth of sulfur (which had been observed to supercool readily by Michael Faraday in 1826[71]) and phosphorus from their melts. According to Tammann,[240b] the leading exponent of such measurements, Gernez was the first to make measurements of this kind. Gernez' data for the linear crystallization velocity of yellow phosphorus (m.p. 44. 2°C) are given in Figure 1-2. These results do not indicate the usual tendency of the crystallization velocity to reach a maximum and then decrease; but then neither do more recent and accurate measurements on this same substance.[196] These investigations of Gernez clearly indicated for the first time the significance of a crystallizing potential and some of the kinetic factors involved in the crystallizing

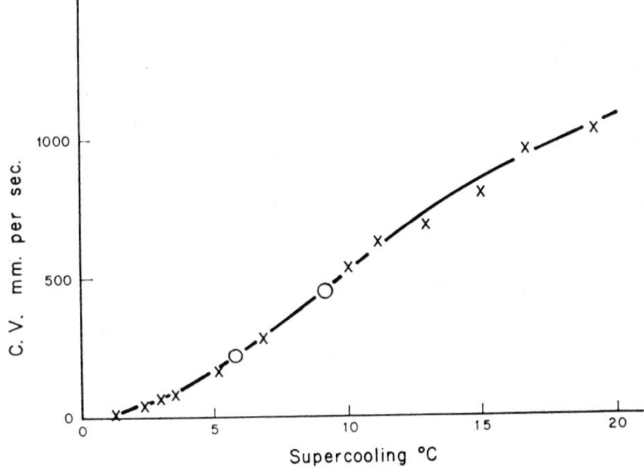

Figure 1-2. Crystallization velocity of phosphorus.[91]

process. Intensive speculations on these aspects of the crystallization of undercooled melts and supersaturated solutions were stimulated further by the work and theories of de Coppet,[48] who contributed and argued in the literature for 35 years.

de Coppet's basic observations were that there appears to be a limit to which supersaturated solutions and supercooled melts remain stable and that the adjustment of such labile systems depends upon the size of the sample being observed. His data suggest that the limits of supersaturation under ordinary conditions of observation do not depend greatly on the initial concentrations (at least for highly soluble substances) but do vary with the time (Table 1-2).

The observations represented in Table 1-2 were made in large tubes. In small tubes the duration of supersaturation is increased considerably in almost inverse proportion to the mass of the solution or melt. Othmer,[189] later, did not find this to be so. de Coppet extended his observations over exceptionally long periods. For instance, his sodium bromide solution took 2½ years to crystallize when in large vials, yet smaller amounts required over 4 years to exhibit crystallization when supercooled to the same extent of 15 degrees or more. Salol was maintained in a highly supercooled condi-

TABLE 1-2

(A) *Supersaturations Sustained by Sodium Sulfate Solutions.*[48]

Na_2SO_4/100 water	—	35	30	25	20
Saturated with respect to the heptahydrate at, °C	19.3	13.3	10	5	0
Crystallization observed at, °C	5 to 5.4°	0 to 1.4°	−4.35	−6.5 to −9.8	−10.4 to −11.5
Supercooling, °C	14	13	14	13	11

(B) *Time Required for $Na_2SO_4 \cdot 7H_2O$ to Crystallize Spontaneously at Different Supercoolings.*[48]

(Initial solution saturated at 19.3°C)

Temp. (°C)	Time (days)	Supercooling (°C)
5–5.9	1	13.8
8–8.9	1	10.8
9–9.9	1.1	9.8
10–10.9	2.1	8.8
11–11.9	7.8	7.8
12–12.9	24.2	6.8

tion for 6 years; and many of the supersaturated solutions prepared in de Coppet's first investigation (1872) were still intact at the time (1907) of his last review and report.*

To de Coppet, the results of his experiments at once suggested a rather simple explanation of the formation of crystal embryos via ordinary collisions. He had no reason to alter this opinion in his last work, even in the face of considerable criticism, principally from the pen of Wilhelm Ostwald. The principles of de Coppet's interpretation were adopted by Tammann,[240] Othmer,[184] Jones and Partington,[130] Kornfeld,[142] Gopal,[96] and others. These principles gradually assumed the form of what is usually referred to as the "Homogeneous Theory of Nucleation."[63] In effect, the theory suggests that crystal embryos are the result of multiple collisions which result in stable nuclei which then continue to grow. The theory considers these centers of growth entirely a matter of chance and thus demands that any supercooled melt or supersaturated solution, no matter how small the degree of supercooling, will adjust to its proper equilibrium condition provided sufficient time elapses for the formation of the first nucleus. It is on this score that many later experimentalists and current theories take exception.

To illustrate the random nature of the nucleation process we may cite a typical example from Tammann (Ref. 240b, p. 240). In 50 crystallizations of piperonal he observed a dispersion of 19.44 about the mean time value. The dispersion about 50 throws of 6 dice was 19.40. This expedient of comparing observation with actual trials of chance operations was introduced by Othmer and Kornfeld after recognizing that agreement with straightforward probability theory was frequently incomplete.[21, 102] Later investigations found the distribution frequency curves to be normal when a sufficient number of observations were made. Figure 1-3 illustrates this. This figure is from the work of Dorsch and Hacker[62] and is a typical example of over 5,000 observations of the spontaneous freezing temperature of supercooled water droplets of various sizes. The form of these curves certainly suggests the fortuitous nature of spontaneous freezing. This, however, does not necessarily signify a homogeneous collisional process, but may equally well indicate fortuitous inoculation with motes which serve

* There seems to be no particular difficulty in preserving supercooled melts and supersaturated solutions for appreciable periods of time.[171] One finds frequent reference to such cases in the literature. The author has several sealed ampules of sodium acetate solutions which were prepared to be saturated at 35°C over 13 years ago and have since been kept at room temperatures without crystallizing. He also has several pure sucrose syrups which have been maintained without crystallizing at a supercooling of 20 to 25°C for over three years. It seems that highly impure solutions are even more reluctant to crystallize.

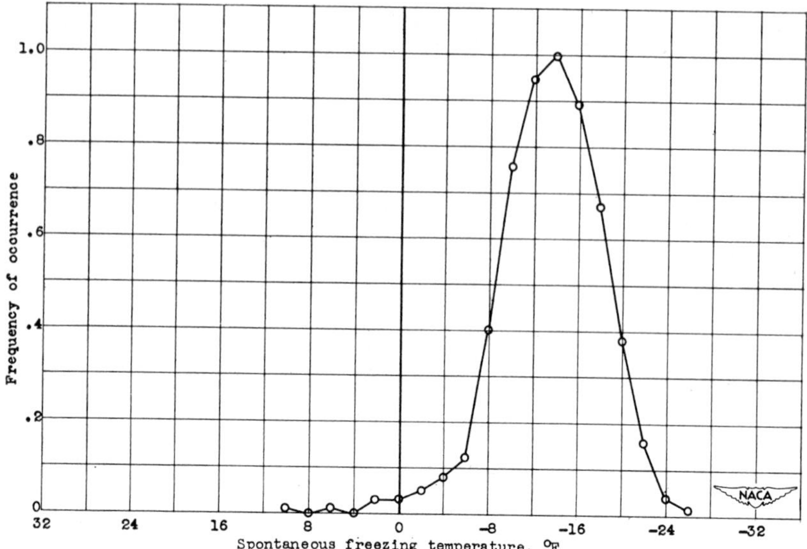

Figure 1-3. Distribution of spontaneous freezing temperatures.[62] Droplet diameter, 59.0 ± 1.5 microns; droplets observed, 692; average spontaneous freezing temperature, −13.3°F; standard deviation, 4.66°F.

as nuclei for the transition to the solid state. The literature is replete with reference to the difficulty, if not the impossibility, of avoiding or eliminating such extraneous nuclei. Their presence in one form or another constitutes the fundamental postulate of the heterogeneous theory of nucleation.

Such observations are quite contrary to the views of de Coppet and his followers but they do not necessarily require that nucleation occurs exclusively by means of foreign agents.[171, 207] For, in that case, one would expect a monotonous reduction in the rate of nucleation as the impurities are isolated by decreasing the size of the sample, but this change is not always observed. This situation was appreciated at an early date and various modifications of the so-called heterogeneous theory were soon developed.

Even de Coppet, in defending his own homogeneous theory, pointed out that the nature of foreign particles and the container walls exerted tremendous influences on the behavior of the crystallizing system. Fuchtbauer[86] emphasized that the colloidal nature of any nucleus (which would include the wall) was dominant in stimulating crystallization. The extreme sensitiveness of this condition would explain the variety of effects observed upon aging, preheating, filtering, etc. Hinshelwood and Hartley[112] substituted a "catalytic activity" to about the same effect; while Richards,

Kirkpatrick, and Hutz[204] postulated a "crystalline adsorbate." Other workers advocating the heterogeneous theory in one form or another include Schaum,[216] Jaffe,[120] Young,[277] Marcelin,[162] Meyer and Pfaff,[171] Tchermak-Seysenegg,[244] Kucharenko,[145] Dorsey,[63] Doucet,[65] and Carpenter.[41]

Thus, throughout the literature on this subject there occurs the implication that true heterogeneous nucleation is an uncertain and indefinite process which is superimposed upon a more fundamental mechanism. There seems to be no question that nucleation in bulk samples generally occurs by an overpowering heterogeneous mechanism, but if these catalytic nucleation centers are eliminated (possibly by isolation of small portions) transformation then proceeds by a homogeneous mechanism.[253c] This latter action, then, is to be considered the more basic mechanism in the adjustment of metastable systems, although by no means in the simple form of de Coppet's theory. Fluctuations replace collisions in the more recent versions of Volmer and Stranski, and their analysis forms the basis of the present-day outlook on matters of crystal growth.

The influence of amount of material on the frequency of nucleation has been observed by many investigators. Tammann, for instance, noted that 6 g of phenol required, on the average, 2810 sec to crystallize, whereas 30 g took only 33 sec under the same conditions. The deviations of single observations were again in accord with probability demands, which was interpreted to signify a homogeneous mechanism resulting from molecular collisions. This particular example is typical of many others. Fuchtbauer[86] reviews older literature on this point, while Turnbull[253a] gives a partial list of more recent work and also adds more extensive data. He found, for instance, that metallic gallium could be supercooled 70°C when in the form of small droplets about 200μ in diameter, whereas only 55°C subcooling was possible in bulk samples. He also mentions that tin and mercury may be supercooled 110 and 46°C, respectively, in small droplets, but only 31 and 14°C when the sample is of appreciable size.

Frulla,[85] in the author's laboratory, has examined the nucleating behavior of droplets of sugar syrup of various sizes, and obtained the same pattern of results. This is illustrated in Table 1-3. Still more elaborate data are to be found in the papers of Dorsch and Hacker,[62] and Heverly.[108] Their curves are approximately cubic parabolas except for the smallest droplets, and this suggests a linear correlation between supercooling and droplet volume.[195] This is empirically in accord with both the homogeneous and heterogeneous theories of nucleation if the maximum degree of subcooling is interpreted as a measure of the rate of nucleation. However, as Turnbull[253a] points out, the ratio of volume change to rate change is hardly compatible with any straightforward probability theory since such a

Table 1-3. Rate of Nucleation of Sucrose Syrups.[85]
(60% supersaturated at 30°C)

Average diam. of droplet	1*	II*	3 mm	2	1	0.1	0.04	0.025
Relative vol. of droplet	—	—	1	0.3	0.03	3×10^{-5}	2×10^{-6}	5×10^{-7}
Relative nucleation rate†	Immediate	1	1	0.8	0.4	0.4	0.6	0.5

* Bulk samples I and II varied in volume from 1 to 5 ml. Type I were prepared without any special care or treatment, while Type II were prepared in sterilized containers and subsequently "cured" to deactivate existing and potential nuclei.

† Mean of at least 50 droplets.

theory would require a thousandfold change in nucleation rate for each tenfold change in diameter of droplet. Nothing like this is observed in the above results, nor in Turnbull's observations, in which a volume change of the order of 10 effected a rate change by a factor of only 10. It seems, then, that the general increase in supercooling observed in smaller samples is a result of the diminished probability of the presence of a foreign nucleating body.

The anomalous behavior of the smallest droplets of Figure 1-4 is significant. The deviations are contrary to what one would expect if electrification[248] had set in. The droplets are not sufficiently small to expect a change according to modern homogeneous theories of nucleation. Hypotheses based upon delayed or transient nucleation may be able to account for this marked effect.[39, 41, 66, 203]

We return now to developments following de Coppet's work. Ostwald objected vehemently to de Coppet's ideas in his great "Lehrbuch" of 1896.[187] He pointed out that the apparent limit of supersaturation evident in de Coppet's own experiments with Glauber's salt and the admitted indefiniteness of these same experiments with samples of different size vitiated the kinetic interpretation which de Coppet had employed. He then presented experiments which indicated that a certain minimum-size fragment was required to induce crystallization in supercooled melts of salol and supersaturated solutions of sodium chlorate, the alums, Rochelle salt, and borax.[188] He found, for instance, that an otherwise stable supersaturated solution of $NaClO_3$ would be caused to crystallize upon the addition of a solute particle only if the size of this grain exceeded 10^{-8} to 10^{-9} g.* These

* Ostwald's critical nucleus would contain 10^8 to 10^{12} molecules and would be several microns in diameter. These values appear to be much too large. More recent estimates[30, 45, 96, 101, 122, 147, 240f] lead to less than 100 molecules per nucleus, or diameters of the order of 100°A, in most cases.

small particles were obtained either by comminution with lactose or other inert carriers, or by spray evaporation of progressively diluted solutions. Ostwald not only regarded this behavior as contrary to de Coppet's hypothesis but from it also developed the concept of a critical-size nucleus. While this same idea is inherent in the earlier works of Lefebvre,[151] Reischauer[202] and Gernez,[91] it finds first clear expression in the writings of Ostwald and has since become an integral part of most theories of crystallization.

In his speculations at this time Ostwald also gave clear expression to several other profound generalizations which have since become intrinsic parts of most current theories of crystallization. These are (a) his concept of supersolubility, (b) his Law of Stages (Stufenregel), (c) his interpretation of Liesegang rings, and, later,[188] (d) the effect of particle size on solubility. Since these subjects virtually form the background for most existing theories of the crystallization process, they will be discussed first in their historical aspects, and later on in more critical form. However, before proceeding, it is significant to point out that in the interim between the commencement of de Coppet's work (1872) and Ostwald's pronouncements (1897), Gibbs' work "On the Equilibrium of Heterogeneous Substances" had appeared in

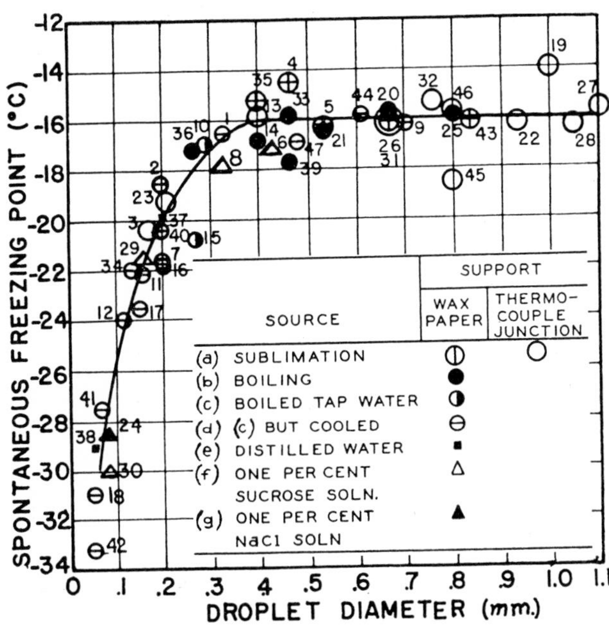

Figure 1-4. Spontaneous freezing point of water droplets as a function of droplet size.[108]

1875–78.[94] The principles and ideas of this masterly work pertaining to the general problem of metastability lay dormant, however, until resurrected by a much later school of theorists.[265]

OSWALD'S CONTRIBUTIONS

Supersolubility

While the concept of a definite supersolubility is contained in the earliest writings on the subject, Ostwald appears to be the first to specify this condition exactly by using the terms "metastable" and "labile."[87] He credits the previous works of Lowitz,[157] Löwel,[156] Schaum,[216] Barus,[11] and even de Coppet,[48] and points out that the principle is inherent in the reports of many other investigators. In effect, a supersaturated solution or supercooled melt will not adjust spontaneously to the equilibrium condition unless the supersaturation or supercooling exceeds certain more or less definite limits. This range of stability is designated as being "metastable." Beyond this limit lies the "labile" region where the metastable condition is relieved automatically by the spontaneous generation of nuclei of the proper crystallizing phase. Within this limit any appropriate "seed" will, of course, cause instantaneous crystallization. The supersolubility curve may be called the solubility curve of particles of critical size, while the solubility curve is that of particles of infinite radius. A schematic representation of these conditions is represented in Figure 1-5.

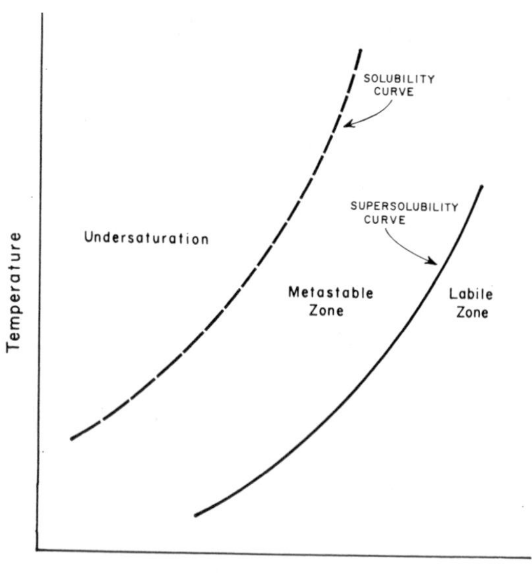

Figure 1-5. Supersolubility curve and regions.

Supersolubility curves and maximum supercooling temperatures have been determined for a great many solutions and melts. While sometimes vague and uncertain, the limits are more often very definite and reproducible so that they may be used for purposes of identification and purity estimation. In the case of binary systems the limits may be traced out as a supersolubility curve entirely analogous and usually parallel to the ordinary solubility curve, but displaced 5 to 20° below on the temperature axis. Although an exact or quantitative interpretation of these curves is not always possible, since they merely represent temperatures at which crystallization becomes appreciable under ordinary operating conditions, they are very useful to the manufacturing chemist, metallurgist, mineralogist, and others.

Miers[172] and Jones, Hartley, *et al.*[103] accepted the supersolubility concept in their works without reservation and in spite of recognized limitations. Miers and Isaac observed a regular decrease in the refractive index of solutions as they were cooled, until a temperature considerably below saturation was secured. At this point a sudden and rapid change occurred with a marked increase in refractive index and visible display of crystals. It was not unusual to observe small "first showers" soon after the temperature fell below the saturation temperature. Such events were considered to be accidental and due to the presence of foreign seeds. In the absence of agitation the first showers were not observed. Miers realized that the rate of cooling and previous history of the sample had an effect on the supersolubility values but even in view of these facts he believed that "the supersolubility curve has a real meaning in the normal order of events, even if spontaneous crystallization can occur in the metastable region."

Jones, Hartley and co-workers[103] ascertained visibly the metastable limit in aqueous solutions of sodium sulfate and alkali nitrates, and in solutions of triphenylmethane in various solvents such as benzene, thiophene, pyrrole, aniline, and pyridine. The supersolubility in some cases extended over the entire phase diagram, as illustrated in Figures 1-6 and 1-7. These workers pointed out the variability of the degrees of supersaturation (cesium nitrate does not supersaturate at all), the fact that it depends upon the rate of cooling and intensity of agitation, and that previous heating above the saturation temperature generally increased the final degree of supersaturation that could be attained. They also admitted de Coppet's stand that any supersaturated solution will crystallize eventually, even though de Coppet himself had maintained a solution of Glauber's salt in the supersaturated condition (about 3°) for over 30 years. The main point that Miers and others developed was that the supersolubility is a real property of solutions and melts under ordinary operating conditions. The practical value of the concept resides in this understanding.

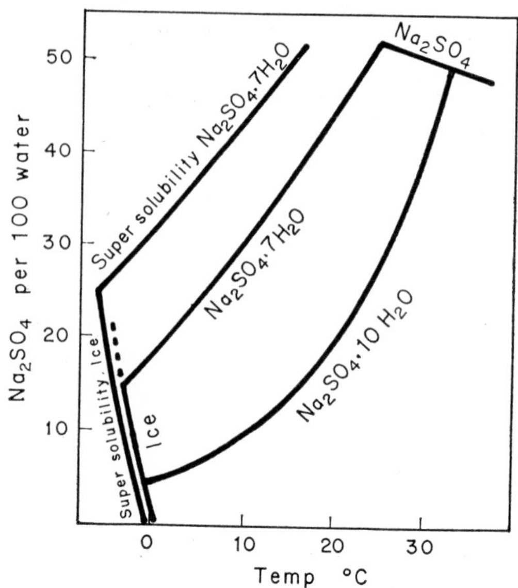

Figure 1-6. Supersolubility in the Na_2SO_4-H_2O system.[103a]

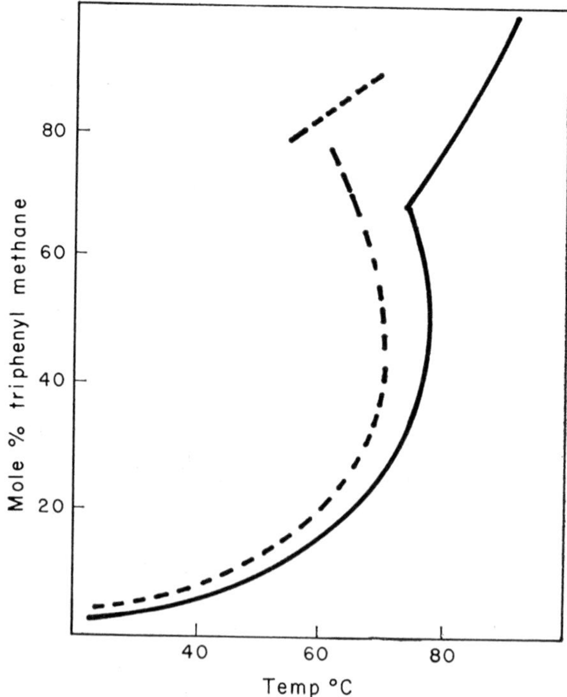

Figure 1-7. Supersolubility of triphenylmethane in benzene.[103d]

—— Solubility

--- Supersolubility

Even previous to the above investigators, Tammann had begun his researches on "The Changes in the State of Matter and their Dependence upon Pressure and Temperature."[240e] These dealt exhaustively with almost all experimental aspects of crystallization from melts and solutions and were to continue for over 40 years. The numerous researches of his school are found mainly in the *Zeitschrift für anorganische Chemie* and in several books.[240] From the very start Tammann recognized that kinetic factors are involved in the adjustment of metastable systems. He expressed these in terms of the rates of the consecutive and simultaneous processes of nuclei formation (K. Z., *Keimezahl*;/cc. sec) and linear growth (K. G., *Kristallisation geschwindigkeit*, or C. V., crystallization velocity; mm/sec). The former could be ascertained by generation at stated conditions followed by development at a more elevated temperature where nucleation was slow but growth appreciable. Rate of growth was measured by the speed with which crystal fronts progressed along a tube after inoculation with an appropriate seed crystal. The methods have been refined[111] in many respects and also criticized severely. These matters will be considered in further detail in Chapter 3 but in the meantime Figures 1-8 and 1-9 may be regarded as typifying the sixteen systems studied by Tammann and his students.

Many other workers have investigated the supersolubility concept since about the turn of the century. Among these may be mentioned Doelter[60] (fused minerals), de Coppet,[48] Schaum[216] (organic melts), Kuster[146] (aqueous solutions), Young,[227] McIntosh,[167] Berkeley[18] and Al'tberg[3] (effects of agitation and shock), Othmer[189] (admits only a very small metastable range), Hinshelwood and Hartley[112] (preheating, curing effects, etc.), Jenkins[124] (nonaqueous solutions), and Jaffe[119] (effects of filtration). The subject has continued to be a lively one even to the present day.[49, 56, 96, 139, 148, 196, 226, 237]

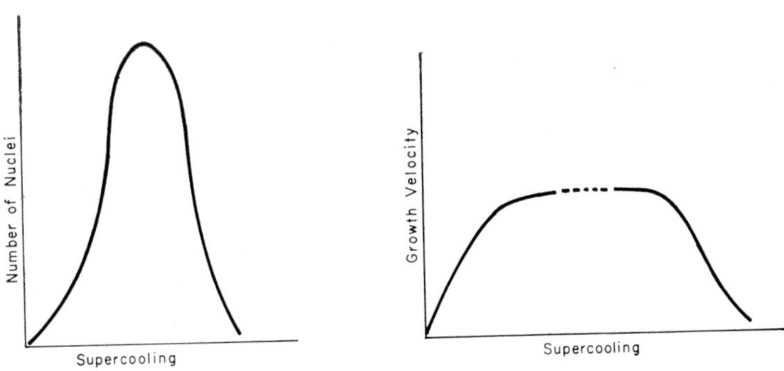

Figure 1-8. Schematic nucleation and growth curves for melts.

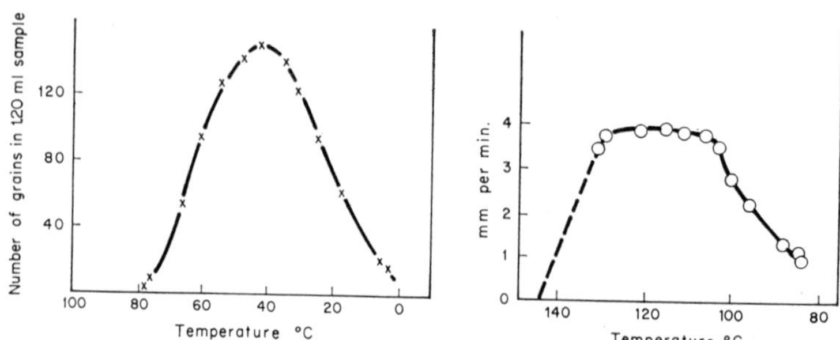

Figure 1-9. Nucleation of piperine (m.p. 129°C) and linear crystallization velocity of triphenylguanidine (m.p. 144.2°C).[240b]

Law of Stages

Several early workers[7, 82] recognized a preferred sequence of adjustment in many metastable systems from which multiple forms were able to separate. Thus, de Coppet found that the unstable heptahydrate separated from supersaturated sodium sulfate solutions long before the stable decahydrate; and, according to Jaffe, an unstable rhombohedric KNO_3 appears first from solution instead of the stable rhombic form.

Ostwald generalized this behavior of supersaturated solutions and supercooled melts in his Law of Stages or *Stufenregel*, according to which *the formation of the unstable phase is generally preferred.* In his own words: "When a given chemical system is left in an unstable state, it tends to change not into the most stable form, but into the form the stability of which most nearly resembles its own; i.e., into that transient stable modification whose formation from the original state is accomplished by the smallest loss of free energy."

Smits[228] states the rule in the following form: "Transformations which proceed spontaneously and with evolution of heat *may* go forward by steps when there are intermediate substances or allotropic forms capable of existence."

Ostwald credits particularly the experiments of Gay-Lussac, Löwel, de Coppet, and Schaum as the basis for this rule, while yet recognizing exceptions. The appearance of multiple phases in order of their relative stabilities was explained by the higher free energy contents of the unstable forms. Molecules of greater kinetic energy can, accordingly, take part more readily in the formation of the unstable form than in the formation of the more stable form. Since these molecules of higher energy are more abundant at the higher temperatures—or smaller supercooling—the probability of formation of the unstable form is at first also greater and this form therefore occurs first upon supercooling. This argument has been described in other ways,[25, 241, 255] of which the most detailed are the treatments of Stranski and Totmanov,[234] and Becker and Döring.[14] Jellinek, however, insists that the law is theoretically unsound.[123, 208]

Ostwald had recognized many exceptions to his rule and many additional ones were soon pointed out. Jones,[129] for instance, found that ice, mono- and decahydrates separated from supersaturated Na_2CO_3 solutions, rather than the heptahydrate expected according to the rule. Tammann[240] studied the rates of nucleation of eight supercooled liquids from which solids could separate in dimorphic form, and concluded that Ostwald's rule is generally not true since only five of these followed the prescribed order. This uncertainty has also been emphasized by Smits,[228] Heisig,[107] Bent and Forziatte,[17] Kohler,[140] Sekera,[224] Jablynski,[118] Fenner,[74] and many other workers. On the other hand, Schmidt,[217] Skrabal,[227] Cohen,[47] Madigan,[158] Bradley,[27] Oldham and Ubbelohde,[184] Tantzov[241] and others report cases in which the rule is followed. Thus, for almost every favorable experiment one can find a contrary report in the literature, and the status of Ostwald's generalization suffered as a result of these contradications. Tammann insisted that kinetic factors alone determined the form precipitated, but Fischer[76] explained how these same factors could account for the many deviations observed. These, and surface energy factors, have since been applied to the question in quantitative form by the modern quasi-thermodynamic theories of crystal growth,[27, 56, 78] and as a result, Ostwald's Law of Stages may now be regarded in an entirely rational and satisfactory manner.

Liesegang Rings

Liesegang[155] discovered, in 1896, that when a gelatin gel of dilute potassium chromate is inoculated with a small crystal of $AgNO_3$, the Ag_2CrO_4 which forms does so in a discontinuous and rhythmic fashion (Figure 1-10). The phenomenon has since been known by his name and appears to be quite general. A flood of papers on this rather spectacular phenomenon soon appeared. By 1932 over 500 papers had been published[106] and the pace has since continued at an unabated rate.[214, 233, 257]

Ostwald realized at once that supersaturation was involved in the formation of these periodic precipitates. He reasoned that a supersaturated solution of Ag_2CrO_4 was formed in the advancing wave front of the counter-diffusing ions, and when this reached the supersolubility limit precipitation ensued until saturation was attained. The process would then be repeated but at another location because the vicinity of the established band had been depleted of the reacting ions.

Morse and Pierce[176] found that the ratio of the distance of any ring from

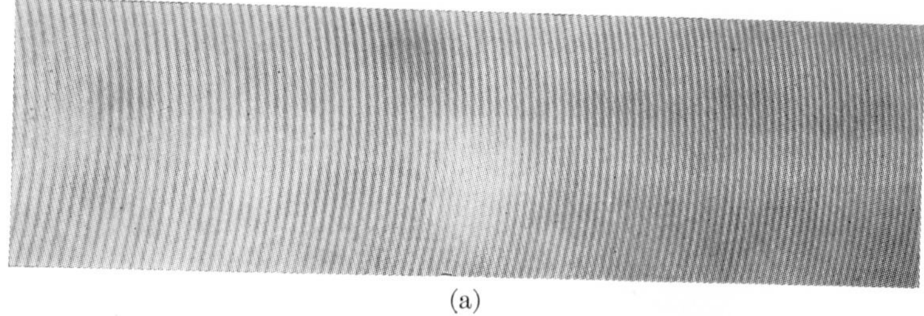

(a)

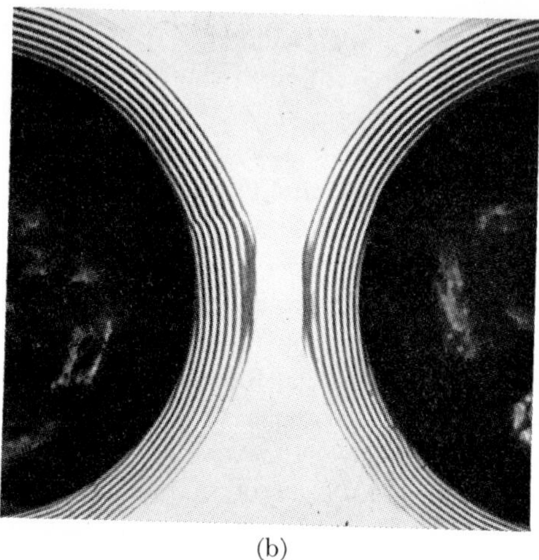

(b)

Figure 1-10. Typical Liesegang rings.
(a) AgI, in capillary, water medium, 350×
(b) Ag_2CrO_4, on flat surface, 5% gelatin medium, 5×

the source of generation, Y_n, to the square root of its time of appearance, t_n, is a constant:

$$\frac{Y_n}{\sqrt{t_n}} = K_1$$

and Jablynski[117] observed that the ratio of the distances of successive rings was also constant:

$$\frac{y_n}{y_{n-1}} = K_2$$

Both these specifications follow from a diffusion theory of interaction coupled with Ostwald's condition of supersaturation.

However, Hatschhek,[105] in 1912, observed that rings of PbI_2 formed in the presence of seeds of this same material and hence Ostwald's theory appeared untenable. Alternative theories soon sprung up but none seemed entirely satisfactory.[107, 257] Morse,[175] in 1930, and the writer[258] independently in 1938, happened to observe that rhythmic precipitation is inhibited in the presence of seeds only if they are sufficiently numerous. Hence kinetic considerations could account for the very serious contradiction reported by Hatschek. A complete quantitative investigation vindicated this contention, and, "In spite of contrary opinions of some authors, Wilhelm Ostwald's supersaturation theory is now adopted by the majority of investigators."[269, 269a, 198] Essentially the only requirement for the formation of rings in the presence of seeds is that the velocity of crystallization be slow compared to the rate of diffusion and interaction. The role of supersaturation in the formation of Liesegang rings of ammonium chloride smoke has been demonstrated recently by Spotz and Hirschfelder[231] and others,[128, 254] but Packter[190] and others[44, 262] still object to its influence.

Particle Size and Solubility

The fourth major contribution of Ostwald in matters dealing with supersaturation concerns the enhanced solubility of very fine particles. By analogy with the Kelvin equation (p. 73) for the dependence of vapor pressure on curvative, he deduced*

$$RT \ln \frac{L}{L_\infty} = \frac{2\gamma V}{r}$$

where L and L_∞ are the solubilities of the material of radii r and ∞ (plane surface) respectively, γ the interfacial tension, V the molar volume, T the absolute temperature, and R the gas constant.

This equation and related ones have been studied extensively both theoretically and experimentally. Direct verification is difficult due to the nature and magnitudes of the quantities involved, as well as the fact that most readily realizable systems display a wide range of particle or droplet sizes rather than uniform ones. For this reason the equation represents a transitory situation since the larger members grow rapidly at the expense of the smaller ones.

Since the concept expressed by this equation is so basic to the development of theories of supersaturation and crystal growth, a detailed exposition will be delayed until a later section. It suffices to say, at this time, that Ostwald himself realized most of the limitations of the equation as well as

* Ostwald's original equation actually contained a numerical factor of 3 rather than the 2 designated here. Freundlich[84] points out Ostwald's error and corrects it accordingly.

the reality of the effect. He interpreted the ordinary analytical procedure of digestion as a practical operation of this principle, and the process of aging by this mechanism has been known since as "Ostwald ripening."[141] This subject of aging of precipitates has been studied extensively by Tezak,[246] Balarev,[6] and many other workers. Tezak adapts Ostwald's term "methorics" to the physics and chemistry of these interboundary reactions.

Ostwald correlated his observations on the critical size of nuclei and metastable limits by means of this equation. In this case, a minimum size crystal, r, which will grow rather than dissolve, is to be associated with a definite supersaturation, or supersolubility value. Kuster[146] and Fuchtbauer[87] developed this relationship still further, and Jones and Partington[130] made it the basis of a rather complete quantitative theory of supersaturation behavior in general. As stated previously, the idea is so fundamental to all modern theories of these phenomena that it will be developed in detail in a following section devoted to this subject.

This concludes our historical presentation of Ostwald's activities in the subjects at hand and some of the immediate reactions of his contemporaries. His chief contribution "rests primarily upon the order and clarity to which he reduced the welter of confused data existing at the time. He is responsible for popularizing most of the concepts and ideas concerning the supersaturated state that are taught elementary students today, and particularly for popularizing some of Gibbs' fundamental contributions on thermodynamic stability and metastable states."[147] Much of the scientific work in this field at this particular period dealt specifically with the many principles pronounced by Ostwald, and many of these have already been mentioned.

Relationship between Solution and Growth

During this period—before, during, and after Ostwald—several lines of approach focused attention on the broad problem of the mechanism of crystal growth. Outstanding among these were the Gibbs-Curie thermodynamic criterion of the equilibrium form of crystals, the Bravais-Donnay-Harker law of the relationship between the faces of a crystal, and the Nernst-Noyes-Whitney theory of the rate of heterogeneous reactions. Although these three main subjects were developed somewhat independently by workers with different interests and problems in mind, they have since become consolidated in most of the modern theories of crystal growth and solution.

Relationships between the Various Faces of a Crystal

One of the truly remarkable features of crystals is the variety of forms which certain substances can assume in contrast to the similarity of forms of other different materials. The thermodynamic consideration of this situation will be postponed until a later section while the more purely crystallographic developments will be outlined here. Considerable details are available in Buckley's book,[34] Barker's "Mineralogical Chemistry,"[8] Wells' review,[273] Groth's "Chemische Kristallographie," Bunn's "Chemical Crystallography," Schoenfliess, and other standard treatises on crystal chemistry.

The point of interest in the present regard is that, to Sohncke,[229] there appeared to be a correlation between the minimum surface energy theory of Curie and the broad generalization of greatest reticular density of Bravais. Now, Bravais had taken Haüy's principle of simplest integers to mean that those faces would be most important according to their reticular density or interplanar spacing. Donnay and Harker[61] elaborated this law by including lattice variations of screw and glide natures. Even though the Bravais-Donnay-Harker rule has been shown[4] to be compatible with the modern theories of crystal growth of Stranski, Kossel, and others, there remain serious objections on purely crystallographic grounds as well as many known cases of the development of high index faces.[168, 273] The over-all conclusion, as with the Gibbs-Curie principle, is that the Bravais condition is an ideal situation which is frequently voided in the case of real crystals. This conclusion is not unexpected when it is recognized that the two criteria under consideration are intimately related. This connection appears reasonable from the following qualitative reasoning: If alternative arrangements are available for a crystal face, that one will appear in which the greatest decrease in free energy is involved. This maximum change will be realized with the establishment of greatest bond strength, which is at the site which offers the greatest area of attachment between crystal and accreting molecules.[36]

In place of this simple thermodynamic reasoning we may reason along kinetic lines to exactly the same conclusion, as follows: If the accommodation coefficients of various faces are fixed we would expect that the velocities of growth of these various faces would depend upon the frequency of lattice points in the various planes—that is, their reticular density. From this conclusion Bravais[31] goes on to demonstrate that preferred planes are those that progress at the slowest rate and extend themselves laterally to the exclusion of more rapidly advancing planes. This fundamental principle may be illustrated in an elementary fashion by the geometric scheme shown in Figure 1-11.

In (A), the central figure is a two-dimensional representation of an octahedral crystal. If the radial growth of the 100 type faces exceeds that of the 111 type faces, progressive growth leads eventually to the exclusion of the

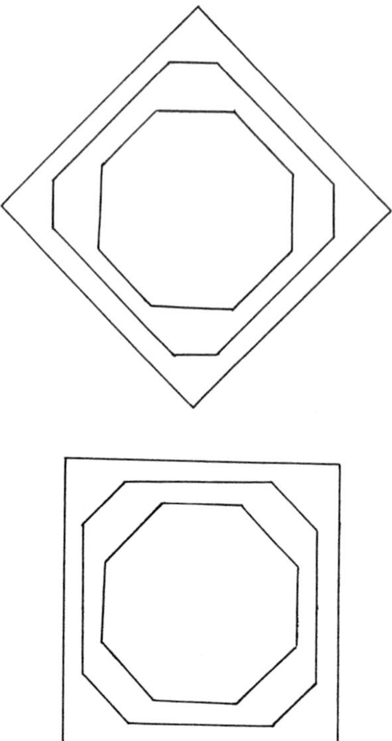

Figure 1-11. Schematic representation of the elimination of high index faces by growth.

faster growing faces. Conversely, (B) indicates the situation should the rate of growth of the octahedral face be greater than that of the regular face. The extension to other configurations and to the reverse process of dissolution is apparent.

Rate of Heterogeneous Reactions

Several successive acts may be visualized as being involved in any heterogeneous reaction:

1. Transport of the reactants to the reaction surface
2. Adsorption of the reactants
3. Reaction on the surface
4. Desorption of the products of reaction
5. Elimination of the products by transfer into the bulk phase

If any one of these steps is considerably slower than the others it will determine the rate of the over-all process. Fortunately, this is frequently the case and considerations of the mechanism of reactions are simplified accordingly. If two or more of the consecutive stages are comparable in rate the observed velocity is the net effect of the interplay of these velocities during the course of the reaction and the kinetics is thereby complicated.

Diffusion is frequently the rate-determining step in the case of solid-liquid reactions owing to the relatively slow rate of this process in solution. This restriction led Noyes and Whitney[182] in 1897 to postulate that a film of saturated solution is formed at the surface of solute and solvent. The velocity of solution would then be determined primarily by the diffusion gradient. This is proportional to the difference in the solubility and the concentration in the bulk solution: i.e.,

$$\frac{dc}{dt} = k(c_s - c)$$

This simple fluid film theory was soon confirmed and amplified by several workers, including Nernst,[179] who generalized the concept for all heterogeneous reactions. Again confirmation followed, but soon several workers, most notably Centnerszwer,[43] pointed out that many heterogeneous reactions proceeded much slower than the rate of transport to or from the active surface. Marc's[161] work on the rate of crystallization, for instance, pointed clearly to the existence of an adsorption layer in which the essential process of crystallization occurred. Many adsorbants, particularly dyestuffs, reduced the crystal growth tremendously yet had little effect upon the reverse process of dissolution; this latter operation being admittedly diffusion-controlled. The adsorption is often preferential so that frequently habit modification ensures. Considerable literature has accumulated on these effects, and the results are discussed in detail by Buckley,[34, 35] France,[80] and others.

Marc showed that in many cases the rate of crystallization is independent of the rate of stirring when this is sufficiently intense, that the growth reaction is bimolecular in many cases, and that the temperature coefficient of reaction is often much higher than the value of 1.5 allotted to most physical processes. All these behaviors suggest the predominance of a surface-controlling reaction rather than a transport process.

These and other criteria have been used by many investigators to ascertain the important step in heterogeneous reactions,[144, 174, 183, 206, 207, 242] and, following Marc, Berthoud,[20] Spangenberg,[230] Jenkins,[124] Walton,[271] and others[53] delineated the primary act in many different types of crystallizations. While this is frequently the diffusion step, this transport stage is by no means the universal rate-controlling one in all crystallizations, or even in dissolution.[131]

Condensation of Water Droplets

Another relevant topic which was initiated during the period under discussion was the condensation of water droplets. This subject has since become very important in the testing of modern theories of nucleation and growth, as well as in the growing practice of rain-making.

According to Volmer,[265] Coulier was the first, in 1875, to observe the formation of droplets produced by the adiabatic expansion of water vapor. The interpretation by means of the Kelvin equation and application to meteorological phenomena followed almost immediately.[2] In 1894, C. T. R. Wilson had planned to study certain spectacular atmospheric optical effects by means of Aitken's techniques but at the very beginning of his experimentation (1891) made an accidental observation which led him astray from his initial intention. Wilson noted that a shower of droplets was produced again and again upon expanding moist air, even when each successive shower effectively removed any pre-existing nuclei. These nuclei were, presumably, being steadily regenerated in the air. They were, of course, ions, although their origin was unknown at the time. It was only in 1910 that Wilson conceived the idea of using this behavior as a means of detecting the several ionizing radiations which had been proposed in other connections in the interim. His original cloud chamber and two of his original photographs of α-tracks are pictured in Figures 1-12 and 1-13.

Figure 1-12. Wilson's original perfected cloud chamber. It was with this instrument that the first photographs were obtained (1911–12).[171]

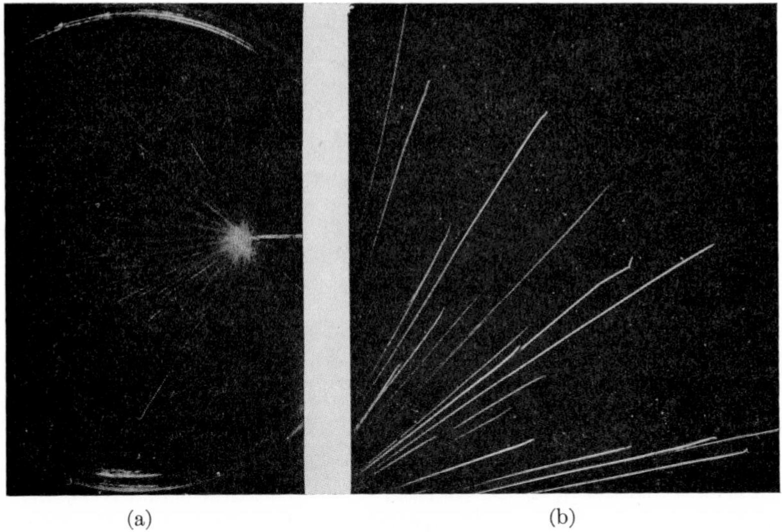

(a) (b)

Figure 1-13.[171]

(a) Alpha tracks from radium. Some particles have traversed before expansion and the tracks have therefore commenced to distintegrate.

(b) Alpha tracks from radium. All particles have traversed immediately after expansion and are therefore well defined.

Wilson's apparatus has been greatly elaborated since its early form but remains our principal means of detecting and measuring many radiations and studying the process of cloud and rain formation (Chapter 6). Continuous models[149] as well as bubble chambers utilizing liquid hydrogen or helium have also been devised.[59]

The Kelvin equation (p. 73) explains the fundamental course of events in an expansion chamber. In its simplest form this equation is:

$$RT \ln \frac{p}{p_\infty} = \frac{2\gamma}{r\rho}$$

Here p/p_∞ is the vapor pressure of a droplet of radius r with respect to the vapor pressure of a plane surface, γ is the surface tension and ρ the density of the liquid, and R and T the usual gas characteristics. The ratio p/p_∞ is related to the expansion ratio of the homogeneous gas phase and is equivalent to the supersaturation. A plot of this equation for water droplets is given in Figure 1-14.

This curve demonstrates very forcibly that the formation of droplets in the absence of nuclei occurs only at very high supersaturations. At low supersaturation the smallest droplets first produced would evaporate rather than grow because of the high vapor pressure. Ordinarily, in the case of water vapor, freed as far as possible from impurities and ions, expansion ratios of about 1.25 are necessary to obtain any appreciable nucleus formation. This corresponds to a supersaturation of about 400 per cent. The frequent occurrence of nucleation below this concentration immediately suggests the strong influence of other factors, probably ions.

Thomson[248] had considered the effect of these on the Kelvin equation, and deduced the following equation:

$$RT \ln \frac{p}{p_\infty} = \frac{1}{\rho}\left(\frac{2\gamma}{r} - \frac{e^2}{8\pi r^4}\right)$$

Here e is the charge per unit surface. Thomson reasoned that the charge opposes the surface tension and thereby reduces the surface energy to an extent proportional to the fourth power of the radius. The effect of this term for unit charge is shown in Figure 1-14 as the dotted line. The maximum occurs just about at the fourfold supersaturation which is usually observed in moist clean air. A charged particle of radius less than 0.6 mμ will not grow, according to this curve, because such growth would require an impossible increase in vapor pressure. Only particles above 0.6 mμ in size are capable of growing. This size, then, constitutes the *critical nucleus* comparable to that already noted in the case of solutions.

It was also recognized that other agencies can act as nuclei to assist the initial formation of water droplets. In his pioneer work on cloud formations,

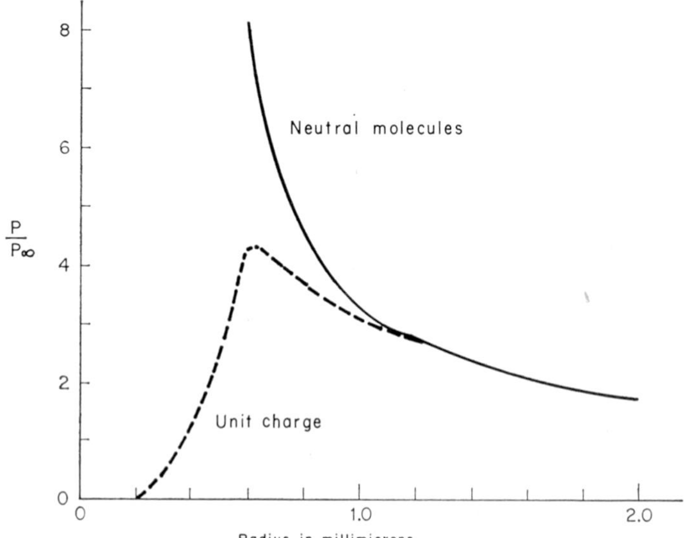

Figure 1-14. Vapor pressure over water droplets.

Aitken emphasized the importance of hydroscopic solid particles. The vapor pressure around such a center is, of course, that of the saturated solution. Since this is much less than that of pure water, condensation ensues even with the attendant dilution. In fact, "our most conclusive evidence to date suggests that the most important nuclei for atmospheric condensation are hydroscopic in nature."[163] These are salt nuclei derived from salt spray and acid nuclei from combustion.

Still other conditions may serve as nuclei for the condensation of water vapor and for other systems, too.[72, 247] A particle which possesses a plane surface may act as a nucleus and induce condensation. The vapor pressure at such a surface will be equal to p_∞ and therefore will lower the vapor pressure of the supersaturated vapor. This necessitates growth. This action will be magnified by a concave surface such as might be presented above a re-entrant crack or porous surface. In this case the vapor pressure becomes considerably less than at a plane surface or one with a convex surface.

It is also possible that agencies which lessen the surface-tension factor may promote adjustments. This and whether or not surface tension depends upon the size of the droplet itself will be discussed in the following two chapters.

Real and Ideal Crystals

Still another topic evolving at the period under consideration was the the definition of real and ideal crystals. These specifications have recently become very important to our understanding of the growth of solids from melts and solutions. The ideal crystal is one with a perfectly regular arrangement throughout the whole crystal, whereas the real crystal deviates from the ideal because of irregularities of growth, thermal motion, plastic deformation, etc. It is now generally realized that the ideal crystal is only a perfect model and that actual crystals always contain defects and surface discontinuities. Much of the early work leading to this idea must be credited to the works of metallographers and metallurgists.

Even the earliest theories of the strength of ionic crystals indicated values much higher than those actually observed.[177] With metals, the theory is much less certain but even so the experimental values are at best less than one-tenth the calculated ones. Obviously surface flaws, cracks, and crevices will lead to inordinately low tensile strength values, but even when these are eliminated (by breaking under water, in the case of NaCl, etc.) the discrepancy between theory and fact still remains.[126] The actual strength of an aluminum single crystal, for instance, is 600,000 psi, while that of polycrystalline material is only about 7,000 psi. Such tremendous differences pointed out the powerful effect of discontinuities and prompted development of the mosaic picture of the structure of solids. This theory suggested that the actual crystal is composed of small blocks of the order of a few hundred to a few thousand lattice distances (10^{-4}–10^{-6} cm). The mosaics are not exactly in alignment and their disarray constitutes the nonideality of the real crystal.

The most significant evidence in favor of this type of structure came from refined X-ray data. The low-angle reflections from an ideal crystal should be exceedingly sharp but this is not the case with most actual crystals. The reflections persist over small but definite angles and the width of the resulting lines, as well as their intensities are caused by a secondary structure of the kind suggested.[1, 113, 121, 276] Direct visual evidence for the mosaic condition of solids is offered in the "fractures" of Zapffe,[278, 249] while their significance in crystallization is discussed by Burgers.[38]

Further support of this proposal is found in the work of Traube,[250, 251] who observed that crystals of arsenic trioxide decrepitate into small blocks, called submicrons, when placed in water. Similarly, many colloids form small entities with specific aggregation patterns when allowed to settle quietly. Goetz *et al.*[95] have also interpreted the persistence of nuclei in melts and solutions as an extension of disorder and order on either side of the transition point and the disorder persisting in the solid state is tantamount to a secondary structure.

The estimated size of the mosaic units is within reach of resolution by the electron microscope, and numerous investigations[9, 10, 23, 100, 164, 199, 213] of this sort have revealed structures that are very suggestive. Figures 1-15

Figure 1-15. Portion of a grain of annealed high purity Cu, etched with $FeCl_3$ reagent. After Barrett.[10]

Figure 1-16. Electron micrograph of sucrose crystal.[197, 259] Water etched, "Formvar" replica, Uranium shadowed, 11,600×. (*Courtesy Stamford Research Laboratory, American Cyanamid Co.*)

and 1-16 display samples of such cases. The dimensions of the discernible block are a few tenths of a micron in both cases. The difficulties and hazards of interpreting these apparent regularities as true secondary structures must be emphasized.[9]

Other properties such as slip phenomena, certain etch patterns, diffusion in crystals, and rates of reaction, solution and crystallization, as well as other phase changes, have also been investigated in this respect, and by and large the weight of experimental evidence favors the reality of secondary structures.[54, 110] These, however, may not in all cases be as extreme as pictured in the mosaic theory.

On the theoretical side, this proposal was endorsed at an early date and encouraged by the work of Zwicky and Smekal.[238] The general theory of ionic crystals due to Born and to Lennard-Jones had led to the conclusion that the excess surface energy of a crystal could be compensated by a contraction of the lattice distances in the surface. Zwicky reasoned that the perfectly regular or ideal crystal would be less stable than a configuration equivalent to a mosaic structure throughout the crystal. This proposal was accepted enthusiastically by many investigators but it does not now appear necessary to assume that this surface effect extends throughout the bulk of the crystal.[186]

Smekal, on the other hand, divided the properties of crystals into two classes: (1) structure-insensitive, and (2) structure-sensitive. Properties such as heat capacity, density, elastic constants, and lattice constants are typical of the first class, while stress limits, magnetic properties, corrosion resistance, and diffusion represent structure-sensitive properties. The former properties are essentially constant and reproducible while the latter may vary considerably from sample to sample, and with the treatment and history of a particular sample. Differences between theoretical and observed properties are also apt to be marked with the sensitive group. Smekal associated these structure-sensitive properties with flaws of various kinds and considered that the practical properties of crystals must be ascribed primarily to these defects and not to the crystalline regularity. An extensive physics of the solid state has developed from these concepts.[77, 88, 98, 137, 178, 221, 222, 223, 236, 239]

The flaws of Smekal were given definite form by the suggestion of Frenkel[83] that ions may leave lattice sites and occupy interstitial positions. Schottky[269a] subsequently proposed that an energetically more favored type of defect involved the displacement of these ions to the surface of the crystal. These displacements leave behind vacant sites or holes which cause rearrangement of the neighboring atoms.

The fraction of Schottky disorder for AgCl and AgBr at 300°C, for instance, has been estimated to be 5.5×10^{-4} and 4.0×10^{-3} respectively, with an energy of displacement amounting to 0.8 ev. Local electron excesses or deficits may also contribute to the disorder in some cases. There are also electrically neutral defects such as cation and anion pair vacancies, or electron occupancy of an anion vacancy (*F*-center). Defects may also be introduced by impurities and by variations in composition.* A simple demonstration of a two-dimensional imperfection as illustrated in Figure 1-17. Complete classifications are to be found in the standard works on solid-state physics and chemistry. The ionic conductivity, magnetic prop-

* The composition of crystals may vary as a result of the incorporation of more particles than regular lattice points, or by a deficiency of such units. Such deviation from the usual strict stoichiometric rate are usually minute, but may be considerable in some cases.[5, 67, 125] The lattices of cuprous oxide, for instance, may be incomplete in copper ions as the result of incompletely occupied metal ion sites. On the other hand, oxygen may occupy the holes in the ferrous ion lattice of FeO to an extent amounting to the composition represented by $FeO_{1.09}$, and as much as 20 or even 30% variations in atomic ratios are observed in other oxides and sulfides. Garner,[88] and A. L. Y. Rees[201] discuss nonstoichiometric compounds in detail.

Figure 1-17. A dislocation in a two-dimensional bubble raft. The dislocation is most easily seen by turning the page by 30 degrees in its plane and sighting at a low angle.[29]

erties, diffusion, and many optical, electronic, chemical, and catalytic[51] properties of crystals are determined by such defects.

The existence of secondary structure, whatever form it may assume, is important to considerations of crystal growth[274] for the following reason. The development of a crystal will, of course, normally proceed in the direction of the most stable form. Since this is the slightly disorganized arrangement, continued extension of the perfect crystal lattice is less probable than the resumption of growth at a distorted point. The defect, then, constitutes the two-dimensional nucleus of growth. Growth then will be intermittent, and will occur more or less as segments of perfect crystals.[235, 273] This pattern of growth, as well as the etch patterns resulting from gentle dissolution,[264] are evidence for the reality of dislocations, while the broadening of X-ray diffraction lines,[46] light scattering,[114] Moiré designs,[26, 194] and electron microscopy[50, 169] supply additional evidence.

The mosaic idea has been developed in an extreme form in another direction by Balarev[6] and others.[145, 251, 266] They consider that growth and many properties of colloidal systems are determined primarily by the mosaic or similar entities themselves, rather than by the whole assembly. Balarev follows Smekal in postulating that any finite crystal cannot be ideal and in equilibrium with its environment. The growth of an actual crystal, therefore, proceeds from a large number of nuclei which are distributed at random over the entire surface of the crystal. Growth of each nucleus ceases when it comes into contact with another growing area. The labyrinth of surfaces and capillary voids produced in this way are highly active in the colloidal sense and Balarev combines observation and theory to explain many behaviors of finely divided, imperfect crystals. His experimental and theoretical investigations of these extensions have been criticized adversely[34, 234, 273] since they lead to many inconsistencies and anomalies.

Packter[190] at first supported Balarev and Tezak's hypothesis that the growth of sparingly soluble metal salts proceeded by coalescence of submicrons of colloidal size, but more recently[190b] concludes that the mechanism is more likely a two-stage one of nucleation and growth. Schaskolsky and Shubnikov,[215] Egli[68] and others,[211, 225] however, still consider that the unit of growth is not the elementary molecule or its equivalent, but a much larger particle.

Impurities

It has long been recognized that contaminating substances often modify the formation and appearance of many crystals. Boyle (1666) noted several examples and Rome de l'Isle[116] first observed that octahedra formed when common salt crystallized from urine. This particular effect was soon recognized to be due to urea,[79] and the example remains a classic one of crystal habit modification.

During this same time mineralogists were noting the variations in habit and color of many ore and mineral specimens, and frequently associated them with impurities. These were often present in only very small amounts. On the preparative side, Ord[185] studied the effects of many substances on the crystalline form of calcium salts, and Gaubert[89] was apparently the first to observe the adsorption of dyestuffs on growing crystals. There soon followed a series of papers on this subject, all of which are discussed in great detail by Buckley. The late Professor W. G. France of Ohio State University has also presented a review of his work[80] of a slightly earlier date and other reviews are also available.[22, 273] These adsorption effects have received important considerations in the growth theories of Niggli, Valeton, Spangenberg, and Bentivoglio.

During this same period von Pickardt,[268] and Padoa and Galeati[191] had been studying the effects of foreign substances upon the crystallization velocity of supercooled melts. With Tammann, these workers found that almost all soluble substances lowered the crystallization velocity. Now, Tammann had explained this general pattern qualitatively by the fact that such second components would depress the freezing point of the first component and therefore decrease the supercooling. However, Freundlich[84] pointed out that the expected change in temperature was wholly inadequate, and he suggested that the pronounced influence of impurities be ascribed to the formation of an adsorbed layer which impeded the otherwise normal crystallization. Application of his adsorption equation to the case of partial coverage of the growing face gave calculated results in agreement with observation. Again, however, this mechanism did not prevail in all cases and many examples were evident where viscosity and solvation effects controlled the rate of adjustment.

The importance of the surface layer was further emphasized by Marc's works on the rate of crystallization from solution. His results with potassium sulfate are illustrated in Figure 1-18 and are typical of the many systems examined. Curve *B* shows the rate of crystallization of potassium sulfate from pure solution under certain conditions, while curve *C* is the same system except that 0.03 per cent of quinoline yellow had been added. The reduction in crystallization velocity is marked. Bismark brown and ponceau red have similar effects, whereas methylene blue in similar concentration does not. The first three dyestuffs actually color the crystals but the last does not. Thus it appears obvious that the inhbition is due to strong adsorption of the impurity. Curve *A* is common for the dissolution of a crystal of K_2SO_4 with or without the presence of these dyestuffs. It is a general pattern, and suggests that the surface reaction is unimportant in the solution process. As already intimated, the rate of diffusion away from the interface is the controlling step in that case.

Adsorption is an atomic phenomenon and on a crystalline body must be highly preferential. In a cubic lattice, such as that of sodium chloride, the (100) planes are occupied by oppositely charged ions while the (111) planes contain only ions of like charge. Valeton[256] considered, therefore, that the

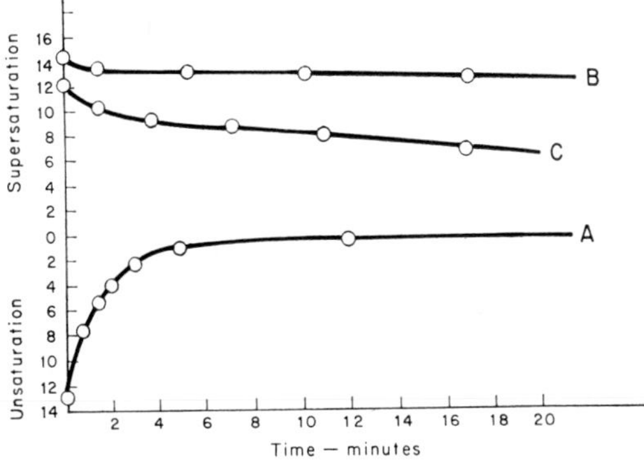

Figure 1-18. Effect of Quinoline Yellow (0.03%) on the rate of solution (A) and crystallization (C) of K_2SO_4 (B).[161]

latter type of plane would have a higher adsorption capacity for appropriate polar materials since the net charge in the regular faces is zero. Octahedral faces should develop in this case since they would be slower growing. This certainly accounts for the situation observed in the development of NaCl crystals in the presence of urea and many other substances. The theory has been extended or criticized by many workers, including Valeton, Spangenberg, Bentivoglio, Bunn, etc.

Paneth and Horowitz[192] were among the first to observe the adsorption of radioactive elements on crystalline precipitates and to use these "tagged" atoms as a means of measuring the total surface of the crystals. The technique has been applied in many directions (e.g., habit modifications) and in the present connection has been employed very successfully by Kolthoff to supplement the dye method of studying the aging of precipitates. Kolthoff *et al.*[141] classify aging phenomena as follows:

1. Perfection of the primary particles as a result of recrystallizations in a liquid film around the particles. This process predominates during the early stages of aging when there is no thermal aging. The primary particles are usually small and imperfect, and are more so the higher the conditions of supersaturation under which they are formed.

2. Agglomeration of primary particles by sharing their water jackets. This process effectively cements together several primary particles with a consequent decrease in surface. At the same time coprecipitated material is expelled with the exuded liquid film. This operation accounts for much of the improved filterability attending the usual digestion process in analytical work.

3. Cementing together of the primary particles in the agglomerate as a result of the perfection process by recrystallization.

4. Ostwald ripening. This process is slow as compared with the perfection and the cementing phenomena. As a rule, the extent of Ostwald ripening is negligible during the early stages of aging and at low temperatures.

5. Perfection of metal precipitates by presence of local elements. The solubility of metallic precipitates is so small that it cannot play a part in the aging of imperfect precipitates of metals. In these cases the recrystallizations resulting in perfection are attributed to the presence of "local elements" which give rise to electrolysis phenomena. The "electrolytic solution tension" at the active surface is greater than at the normal surface; hence, the potential at the active surface is more negative than at the normal surface. Consequently, metal ions enter the liquid film at the active surface and are deposited again at a more normal surface.

6. Transformation of a metastable modification into another metastable

or into the stable modification. Such a case occurs relatively rarely. It has been found with calcium oxalate. When this substance is precipitated at room temperature from relatively concentrated solutions, the metastable di- and trihydrates separate. These are transformed relatively quickly into the stable monohydrate. The speed of transformation will, no doubt, be influenced by the properties of the liquid medium with which the precipitate is in contact.

7. Thermal aging in the dry state. A thermal aging of highly imperfect precipitates with a high melting point was found to occur at temperatures near 300°C (e.g., lead sulfate, lead chromate and barium sulfate). The silver halides show a pronounced thermal aging at room temperature.

8. The above cases are all examples of physical aging. Chemical aging seems to occur especially when dealing with amorphous precipitates, the primary particles of which have a pronounced reactivity and which are of such a chemical composition that they can react chemically with one another. Cases of chemical aging are found with the hydrous oxides and hydroxides, as in the polymerization of *ortho*-ferric hydroxide.

The limit of strong adsorption is total incorporation into the crystal lattice, or isomorphism. Between the extremes we find the phenomena of syncrystallization, overgrowth, parallel growth, and mixed and double crystals. These century-old subjects have been designated, collectively, as "epitaxis," on which subject the classic paper is that of Royer[212] who specified the following conditions for oriented growth:

1. The lattice spacings of the crystals must be almost identical or in simple integer ratio
2. Epitaxis is reciprocal
3. Both crystals must have the same type of bonding

While these conditions generally prevail, we now realize that considerable latitude is permissible.[61] Johnson,[127] for instance, finds oriented overgrowth of Ag on Au even though a 10 per cent difference in lattice constants exists. This is considerably more than the 5 per cent allowed by Goldschmidt's rule, but even still higher differences have been reported.[33, 97] Interest in this subject has been revived recently by the importance of epitactic materials as nucleation catalysts[253, 272] as well as in other applications.[13, 58, 138, 180]

Superheating of a Solid: 1-1 and 1-g Transitions

Superficially, it does not appear reasonable that the metastable condition should not be reciprocal for all transitions. Yet contrary to the frequent occurrence of supercooling and supersaturation of ordinary liquid systems, we have the generalizations that overheating a solid and supersaturation of partially miscible liquids are impossible.[20, 73, 81, 165, 193, 210, 280] Explanations have been offered based on kinetic[99, 146, 240b] and on surface energy[83] considerations but experimental work has revealed many exceptions to these unidirectional changes.

Davies[55] was the first to observe liquid-liquid supersaturation. Nitrobenzene supersaturates its complimentary water layer by an amount corresponding to 0.1 to 1.4°. Oddly, the nitrobenzene layer does not supersaturate with water. CS_2 in water supercools rather readily as much as 3° and the *cis-trans* isomers of benzaldoxime[75] have also been observed to mutually supersaturate in the liquid state. Gopal and Rastogi[96] conclude from theoretical analysis and experimental trial that appreciable supersaturation of the 1-1 kind can be realized if the interfacial tension between components is high and the relative internal pressures equal.

The superheating of solid P_2O_5 was first reported by Hill, Faust, and Kendricks[109] and soon confirmed by Smits.[228b] Frenkel and Turnbull recognize the impossibility of superheating a solid because the free surface energy of a liquid is smaller than that of any face of the corresponding crystal; but they reason that it might be possible to trespass this condition if the surface could be maintained at a temperature below the melting point, or if coated with a coherent infusible crystalline film. The superheating of tin[134] by at least 2°C and other solids[132, 143, 220, 232] has been observed under the first of these conditions.

The proper transition of liquid to gas is also subject to considerable impedance. The attendant delay has been considered under the subjects of superheating, boiling, and bumping of liquids,[15, 19, 133, 150, 153, 160, 181, 275] tensile strength of liquids,[16, 32, 64, 245] and supersaturation of gas in liquids.[12, 104, 133, 159, 170, 205, 243]

In addition to the subjects already discussed many other topics which are now realized have a bearing on the general subject of crystal growth were being investigated in the late 19th and early 20th centuries. At the same time the first quantitative theories were beginning to extend the qualitative descriptions of the workers in these fields and this evolution of our modern theories will be outlined in the following chapters.

REFERENCES

1. Addink, N. W. H., *Nature*, **157**, 764 (1946).
2. Aitken, J., *Collected Scientific Papers*, Cambridge U. Press, (1923).
3. Al'tberg, V. Ya., *Acta Physicochem*, **11**, 287 (1939).
4. Amelinckx, S., *J. chim. phys.*, **47**, 213 (1950).
5. Anderson, J. S., *Trans. Roy. Soc. London*, **A185**, 64 (1946).
6. Balarev, D.
   (a) "Der disperse Baue der festen Systeme," Dresden, 1939.
   (b) *Koll. Z.*, **106**, 116 (1944).

(c) *Annual Repts. on Prog. Chem.* (*Chem. Soc. London*), **43,** 8 (1946).
(d) *Mikrochemie der Mikrochem. Acta*, **36/37,** 214 (1951), *C.A.*, **45,** 4990.

7. Bancroft, W., *J. Phys. Chem.*, **1,** 1212 (1896).
8. Barker, T. V., *Annual Repts. Prog. Chem.* (*Chem. Soc. London*), (1913–17).
9. Barnes, R. B. and Burton, C. J., *J. Appl. Phys.*, **16,** 730 (1945).
10. Barret, C. S., "Structure of Metals," New York, McGraw-Hill Book Co., 1943.
11. Barus, P., *Am. J. Sci.*, **42,** 141 (1891).
12. Bateman, J. B. and Lang, J., *Can. J. Res.*, **E23,** 22 (1945).
13. Bauer, E., *Z. Krist.*, **110,** 372 (1958); *C.A.*, **52,** 1932.
14. Becker, R. and Doring, W., *Ann. Physik*, **24,** 719 (1935).
15. Bennett, J. S., *Science*, 644 (1947).
16. Benson, S. W., *et al.*, *J. Chem. Phys.*, **17,** 914 (1949); **18,** 215 (1950).
17. Bent, H. E. and Forziate, A. F., *J. Am. Chem. Soc.*, **58,** 2222 (1936).
18. Berkeley, Earl of, *Phil. Mag.*, **24,** 254 (1912).
19. Bernath, L., *Ind. Eng. Chem.*, **44,** 1310 (1952).
20. Berthoud, A.,
    (a) *J. chim. phys.*, **10,** 624 (1912).
    (b) **8,** 837 (1910), *C.A.*, **4,** 3031.
21. Biilmann, E., and Klett, H., *K. danske vidinsk.* (*Math. fys. medd.*) **12,** 516 (1932).
22. Bliznakov, G., *Fortschr. Mineral.*, **36,** 149 (1959); *C.A.*, **53,** 10897.
23. Boardman, J. F. C., Heyz, R. H., Terry, G. C., *Nature*, **182,** 1762 (1958).
24. Boisbaudran, L. de, *Compt. rend.*, **63,** 95 (1866).
25. Borelius, G., *Ann. Physik.*, **(v) 33,** 517 (1938).
26. Bowden, F. D., *J. Col. Sci.*, **11,** 555 (1956); *Proc. Roy. Soc.*, **A236,** 119 (1956).
27. Bradley, A. J., *Proc. Phys. Soc.*, **52,** 80 (1940).
28. Bradley, R. S., *Quart. Rev.*, **4,** 315 (1951).
29. Bragg, W. L. and Nye, J. F., *Proc. Roy. Soc.* (*London*), **A190,** 474 (1947). Bragg, W. L. and Lomer, W. M., *Proc. Roy. Soc.* (*London*), **A196,** 171 (1941).
30. Bransom, S. H., Dunning, W. J., and Millard, B., *Discussions Faraday Soc.*, **5,** 92 (1949).
31. Bravais, A., *J. de l'Ecole Polytechnique*, 167 (1851).
32. Briggs, L. S., *J. Appl. Phys.*, **21,** 721 (1951); **26,** 100 (1955).
33. Bru, L. and Gharpurey, M., *Proc. Phys. Soc.* (*London*), **64A,** 283 (1951).
34. Buckley, H. E., "Crystal Growth," Chap. 11, New York, John Wiley & Sons, 1951.
35. Buckley, H. E., *Mem. & Proc. Manchester Lit. & Phil. Soc.*, 77–123 (1951), 2–3 (1952).
36. Buerger, M. J., *Am. Mineralogist*, **32,** 593 (1947). Chap. 6 "Phase Transformations in Solids", New York, John Wiley & Sons, 1951.
37. Bunn, C. W., *Discussions Faraday Soc.*, **5,** 364 (1949).
38. Burger, W. G., *Proc. Koninkl. Ned. Akad. Wetenschap.*, **50,** 595, 719 (1947).
39. Cahn, R. W., *Proc. Phys. Soc.*, **63A,** 323 (1950).
40. Cambridge Monograph No. 4, Cambridge Instrument Company Ltd., London (1952).
41. Carpenter, L. C., Connell, L. J., and Osborn, A. B., *Nature*, **163,** 23 (1949).
42. Carey, E. J., *Biodynamica*, **3,** 251 (1941).
43. Centnerszwer, N., *Z. physik. Chem.*, **141A,** 297 (1927).
44. Chatterji, A. C. and Rastogi, M. C., *J. Indian Chem. Soc.*, **28,** 283 (1951), *C.A.*, **48,** 7393.

45. Christiansen, J. A., and Nielsen, A., *Acta. Chem. Scand.*, **5,** 673 (1951), *C.A.*, **46,** 4328.
46. Cochran, W., *Acta Cryst.*, **9,** 259 (1956).
47. Cohen, E.—cited by Moesveld, *J. Chem. Ed.*, **25,** 310 (1948).
48. Coppet, L. C., de, *Bull. soc. chim.*, **17,** 146 (1872); *Ann. Chim. et Phys.*, **6,** 275 (1875); **10,** 457 (1907).
49. Correns, C. W., *Naturwiss.*, **40,** 620 (1953), *C.A.*, **48,** 9143.
50. Cosslett, V. E., *Endeavor*, **15,** 160 (1956).
51. Cratty, L. E., and Granato, A. V., *J. Chem. Phys.*, **26,** 96 (1957).
52. "Crystal Growth," *Discussions Faraday Soc.*, **5,** 365 (1949).
53. Crystal Growth Symposium, Am. Chem. Soc., *Ind. Eng. Chem.*, **44,** 1269 (1952).
54. Davey, W. P., "Crystal Structure." Chap. 12, New York, McGraw Hill Book Co., 1934.
55. Davies, *J. Am. Chem. Soc.*, **38,** 1166 (1916).
56. DeBoer, J. H., *Discussions Faraday Soc.*, **23,** 177 (1957).
57. DeRooster, J., *Bull. Soc. Chem. Belges*, **57,** 187 (1949).
58. Dev, A. E., *Proc. Roy. Soc. (London)*, **A236,** 7–9 (1956).
59. Dodd, C., *Endeavor*, **15,** 206 (1956); *Science*, **124,** 779 (1956).
60. Doelter, Z. C., "Handbuch der Mineral Chemie," (1912).
61. Donnay, J. D. H. and Harker, D., *Am. Mineral.*, **22,** 446 (1937).
62. Dorsch, R. G., and Hacker, P. T., *Natl. Advisory Comm. Aeronautics*, Washington, D.C., Tech. Note **#2142,** (1950).
63. Dorsey, N. E., *T. Am. Phil. Soc.*, **38,** 301 (1948).
64. Dorsey, W., *Z. physik. Chem.*, **B36,** 371 (1936); **B37,** 292 (1937).
65. Doucet, G., *Groupe. franc. devel. aero. Tech.*, **#35,** 30 pp. (1946); *C.A.*, **43,** 1620.
66. Dunning, W. J., in Garners, "Solid State Chemistry," London, Butterworth's, 1955.
67. Dunwald, H. and Wagner, C., *Z. physik. Chem.*, **B22,** 212 (1933).
68. Egli, P. H., *Sci. Monthly*, **68,** 270 (1949).
69. Engel, O. G., *J. Research Nat. Bur. Standards*, **50,** 249 (1953).
70. Fahrenheit, D., *Phil. Trans. Roy. Soc.*, **33,** 78 (1924).
71. Faraday, M., *Quart. J. Sci.*, **21,** 392 (1826).
72. Farley, F. J. M., *Proc. Soc. Phys. London*, **A212,** 530 (1952).
73. Fawcett, W. J., *T. Roy. Soc. Canada*, **III, 7,** 219 (1913).
74. Fenner, *Am. J. Sci.*, **36,** 342 (1913).
75. Findlay, A., "Phase Rule," New York, Longmans-Green and Co., 1938.
76. Fischer, W. M., *Chem. Ztg.*, **36,** 527 (1912).
77. Fisher, J. C., Johnstone, W. G., Thomson, R. and Vreeland Jr., J., "Dislocations and Mech. Properties of Crystals," New York, John Wiley & Sons, 1957.
78. Ford, G. F. and LaMer, V. K., *J. Am. Chem. Soc.*, **72,** 1959 (1950).
79. Fourcroy and Vauguelin, *Ann. de Chemie*, **32,** 130 (1810).
80. France, W. G., in Alexander's "Colloid Chemistry," **Vol. 5,** P. 443–57, New York, Reinhold Publishing Corp., 1944.
81. Frank, F. C., *Proc. Roy. Soc.*, **170A,** 182 (1939).
82. Frankenheim, L., *Pogg. Ann.*, **39,** 380 (1836).
83. Frenkel, J., "Kinetic Theory of Liquids," P. 425, Oxford Press, 1946.
84. Freundlich, H., "Colloid and Capillary Chemistry," p. 155, New York, E. P. Dutton and Co., 1922.
85. Frulla, F., *M. S. Thesis*, College of the Holy Cross, 1951.
86. Fuchtbauer, C., *Z. physik. Chem.*, **48,** 549 (1904).

87. Gapon, E. N., *J. Russ. Phys. Chem. Soc.*, **61**, 1721 (1929); *C.A.*, **24**, 2359.
88. Garner, W. E., "Chemistry of the Solid State," New York, Academic Press, 1955.
89. Gaubert, P., *Bull. Soc. franc. Mineral*, (1894–1932).
90. Gay-Lussac, J. L., *Ann. chim.*, **87**, 225 (1813); p. 296 (1819).
91. Gernez, D., *Compt. rend.*, **60**, 833, 1027 (1865); **61**, 289 (1865); **95**, 1278 (1882).
92. Gibbs, J. Willard, "Collected Works," New York, Longmans, Green and Co., 1928.
93. Gibbs, J. Willard, "Commentary," New Haven, Conn. Yale U. Press, 1936.
94. Gibbs, J. Willard, *Trans. Conn. Acad.*, **III**, 108–248 (1875–6), 343–524 (1877–8).
95. Goetz, A., and co-workers, *Phys. Rev.*, **31**, 193 (1930); **37**, 1044 (1931); **40**, 643 (1932).
96. Gopal, R., *J. Ind. Chem. Soc.*, (a) **21**, 103 (1944); (b) **24**, 281 (1947); (c) **27**, 43 (1950); (d) with Rastogi, R.P., **27**, 401 (1950).
97. Gorunova, N. A., *Doklady Akad. Nauk. USSR*, **75**, 51 (1950); *C.A.*, **45**, 3678.
98. Gray, T. J., "The Defect Solid State," New York, Interscience, 1957.
99. Greig, J. W. and Barth, T. F. W., *Am. J. Soc.*, **35A**, 93 (1928).
100. Gulbransen, *Anal. Chem.*, **18**, 391 (1946).
101. Hamburger, L., *Chem. Weekblad.*, **35**, 886 (1938).
102. Hammer, C., *Ann. Phys.*, **(5) 33**, 445 (1938).
103. (a) Hartley, H., Jones, B. M. and Hutchinson, G. A., *J. Chem. Soc.*, **93**, 825 (1908).
    (b) Jones, B. M., *J. Chem. Soc.*, **93**, 1739–47 (1908).
    (c) Hartley, H., and Barrett, W., *J. Chem. Soc.*, **95**, 1178–85 (1909).
    (d) Hartley, H. and Thomas, H. G., *J. Chem. Soc.*, **89**, 1612 (1906).
104. Harvey, E. N. *et al.*, *J. Cell and Comp. Physiol.* **24**, 1, 23 (1944); **28**, 325 *J. Am. Chem. Soc.*, **67**, 156 (1945); **68**, 2119 (1946), *J. Phys. Chem.*, **51**, 556 (1947).
105. Hatschek, E., *Koll. Z.*, **10**, 124 (1912).
106. Hedges, E. S., "Liesegang Rings and other Periodic Structures," Chapman & Hall, London, 1932.
107. Heisig, G. B., *J. Am. Chem. Soc.*, **60**, 360 (1938).
108. Heverly, J. R., *Trans. Am. Geophys. Union*, **30**, 205 (1949).
109. Hill, Faust, and Kendricks, F. B., *J. Am. Chem. Soc.*, **65**, 794 (1943).
110. Hill, R. A. W., and Wallace, A. A., *Nature*, **178**, 692 (1956).
111. Hillig, W. B. and Turnbull, D., *J. Chem. Phys.*, **24**, 914 (1956).
112. Hinshelwood, C. and Hartley, H., *Phil. Mag.*, **43**, 78 (1922).
113. Hirsch, P. B., *Progress in Metal Physics*, **6**, 236 (1956).
114. Humphreys-Owen, S. P. F., *Phys. Soc. Proc.*, **69B**, 350 (1956).
115. "International Critical Tables," IV P. 236, New York, McGraw-Hill Book Co., 1926.
116. Isle, Rome de l', "Crystalographie," Paris, 1783.
117. Jablynski, M., *Bull. Soc. Chem.*, **(4)**, **33**, 1592 (1923).
118. Jablynski, M., *Roczniki Chem.*, **2**, 485 (1922).
119. Jaffe, G., *Z. physik. Chem.*, **22**, 325 (1897).
120. Jaffe, G., *F. physik. Chem.*, **43**, 565 (1903).
121. James, P. W., "X-Ray Diffraction," London, 1948.
122. James, T. H., "Advances in Catalysis," New York, Academic Press, 1950.
123. Jellinek, K., "Lehrbuch der physikalischen Chemie," Vol. 2, p. 562, Stuttgart, 1915.
124. Jenkins, J. D., *J. Am. Chem. Soc.*, **47**, 903 (1925).

125. Jette, E. R., and Foote, F., *J. Chem. Phys.*, **1**, 29 (1933).
126. Joffe, A. F., "Physics of Crystals," New York, McGraw-Hill Book Co., 1928.
127. Johnson, G. W., *J. Appl. Phys.*, **21**, 1057 (1950); **22**, 797 (1951).
128. Johnston, W. H. & Mannu, P. J., *Ind. Eng. Chem.*, **44**, 1304 (1952).
129. Jones, B. M., *J. Chem. Soc.*, **95**, 1672 (1909).
130. Jones, B. M. and Partington, J. R., *J. Chem. Soc.*, **107**, 1019 (1915); *Z. phys. Chem.*, **88**, 291 (1914).
131. Joos, G., Enderlein, H. D., and Schadlich, *Z. physik. Chem.*, (Frankfurt) **19**, 397 (1959).
132. Kamenetskaya, D. S. and Piletskoya, I. B., *Doklady akad. Nauk. U.S.S.R.*, **94**, 689 (1954), *C.A.*, **49**, 13719.
133. Kendrick, F. B., Wismer, K. L. and Wyath, K. S., *J. Phys. Chem.*, **28**, 1308 (1924).
134. Khaikin, S. and Benet, H., *Compt. rend. acad. sci., U.S.S.R.*, **23**, 31 (1939).
135. Kirkaldy, J. S., *Canadian J. Phys.*, **37**, 739 (1959).
136. Kirkwood, J., *J. Chem. Phys.*, **18**, 991 (1950).
137. Kittell, C., "Introduction to Solid State Physics," New York, John Wiley & Sons, 1956.
138. Kleber, W. and Weis, J., *Z. Krist.*, **110**, 30 (1958).
139. Koda, K., *Kagaku Kenkyushe Holsoku*, **32**, 218 (1956); *C.A.*, **52**, 839.
140. Kohler, *Koll. Z.*, **19**, 65 (1916).
141. Kolthoff, I. M. and co-workers, *J. Am. Chem. Soc.* and *J. Phys. Chem.*, (1934 to date); *Science*, **84**, 376 (1936); *Tekniska Samfundets Handlinger*, **3**, 132 (1939); Kolthoff, I. M. and Sandell, E. B., "Inorganic Quantitative Analysis," New York, Macmillan Co., 1952.
142. Kornfeld, G., *Monatsh.*, **37**, 609 (1916).
143. Kracek, F. C., in "Phase Transformations," p. 264, New York, John Wiley & Sons, 1951.
144. Krasil'schikov, A. I., *Uspekki Khim.*, **5**, 367 (1936).
145. Kucharenko, J. A., *Planter Sugar Mfg.*, p. 75 (1928).
146. Kuster, F. W., *Z. anorg. Chem.*, **33**, 363 (1903).
147. La Mer, V. K., *Ind. Eng. Chem.*, **44**, 127 (1952); with Pound, G. M., *J. Phys. Chem.*, **19**, 506 (1951).
148. Landolt-Bornstein, "Physikalisch-Chemische Tabellen," 5th ed., Berlin, Julius Springer, 1923–36.
149. Langsdorf, A. Jr., *Ind. Eng. Chem.*, **44**, 1298 (1952).
150. Larson, R. F., *Ind. Eng. Chem.*, **37**, 1004 (1945).
151. Lefebvre, E., *Compt. rend.*, **70**, 684 (1870).
152. Leicester, H. L., and Klickstein, "Source Book in Chemistry," p. 9, New York, McGraw-Hill Book Co., Inc., 1952.
153. Lenher, S., *J. Phys. Chem.*, **33**, 1579 (1929); *J. Am. Chem. Soc.*, **51**, 2948 (1929).
154. Lieben, *Wien. Akad. Ber.*, **12**, 771 (1854).
155. Liesegang, R. E., *Phot. Archiv.*, **21**, 221 (1896).
156. Löwel, *Ann. chim. phys.*, 1850–1857; i.e. **(3) 49**, 32 (1857).
157. Lowitz, J. T., *Crell's Chem. Annalen*, **1**, 3 (1795).
158. Madigan, S., *Phys. Rev.*, **51**, 61 (1937).
159. Marbee, E. C., *Chem. and Engr. News*, **27**, 2198 (1949).
160. Marboe, T. E. C. and Weyl, W. A., *Trans. Soc. Glass. Tech.*, **32**, 282 (1948).
161. Marc, K., *Z. physik. Chem.*, **61**, 385 (1908); **67**, 470 (1909); **68**, 104 (1909); **73**, 685 (1910).
162. Marcelin, A., *Compt. rend.*, **148**, 631 (1910).

163. Mason, B. J. and Ludlam, F. H., *Reports on Progress in Physics*, p. 158 (1951).
164. Mattheus, R. E. F., Horne, R. W., Green, E. M., *Nature*, **178,** 635 (1956).
165. McBain, J. W., *J. Chem. Soc.*, **127,** 852 (1925); **128,** 421 (1926).
166. McCracken, E. C., *Science*, p. 453 (1947).
167. McIntosh, D., *Proc. Trans. Roy. Soc. Canada*, **13,** (**III**), 265 (1919).
168. McLachlan, Dan, Jr., Carlson, A., Christensen, C. J. and King, A., *Bull. #57*, U. of Utah (1952).
169. Menter, J. W., *Proc. Roy. Soc.*, **236A,** 119 (1956).
170. Metschl, J., *J. Phys. Chem.*, **28,** 417 (1924).
171. Meyer, J. and Pfaff, W., *Z. anorg. Chem.*, **217,** 257 (1934); **222,** 382 (1935); **224,** 305 (1935).
172. Miers, H. A., *J. Inst. Metals*, **37,** 331 (1927); *Rice Inst. Pamphlet* (1919). Miers, H. A. and Issac, F., *J. Chem. Soc.*, **89,** 413–54 (1906).
173. Mitscherlich, E., "Collected Works," Berlin, 1896. Polymorphs were recognized at an earlier date (1815) by J. N. Fuchs, who called them *vicariates*.
174. Moelwyn-Huges, E. A., "Kinetics of Reactions in Solution," p. 267, Oxford, 1947.
175. Morse, H. W., *J. Phys. Chem.*, **34,** 1554 (1930).
176. Morse, H. W. and Pierce, G. W., *Z. physik. Chem.*, **45,** 589 (1903).
177. Mott, N. F.
    (a) "Atomic Structure and the Strength of Metals," London and New York, Pergamon, 1956.
    (b) "Dislocations and the Mechanical Properties of Crystals," Int. Conf. 1956, New York, John Wiley & Sons, 1957.
178. Mott, N. F. and Gurney, R. W., "Electronic Processes in Ionic Crystals," Cambridge Press, 1941.
179. Nernst, W., *Z. physik. Chem.*, **47,** 52 (1904).
180. Neuhaus, K., *Fortschr. Min.*, **29/30,** 136–296 (1950–51).
181. Nichols, W. B., Carmichael, L. T. and Sage, B. H., *Ind. Eng. Chem.*, **49,** 1165 (1957), **33,** 443 (1941).
182. Noyes, A. A. and Whitney, W. R., *Z. physik. Chem.*, **23,** 689 (1897).
183. Noyes, R. M., *J. Chem. Phys.*, **22,** 1349 (1954).
184. Oldham, S. W. H., and Ubbelohde, A. R., *Proc. Roy. Soc.*, **176A,** 50, 65 (1940).
185. Ord, "Urinary Calculi," London, 1879.
186. Orowan, *Repts. Progr. in Phys.*, **7,** 195 (1948–49).
187. Ostwald, Wilhelm, "Lehrbuch," Vol. II, Leipzig, Engelmann, 1896–1902. (It is from Ostwald's account that much of the material of this present sketch is drawn.)
188. Ostwald, Wi., *Z. physik. Chem.*, **22,** 289 (1897); **23,** 365 (1897); **34,** 503 (1900).
189. Othmer, P., *Z. anorg. Chem.*, **91,** 209 (1915).
190. Packter, A.
    (a) *J. Chem. Soc.*, p. 239 (1956).
    (b) *J. Phys. Chem.*, **59,** 1140 (1955); **62,** 1025 (1958).
    (c) *J. Coll. Sci.*, **10,** 46 (1955); **11,** 96, 150 (1956).
    (d) *Koll. Z.*, **142,** 109 (1955).
191. Padoa and Galeati, *Gazz. Chim. ital.*, **35,** 181 (1904).
192. Paneth, F. and Horowitz, *Z. physik. Chem.*, **89,** 513 (1915).
193. Partington, J. R., "Treatise on Physical Chemistry," Vol. 3, p. 487, New York, Longmans, Green and Co., 1952.
194. Pashley, D. W., Menter, J. W. and Bassett, G. A., *Nature*, **179,** 752 (1957).

195. Pound, G. M. and LaMer, V. K., *J. Am. Chem. Soc.*, **74**, 2323 (1952) find the nucleating power proportional to the area of the droplet.
196. Powell, R. E., Gilman, T. S., and Hildebrand, J. H., *J. Am. Chem. Soc.*, **73**, 2525 (1951).
197. Powers, H. E. C., *Int. Sugar J.*, **58**, 246 (1956); Nature **178**, 139 (1956).
198. Prager, S., *J. Chem. Phys.*, **25**, 279 (1956).
199. Price, W. C. and Wyckoff, R. W. G., *Nature*, **157**, 764 (1946).
200. Reamer, A. H. and Sage, B. H., *Chem. and Eng. Data*, **5**, 38 (1960).
201. Rees, A. L. Y., "Chemistry of the Defect Solid State," London, Methuen Co., 1954.
202. Reischauer, C. S., *Lieb. Ann.*, **115**, 116 (1860).
203. Reiss, H., *J. Chem. Phys.*, **18**, 529 (1950).
204. Richards, T. W., Kirkpatrick, E. C., and Hutz, C. H., *J. Am. Chem. Soc.*, **58**, 2234 (1936).
205. Richardson, T. N. and Bailey, K. C., *Nature*, **131**, 762 (1933).
206. Riddiford, A. C., *Quarterly Rev.*, **6** No. 2, 157 (1952); *J. Phys. Chem.*, **56**, 745 (1952).
207. Rix, W., *Z. Krist.*, **96A**, 155 (1937).
208. Robinson, P., *J. Phys. Chem.*, **34**, 206 (1930).
209. Roller, P. S., *J. Phys. Chem.*, **39**, 221 (1935).
210. Rothmund, *Z. physik. Chem.*, **26**, 443 (1898).
211. Rothstein, J., *J. Chem. Phys.*, **23**, 219 (1955).
212. Royer, L., *Bull. soc. franc. mineral.*, **51**, 7 (1928).
213. Savost'yanova, *Uspeki Fiz. Nauk.*, **22**, 1, 168 (1938); *C.A.*, **34**, 6504.
214. Schaffs, W., *Koll. Z.*, **133**, 65 (1953); **137**, 12, 121 (1954).
215. Schaskolsky, M. and Schubnikov, A., *Z. Krist.*, **A85**, 1 (1933).
216. Schaum, K., *Z. physik. Chem.*, **25**, 722 (1898).
217. Schmidt, G. C., *Jahr. Radioak. Electron.*, **5**, 115; *C.A.*, **2**, 2643.
218. Schoen, H. M., Grove, C. S., Jr., and Palermo, J. A., *J. Chem. Ed.*, **33**, 373 (1956).
219. Schweigger, *Schweigg. J.*, **9**, 79 (1813).
220. Sears, G. W., *Phys. & Chem. Solids*, **2**, 37 (1957); *C.A.*, **52**, 29.
221. Seegar, A., "Theory of Crystal Imperfections," Chap. 7, Crystal Physics I; "Handbuch der Physik," S. Flugge, Ed. Berlin, Springer, 1955.
222. Seitz, F., "Modern Theory of Solids," New York, McGraw-Hill Book Co., 1940.
223. Seitz, F. and Turnball, D., "Solid State Phys." New York, Academic Press, 1956.
224. Sekera, F., *Koll. Z.*, **27**, 28 (1920).
225. Sheftal, N. N., Acad. Sci. USSR, "Growth of Crystal," p. 7, New York, Consultants Bur. New York, 1958.
226. Shlykov, A. S. and Gorbachev, S. V., *Zhur. Priklad. Khim.*, **29**, 607, 797, 1027, 1396 (1956); *C.A.*, **51**, 809.
227. Skrabal, A., *Chem. Ztg.*, **32**, 539; *C.A.*, **2**, 3300.
228. Smits, A., "Theory of Allotrophy," New York, Longmans-Green and Co., 1922.
    (a) *Z. Phys. Chem.*, 22, 545 (1897).
    (b) *Z. Phys. Chem.*, 46B, 43 (1944).
229. Sohncke, L., "Entwickelung einer Theorie der Kristallstruktur," Leipzig, 1879.
230. Spangenberg, K., "Wachstum u Autlosen der Kristalle," Handb. Naturwiss. Vol. X, 326–401, Jena, Fisher, 1934.
231. Spotz, E. L. and Hirschfelder, J., *J. Chem. Phys.*, **19**, 1215 (1951).

232. Staveley, H. and co-workers, *Quart. Rev.*, **3,** 65 (1949); *J. Chem. Soc.*, p. 2572 (1951); 1727 (1952).
233. Stern, K., *Chem. Rev.*, **54,** 79 (1954); Bibliography, U. Arkansas (1955).
234. Stranski, I. N., *Koll. Beihefte*, **32,** 197 (1931); *Naturwiss*, **37,** 13, 289 (1950); with Totomanov, D., *Z. phys. Chem.*, **163A,** 399 (1933).
235. Straumanis, M., *Z. physik. Chem.*, **13B,** 316 (1931); **19B,** 63 (1932).
236. Structure of Solids Discussions, *Deut. Min. Gesellschaft*, Berlin, Springer, 1951.
237. Suchman, H. and Saulwald, F., *Z. physik. Chem.*, **195,** 295 (1950).
238. Symposium on Ideal and Real Crystals, *Z. Krist.* **89A,** 193–416 (1934).
239. Symposium, "Imperfections in Nearly Perfect Crystals," New York, John Wiley & Sons, 1950.
240. Tammann, Y.
    (a) "Kristallisieren und Schmelzen," Leipzig, 1903.
    (b) "Aggregatzustande," English translation, "The States of Aggregation," by Mehl, R. F., New York, D. Von Nostrand Co., 1925.
    (c) "Metallography," translated by Dean, R. S. and Swenson, L. G., New York, D. Van Nostrand Co., 1925.
    (d) "Der Glaszustand," Leipzig, 1933.
    (e) *Z. phys. Chem.*, **25,** 472 (1898).
    (f) with Gronow; *Z. anorg. Chem.*, **200,** 57 (1931).
241. Tantzov, N. V., *J. Russ. Phys. Chem. Soc.*, **48,** 1654 (1916); **58,** 947 (1926).
242. Taylor, H. S., "Treatise on Physical Chemistry," Chap. VX, New York, D. Van Nostrand Co., 1930.
243. Taylor, J. E. and Feltis, T. J., *J. Am. Chem. Soc.*, **74,** 1331 (1952).
244. Tchermak-Seysenegg, *Z. Krist*, **101,** 230 (1939).
245. Temperley, H. H. V., *Proc. Phys. Soc.*, **55,** 376 (1943).
246. Tezak, B., *Arkiv. Kem.*, **19,** 23 (1947–1951); *C.A.*, **46,** 9937.
247. Thomas, D. G. and Stavely, A. K., *J. Chem. Soc.*, p. 4569 (1952).
248. Thomson, J. J., "Conduction of Electricity Through Gases," p. 149 (1903).
249. Tolansky, W. "Interferometry," p. 74, Oxford Press, 1948.
250. Traube, J., *Z. Elektrochem.*, **35,** 626 (1929).
251. Traube, J. and von Behren, W., *Z. physik. Chem.*, **138,** 85 (1928).
252. Triewald, M., *Gehler's Phys. Worterb.*, **1,** 678 (1787).
253. Turnbull, D.
    (a) "Seminar on Physical Metallurgy," p. 282, Cleveland, Ohio, Am. Soc. Metals, 1950.
    (b) *J. Chem. Phys.*, **18,** 198 (1948).
    (c) *J. Appl. Phys.*, **20,** 817 (1949); *T. Am. Men. Met. Eng.*, **175,** 774 (1948).
    (d) *Acta Met.*, **1,** 8 (1953).
    (e) *Ind. Eng. Chem.*, **44,** 1292 (1952).
254. Twomey, S., *J. Chem. Phys.*, **31,** 1684 (1959).
255. Ubbelohde, A. R., *Trans. Faraday Soc.*, **33,** 1198 (1937).
256. Valeton, J. J. P., *Physik. Z.*, **21,** 606 (1920); **59,** 335 (1924).
257. Van Hook. A., in Alexanders "Colloid Chemistry", **V,** New York, Reinhold Publishing Corp., 1944.
258. Van Hook, A., *J. Phys. Chem.*, **42,** 1191 (1938).
259. Van Hook, A., *Proc. Am. Soc. Sugar Beet Tech.*, **6,** 573 (1954).
260. Van Hook, A., and Frulla, F., *Ind. Eng. Chem.*, **44,** 1305 (1952).
261. Van Hook, A., and Bruno, A. J., *Discussions Faraday Soc.*, **5,** 112 (1949).

262. Van Oss, C. J. and Hirsch-Ayalon, P., *Science*, **129,** 1365 (1959).
263. Violette, Ch., *Compt. rend.*, **60,** 831 (1865).
264. Vogel, *Phys. Rev.*, **90,** 489 (1953).
265. Volmer, M., "Kinetic der Phasenbildung," Dresden, Steinkopf, 1939.
266. Von Behren, W. and Traube, J., *Z. phys. Chem.*, **A1216,** 1 (1929).
267. Von Lippmann, E. O., *Chem. Ztg.*, **52,** 257 (1931).
268. von Pickardt, *Z. physik. Chem.*, **42,** 327 (1902).
269. Wagner, C.,
    (*a*) *J. Coll. Sci.*, **5,** 85 (1950).
    (*b*) with Schottky, W., *Z. phys chem.*, **11B,** 163 (1930); **38B,** 295 (1937).
270. Walden, P., *Chem. Ztg.*, **55,** 373 (1931).
271. Walton, A., *J. Am. Chem. Soc.*, **38,** 317, 1161 (1916); **40,** 1168, 1184 (1918).
272. Weickmann, H. "Conference on Interfacial Tension," Boston U., p. 21, 1951.
273. Wells, A. F., *Annual Repts. Prog. Chem.* (*Chem. Soc. London*), (1947, 1949).
274. Wells, A. F., *Discussions Faraday Soc.*, **5,** 198 (1949).
275. Westwater, J. W. and Santagelo, J. G., *Ind. Eng. Chem.*, **47,** 1605 (1955).
276. Wilson, A. J. C., "X-ray Optics," New York, John Wiley & Sons, 1939.
277. Young, S. W. and students, *J. Am. Chem. Soc.*, **26,** 1413 (1904), **28,** 315 (1906), **33,** 148 (1911), **35,** 1067 (1913).
278. Zapffe, C. A. and Worden, C. O., *Acta Cryst.*, **2,** 377 (1949).
279. Zdanovskii, A. B., *Freiberger Forschimgsh.*, **A123,** 119 (1959); C. Z. 53, 7320.
280. Zernicke, J., "Classical Phase Theory," Kluwer's Publ. Co., 1957.
281. Ziz, *Schweigg. J.*, **15,** 160 (1815).

Chapter 2

BASIC PRINCIPLES

PHASE RULE

Were time of no moment, questions of the nature of product and yield in crystallization processes would be adequately answered by the phase rule. In the simplest and very practical case of the separation of a pure component from two-component systems in which no compounds are formed, the yield is merely the difference in solubilities at the terminal operating temperatures. The addition of a third component may, at times, substitute for changing temperature, and may "salt-out" or "salt-in" the desired product. Thus, NaCl and KCl do not form hydrates, double salts, or solid-solid solutions at ordinary temperatures, and only mutually lower the solubility of each other in water, as illustrated in Figure 2-1.

The area to the left of the line represents undersaturated solutions, while all compositions to the right are oversaturated. The solution is saturated simultaneously with both salts at the point of intersection. The isothermal removal of water would be represented by the diagonal and indicates that KCl would first separate and continue to do so until the NaCl/KCl mole ratio reached a value of approximately 88/42, after which the two salts would continue to separate at this same ratio.

In the reciprocal salt pair $NaNO_3$-KCl, the essential features enabling the separation of KNO_3 are the relatively low and high temperature coefficients of solubility of NaCl and KNO_3, respectively. A salt-mixture solution is thus evaporated to incipient NaCl crystallization and is then cooled. Most of the KNO_3 crystallizes in this operation and relatively little NaCl. A simple recrystallization improves the product tremendously. Complete and detailed phase-rule considerations of this conversion are to be found in Findlay's "Phase Rule."[43]

If the system is one in which solvates may form, a simple weight balance enables the calculation of product; i.e., if the composition of the solution is expressed as y fraction of component A, and separation occurs into fractions w_1 of composition y_1, and $(1 - w_1)$ of composition y_2:

$$y = y_1 w_1 + y_2(1 - w_1)$$

$$w_1 = \frac{y - y_2}{y_1 - y_2}$$

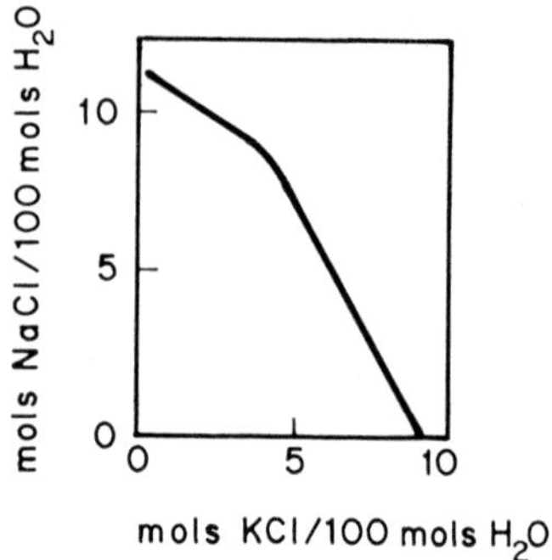

Figure 2-1. KCl-NaCl-H_2O system, 25°C.

If the separation is effected by the removal of fraction w_2 :

$$y = y_1w_1 + y_2(1 - w_1 - w_2)$$

This is illustrated in the basic Na_2SO_4–H_2O diagram shown in Figure 2-2, from which a simple graphic solution is apparent.

The addition of a second solute species complicates the phase diagram and usually restricts the range of pure components. Na_2CO_3 alters the Na_2SO_4–H_2O system as illustrated in Figure 2-3.

The basic Na_2SO_4–H_2O diagram is evident in the upper boundary of the figure. Each salt mutually reduces the solubility of the other. Up to 26°C the solid phases consist of the decahydrates of both salts with a slight reciprocal solubility of each in the other. The solid-solid solution line AC represents this situation. The highest concentrations along this line are 6.8 more per cent of the carbonate in the sulfate (as anhydrous salts), and 4.8 per cent sulfate in carbonate. The double salt $Na_2CO_3 \cdot 2Na_2SO_4$ appears above 26°C and is stable in its own solution above 67°C.

The diagram exposes the fact that crystallization of either single salt

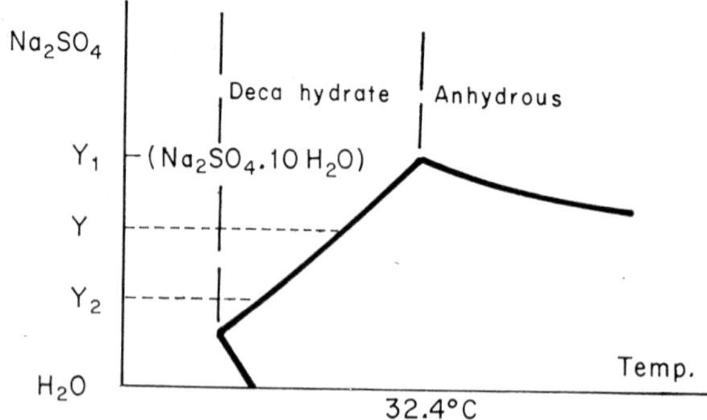

Figure 2-2. Na_2SO_4-H_2O system.

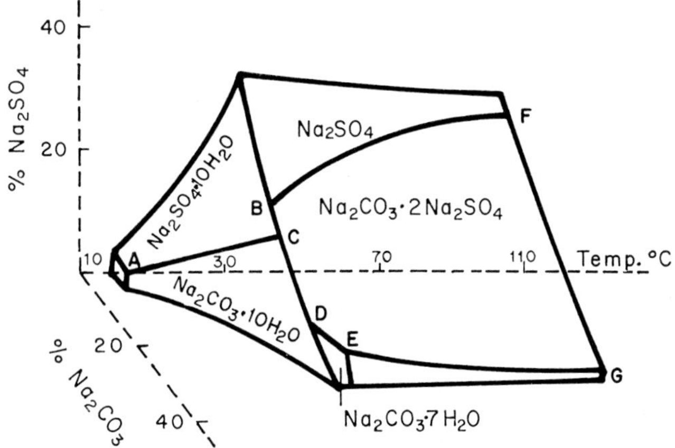

Figure 2-3. The Na_2SO_4-Na_2CO_3-H_2O system.[27]

from mixed solutions will be greatly restricted above the transition temperature of 26°C. Between 26° and 40°C the double salt precipitates with relatively large proportions of admixed carbonate and sulfate, but this proportion decreases rapidly at higher temperatures.

These data of Caspari have been represented in the usual triangular by Hougen and Watson.[68] This form, Figure 2-4, expedites the calculation of yields, as, for instance, the calculation of the production of crystals by

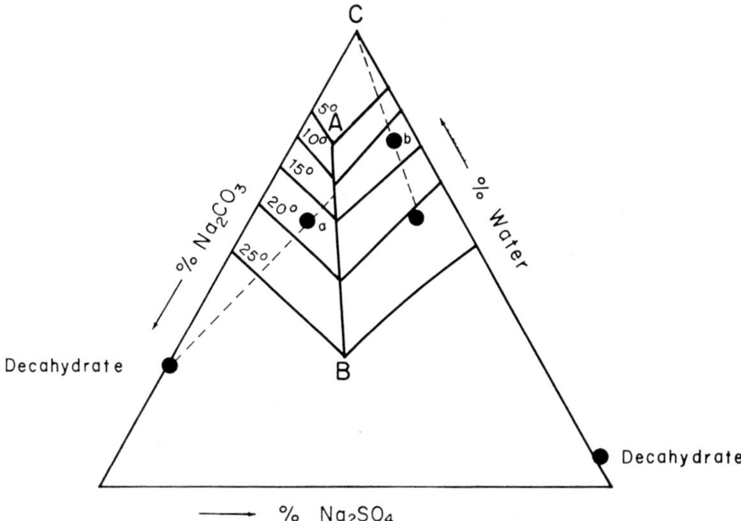

Figure 2-4. Solubility in the system Na_2CO_3-Na_2SO_4-H_2O at low temperatures. After Hougen and Watson.[68]

the cooling of a mixed solution. If the initial situation is represented by point *a*, cooling falls along the line drawn between this point and the sodium decahydrate point. This hydrate will separate upon cooling until the line *AB* is reached, at which point the two decahydrates will separate along the same line. Glauber's salt will separate, of course, from compositions to the right of line *AB*. Evaporation of water is tantamount to movement along the straight line at fixed salt ratio—i.e., *bc*.

The classic works of phase-rule chemistry[12, 139, 160, 174, 182] are replete with extended examples of these equilibrium calculations. The basic data in all cases are represented in the complete phase diagram, and the proper computational procedure is contained in the principle of conservation of mass.

Many instances are known where complete equilibrium conditions do not prevail and it is then sometimes possible to isolate metastable modifications under conditions appropriate to more stable forms. Gay-Lussac, Lowel and many other early workers (see Chapter 1), for instance, recognized the frequent occurrence of the metastable $Na_2SO_4 \cdot 7H_2O$ in the decahydrate range. The solubility of the heptahydrate exhibits a metastable eutectic with ice at $-3.55°C$ and a metastable transformation to the decahydrate at 24.2°C. This region is indicated schematically in Figure 2-5.

Another well-known example is the dextrose-water system. This sugar has a stable transition of the monohydrate to the anhydride at 52°C, yet, as long ago as 1882, Behr[8, 118] realized that either form would crystallize in the hydrate region according to the seeding material. Both forms may be produced commercially at about the same temperature.[118] Metastable polymorphs are generally easy to separate, and if the transformation speed of the unstable to the stable is relatively small, it is even possible to crystallize the two simultaneously from the same solution.[69, 114]

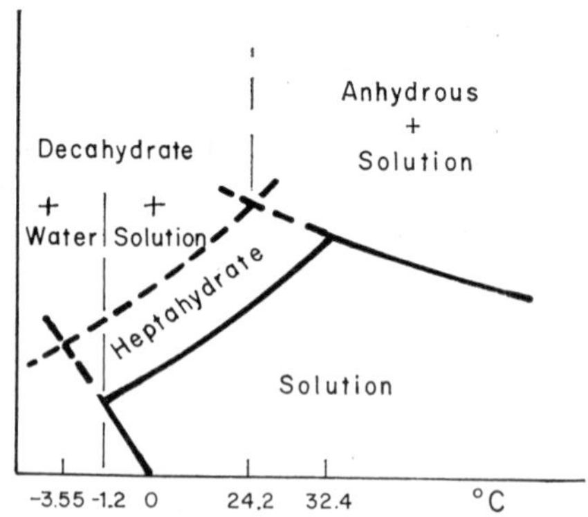

Figure 2-5. Metastability in the Na_2SO_4-H_2O system. Schematic.

These few examples, out of many, suggest very strongly that rate considerations may prevail over equilibrium matters.

CRYSTALLOGRAPHIC PRINCIPLES

The science of crystallography is based on three fundamental principles:

1. Law of Constancy of Interfacial Angles
2. Law of Rational Indices
3. Symmetry

The first of these principles was enunciated clearly by Nicolaus Steno in 1669 and is frequently designated by his name. It states that the angles between specified external surfaces of a given substance remain constant no matter how these faces develop. This law recognizes the remarkable identity and uniformity of form in crystals, as well as a variety of appearances (habit) due to the unequal development of faces.*

Haüy's law of rational indices was published in 1784 and refers to the orderly arrangement of the crystal units in space. If these units are planes representing the various faces of the crystal and are referred to a three coordinate axes system, then the relative intercepts of the planes on these axes can be expressed as small whole numbers. These ratios are designated the *Weiss indices* (a,b,c) of the plane. The *Miller indices* are more generally used and are obtained from the reciprocal of the Weiss coefficients after multiplication by the least common factor to give integer values.

In 1830, Hesel deduced that there were 32 classes of solids bounded by plane surfaces and subject to the condition of rational indices. Bravais[19] later proved that only 14 different symmetrical arrangements or space lattices are possible if shape considerations are excluded. These 14 space lattices fall into seven groups, which are the seven crystal systems. To arrive at this figure, Bravais stipulated that the fundamental building units of the crystal be arranged to be parallel and symmetric to each other. If a more general concept of homogeneity is substituted for these somewhat restricted conditions, 65 typical ways of arranging points in space are realized. These 65 *Sohncke groups* are augmented to a total of 230 *space groups* if mirror-image symmetry is also admitted. The seven systems of crystals

* The constancy of interfacial angles has led to an elaborate system of identification of crystals. In the first volume of "Barker's Index of Crsytals"[129] over 3,000 crystals are catalogued according to this criterion. An additional 3,571 are included in the second volume (1956), and 1500 more are planned for later volumes, thus developing Federov's early plan (1920) in a most exhaustive fashion. Systematic publication of similar crystallographic data on new compounds has also been inaugurated by the Armour Research Foundation. These notes are to be found in the current issues of *Analytical Chemistry*.

are classified according to these conditions as shown in Table 2-1. Their characteristics are summarized in Table 2-2 and Figure 2-6.

The third law of crystallography simply states that crystals always have the same elements of symmetry in one, two or three dimensions. Plane symmetry is defined by means of imaginary planes which divide the crystal into two exact and mirror-image parts. An axis of symmetry is a line with respect to which the faces, edges, and corners of the crystal duplicate at simple fractions of complete rotation. Points or centers of symmetry specify the situation when to every face there is a corresponding face at the opposite

TABLE 2-1. THE SEVEN CRYSTAL SYSTEMS

System	No. of the 32 Classes	No. of the 14 Bravais Lattices	No. of the 65 Sohncke Groups	No. of the 230 Space Groups
Cubic	5	3	13	36
Hexagonal	5	1	12	22
Trigonal	7	1	11	30
Tetragonal	7	2	16	68
Orthorhombic	3	4	9	59
Monoclinic	3	2	3	13
Triclinic	2	1	1	2
	32	14	65	230

TABLE 2-2. CHARACTERISTICS OF THE SEVEN CRYSTAL SYSTEMS

System	Axial Lengths	Axial Angles*	Typical Representatives
Cubic (regular or isometric)	$a = b = c$	$\alpha = \beta = \gamma = 90°$	NaCl, CaO, Cu, alums, diamond
Hexagonal	$a = b \neq c$†	$\alpha = \beta = 90°;\ \gamma = 120°$	Quartz, Zn, ice, beryl, graphite
Trigonal (rhombohedral)	$a = b = c$	$\alpha = \beta = \gamma \neq 90°$	Al_2O_3, Bi, calcite
Tetragonal	$a = b \neq c$	$\alpha = \beta = \gamma = 90°$	SnO_2, TiO_2 (rutile), $ZrSiO_4$ (zircon), urea
Orthorhombic (or rhombic)	$a \neq b \neq c$	$\alpha = \beta = \gamma = 90°$	$HgCl_2$, K_2SO_4, I_2, KNO_3, NH_4NO_3, topaz
Monoclinic	$a \neq b \neq c$	$\beta \neq 90°;\ \alpha = \gamma = 90°$	$KClO_3$, S, sucrose, borax, Glauber's salt
Triclinic	$a \neq b \neq c$	$\alpha \neq \beta \neq \gamma \neq 90°$	$CuSO_4 \cdot 5H_2O$, H_3BO_3

* α, β and γ are the angles between the axes a, b, and c (or h, k, and l) respectively.

† Three equal axes at 60° to each other, all in one plane, and a fourth perpendicular to the plane but not equal in length.

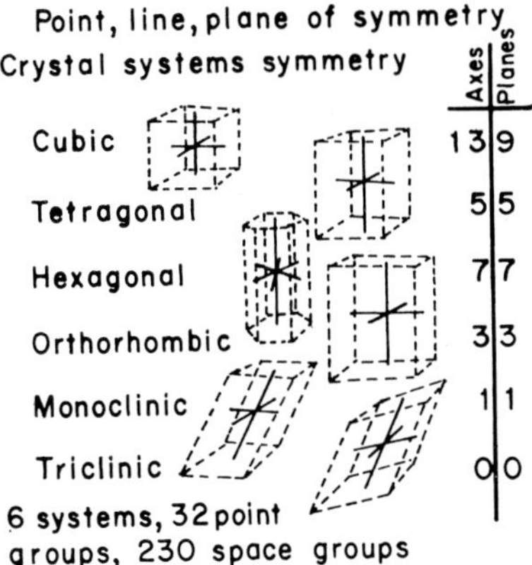

Figure 2-6. Illustrating the axes of the several crystal systems, and the simplest representative crystal outline.

side of the crystal. The symmetry characteristics of the seven crystal systems are indicated in Table 2-3.

The cubic or regular system represents the highest degree of symmetry of all the crystallographic systems. Starting with the simple cube itself, we can generate polyhedra within the same system by mere addition of faces oblique to each axis. Only a few of the many possibilities are illustrated in Figure 2-7, where the naturally rare 48-face diamond is an example of the hexakisoctahedron. Complex molecules are more inclined to appear with a low order of symmetry, while simple molecules are more likely in the cubic or hexagonal systems with a high order of symmetry. In fact, Donnay *et al.*,[38] point out that there is no known member in 41 of the space groups, and only single examples in 32. Thus only ⅔ of all possible space groups are found in nature to any appreciable extent, and the most populated of all space groups is the monoclinic, $C_{2h}^5 - P2_1/C$. Nine per cent of all known substances (including 22 per cent of known organic crystals) belong to this kind.

TABLE 2-3. SYMMETRY CHARACTERISTICS OF THE SEVEN CRYSTAL SYSTEMS

Cubic, more than one axis of three- or fourfold symmetry.
Hexagonal, one axis of sixfold symmetry.
Trigonal, one axis of threefold symmetry.
Tetragonal, one axis of fourfold symmetry.
Orthorhombic, two or more axes of twofold symmetry, or one axis of twofold symmetry and two planes of symmetry.
Monoclinic, one axis of twofold symmetry, or one plane of symmetry.
Triclinic, no planes or axis of symmetry. May have center of symmetry.

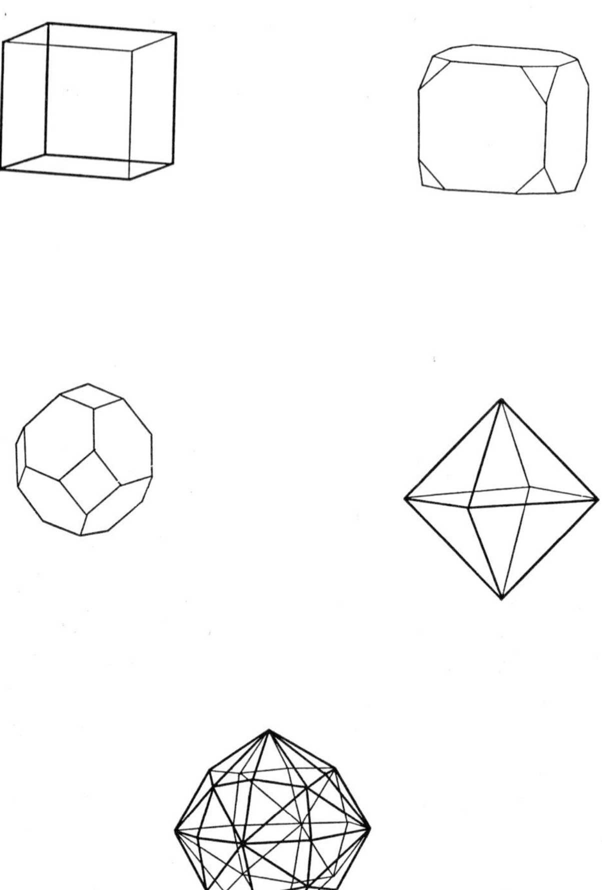

Figure 2-7. A few possible forms in the cubic system.

Stereographic projection

Any ordinary sketch of a crystal is, of course, in perspective, and is quite useless for representing angles and directions. Various schemes have been devised to alleviate this difficulty and one of the most convenient is by stereographic projection. This representation consists of the projection onto a selected plane (such as the equatorial plane of a reference sphere) of the points at which normals to the various faces cut the surface of a sphere whose center is placed at the center of the crystal. This arrangement specifies the spatial relationships of all faces but not the relative extent of their development. The various crystal angles may then be calculated readily by the following formulas of spherical geometry:

$$\frac{\sin \alpha}{\sin a} = \frac{\sin \beta}{\sin b} = \frac{\sin \gamma}{\sin c}$$

$$\cos a = \cos b \cos c + \sin b \sin c \cos \alpha$$

$$\cos \alpha = -\cos \beta \cos \gamma + \sin \beta \sin \gamma \cos a$$

where α, β and γ refer to the solid angles and a, b and c the plane angles, respectively. These relationships enable the computation of true axial ratios from measured dimensions and angles and are very useful in growth calculations. The method is illustrated in Figures 2-8 and 2-9 with a simple cubic model as well as with a more complicated case.

The foregoing classification of crystals is based exclusively upon geometric consideration. But there are many other arrangements which are useful for various purposes; one of these[60] is outlined in Table 2-4.

X-RAY CRYSTALLOGRAPHY

The ultimate form of a crystal is the result of the repetition of the fundamental unit cell in space. These unit cells pack together in the same way, but at different speeds in different directions during crystallization, so that the external form, or habit, is not always a simple indicator of the true inner structure. This information has become available only since the brilliant X-ray diffraction studies of von Laue, Bragg, and others. Excellent treatises on X-ray crystallography are available; the books of Bragg,[17] Bunn,[25] Wilson,[185] and others[52, 73, 82, 107, 137, 140] are representative. For recorded data on crystals most crystallographers depend on the *Strukturbericht* and Tabellen,[71] which have been continued lately by the *Structure Reports*[156] and Tables[72] of the International Union of Crystallography. Compendiums, such as that of Wyckoff,[181] are also widely used, while Schoenflies[14] is generally regarded as the ultimate reference in point group theory and related matters. Hodgkin and Pitt[63] have an excellent review of work on organic structures.

Direct X-ray examination of crystals reveals their symmetry features, but a Fourier analysis of the interference pattern is necessary in order to reveal the details of the atomic make-up of the scattering centers. The Patterson analysis is one of the most powerful of several methods and has served to illuminate the structure of very many extremely complicated molecules. General discussions will be found in the texts previously mentioned as well as in many other standard works. Many problems and appli-

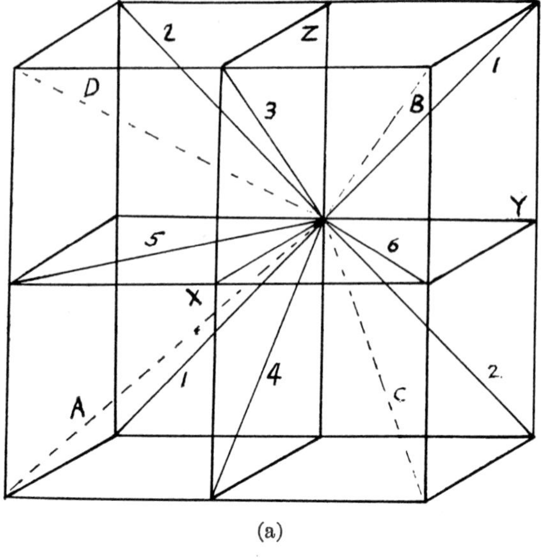

(a)

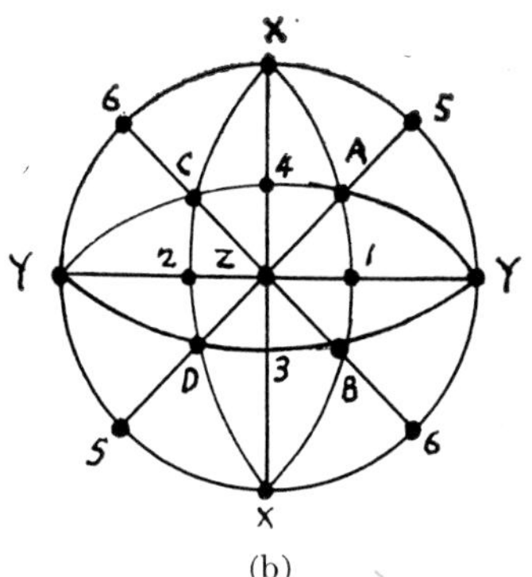

(b)

Figure 2-8. Cubic crystal.
(a) Four unit cells in perspective.
(b) Stereographic projection.

cations of these methods appear especially in the pages of *Acta Crystallographica.*

The direct revelation of individual atoms within a crystal is a much more recent development. Single macromolecules of molecular weight in the order of 1,000,000 have been resolved in the electron microscope,[138] while the even more powerful two-wave-length and field-ion microscopes reveal even much smaller entities such as the atoms of FeS_2[22a] and W.[116]

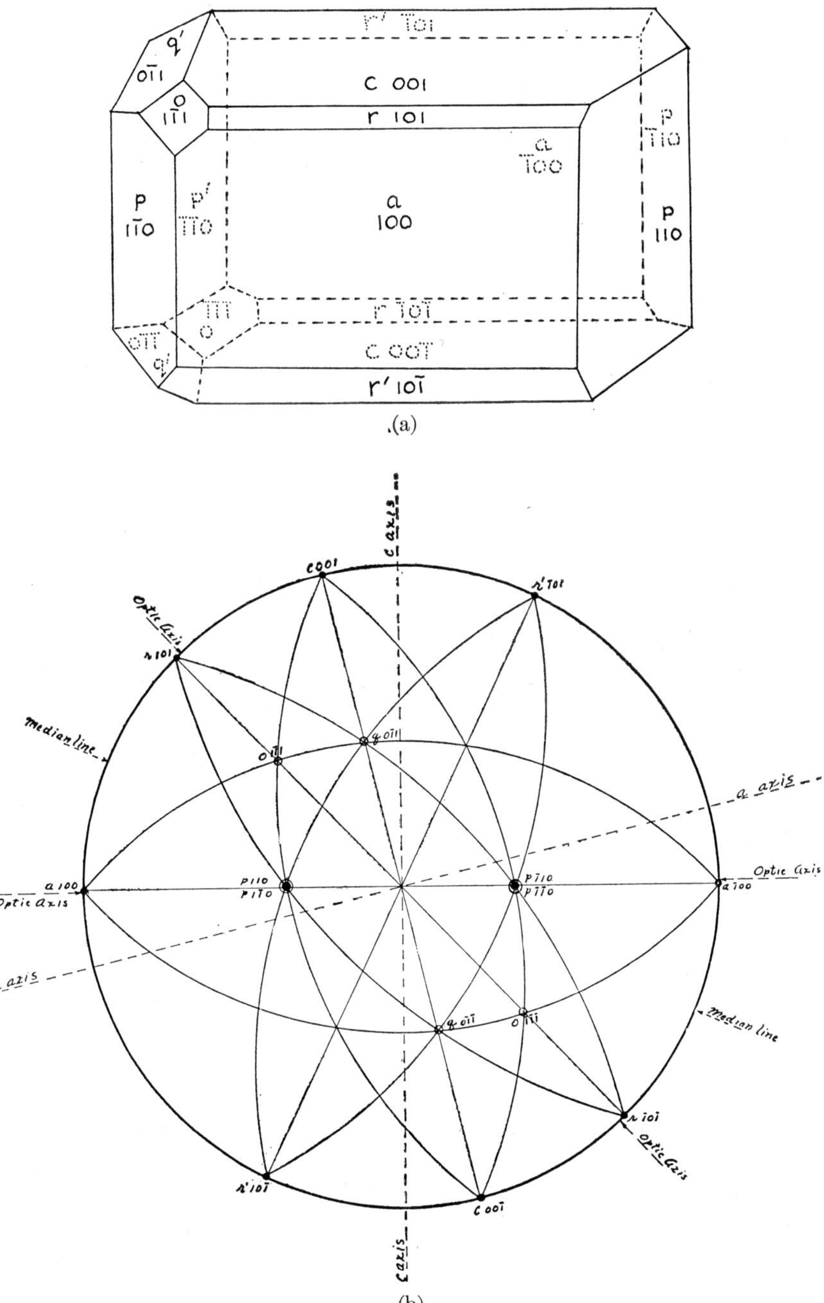

Figure 2-9. Sucrose crystal. Monoclinic; a:b:c 1.2595:1:0.8782 103°30′. (a) Perspective; (b) Stereographic net. After C440.[6]

TABLE 2-4. CLASSIFICATION OF CRYSTAL TYPES

Type	Examples	Bonding Energy (kcal/mole)	Characteristics
Ionic (electrostatic, or coulombic)	NaCl, LiF	180, 240	Strong infrared absorption; low electrical conduction at low temp., good at high temp.
Covalent	Diamond, SiC	170, 283	Hard; low conduction at low temp. if pure
Metallic	Na, Fe	26, 96	High electrical conduction
Molecular or van der Waals	A, CH_4 Most organic crystals	1.8, 2.4	Low melting and boiling points, compressible
H-bonded	Ice, HF	12, 7	Tendency to polymerize

External Form or Habit

Figure 2-10 illustrates that the form of a crystal may be different even though the crystallographic foundations are identical. In this schematic figure the background grid represents the cubic system and each square the unit cell. If these are assembled about a point of origin in a uniform manner in all directions, the equant form (*a*) of the regular cube results. If, however, the addition along the three axes differs, forms such as *b* and *c* would result. The particular case illustrated in Figure 10(b) would be described as *prismatic* or *columnar* when found in three dimensions. If the development normal to the plane of the illustration approximated the lengthwise growth of the face, the crystal would be described as being *tabular*. On the other hand, if the thickness were small compared to the length and breadth, the habit would be designated as *platy*, *micaceous*, or *lamellar*. *Blades* and *laths* would account for the intermediate cases. *Needles* or *acicular growth* indicate the predominance of growth in one direction, and if extreme the term *fibrous* is used. Such terms apply to individual crystals.

It is common for crystals to grow together or to extend variously in different directions during growth. The treelike patterns frequently observed in these cases are known as *dendrites* and the growth or aggregation as *dendritic* or *arboraceous*. If the aggregated crystal consists of small crystals grouped about a center, it is called a *spherulite*.

In addition to these general terms describing habit, additional ones are used to designate particular faces or combinations thereof. A few of these follow:

Prism: A form consisting of three or more intersecting planes whose intersections are parallel and vertical.

Pyramid: A solid defined by three or more similar planes having a common point of intersection. (*Bipyramid*—two such pyramids placed base to base.)

Pinacoid: A face parallel to two axes and cutting the third.

Dome: A face parallel to one axis and cutting the other two.

Sphenoid: Two faces whose intersection is parallel to a two-faced axis.

Holohedrism: Development of all the faces of a form.

Hemihedrism: Development of half the faces of a form.

Hemimorphism: Different development on opposite ends of an axis of symmetry, i.e., optical antipodes.

Truncation: The replacement of an edge between similar faces: i.e., the (111) faces truncate the (100) faces in an octahedron.

Vicinal faces: Faces with high Miller indices.

Twin Crystals: The intergrowth of two crystals as a unit. If the two members of the unit coincide by rotation about an axis they are said to exhibit *rotation twinning*, whereas they are designated *reflection twins* if a coincidence occurs by reflection through a plane.

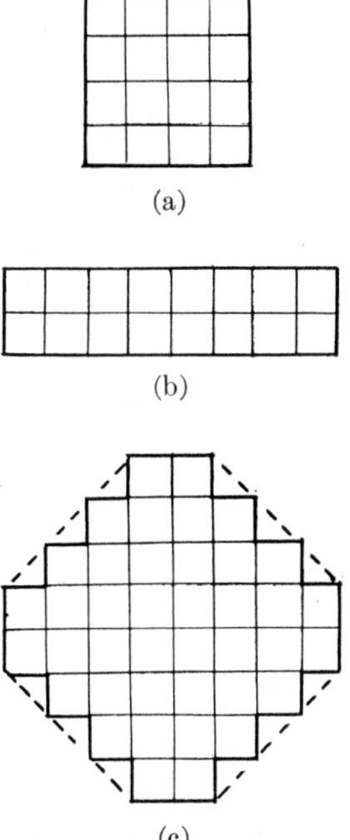

Figure 2-10. Two-dimensional schematic representation of different habits of a regular crystal.

Growth of External Form

In general, crystals develop their most characteristic habit when grown slowly from their mother liquid in an unimpeded manner. If grown rapidly, certain faces are apt to be absent or undeveloped. Mechanical restriction, such as contact with the sides or bottom of the container or clamp, usually leads to the exaggeration of the face or faces involved. Impurities may also impede the rate of growth of certain faces and thus lead to their preferred development, although Kern[79] feels that these are secondary effects. Thus, the addition of urea to solutions from which NaCl cubes deposit leads to the prominent development of the octahedra faces in addition to those normally present. The modification of crystal habit by environment is referred to throughout the papers in the Faraday Society symposium A-37 and in most of the standard works on crystallography. Lindenberg[105] has a general paper on the influences of solvents and co-solutes on the morphology of crystals, while Pozdynakov,[130] for example, discusses in detail the effects of pH and impurities on the form of large single crystals of Li_2SO_4. Professor Buckley has studied this subject of crystal-habit modification very systematically, and no better reference can be made than to his book.[A-1]

It is also generally presumed that a definite crystal form will be generated and conserved by continued growth under constant environmental conditions. While this may be true under simple and ideal conditions it is by no means always the case in actual circumstances. The first question of what particular crystalline form appears from a homogeneous atmosphere is essentially the subject of the Law of Successive Equilibria, whose historical and main features have already been discussed in Chapter 1, p. 16. The preservation of any particular established form is then primarily a question of the equilibrium form of crystals.[64, 183] Gibbs* formulated his criterion of equilibrium in the following words:

I. "For the equilibrium of any isolated system it is necessary and sufficient that in all possible variations of the state of the system which do not alter its energy, the variation of its entropy shall either vanish or be negative.

The following form, which is easily shown to be equivalent to the preceding, is often more convenient in application:

II. "For the equilibrium of any isolated system it is necessary and sufficient that in all possible variations of the state of the system which do not alter its entropy, the variation of its energy shall either vanish or be positive."

* Ref. 1, 93, Vol. 1, p. 354.

In Gibbs' nomenclature

$$(\delta\eta)_\epsilon \leqq 0 \quad \text{and} \quad (\delta\epsilon)_\eta \geqq 0$$

Here, η and ϵ are the entropy and energy of the system, respectively. He applies these criteria to the surfaces of discontinuity between solids and fluids and, after recognizing the restrictions imposed by the geometry of the crystal, writes the criterion as a minimum of the surface energy. In his own words, "On the whole, it seems not improbable that the form of very minute crystals in equilibrium with solvents is principally determined by equation (665), (i.e., by the condition that $\sum(\sigma s)$* shall be a minimum for the volume of the crystal except so far as the case is modified by gravity or the contact of other bodies)." He goes on in this same sentence to imply extenuating circumstances: "but as they grow larger (in a solvent no more supersaturated than is necessary to make them grow at all), the deposition of new matter on the different surfaces will be determined more by the nature (orientation) of the surfaces and less by their size and relations to the surrounding surfaces." That these circumstances may be kinetic ones is stated quite clearly in the following words.†

"The manner in which crystals actually grow or dissolve is often principally determined by other differences of phase in the surrounding fluid than those which have been considered in the preceding paragraph. This is especially the case when the crystal is growing or dissolving rapidly. When the great mass of the fluid is considerably supersaturated, the action of the crystal keeps the part immediately contiguous to it nearer the state of exact saturation. The farthest projecting parts of the crystal will therefore be most exposed to the action of the supersaturated fluid, and will grow most rapidly. The same parts of a crystal will dissolve most rapidly in a fluid considerably below saturation.

"But even when the fluid is supersaturated only so much as is necessary in order that the crystal shall grow at all, it is not to be expected that the form in which $\sum(\sigma s)$ has a minimum value (or such a modification of that form as may be due to gravity or to the influence of the body supporting the crystal) will always be the ultimate result. For we cannot imagine a body of the internal structure and external form of a crystal to grow or dissolve by an entirely continuous process, or by a process in the same sense continuous as condensation or evaporation between a liquid and gas, or the corresponding processes between an amorphous solid and a fluid. The process is rather to be regarded as periodic, and the

* σ is the specific surface free energy (capillary constant), and s the area.

† Ref. 1.93, Vol. 1, p. 324–5.

formula (664)* cannot properly represent the true value of the quantities intended unless δN is equal to the distance between two successive layers of molecules in the crystal, or a multiple of that distance.

"Since this can hardly be treated as an infinitesimal, we can only conclude with certainty that sensible changes cannot take place for which the expression (664) would have a positive value."

Curie[31] arrived at the same condition for equilibrium, but in a different manner. Curie believed that the principle held for macroscopic crystals, and that a crystal can change its shape as required by theory by one face growing and another diminishing. He postulated that the perpendicular distance h from the point of origin of a crystal to individual faces is proportional to the free energy of the face, or its capillary constant, σ: i.e.,

$$\frac{h_1}{\sigma_1} = \frac{h_2}{\sigma_2} = \cdots \frac{h_i}{\sigma_1} = \text{constant}\dagger$$

Each face has a specific capillary constant and crystals assume that habit which gives them the minimum surface energy. The relative areas of the faces, therefore, depend on their capillary constants.

Wulff,[190] in 1901, represented this same principle geometrically, and identified the capillary constants with the velocities of growth of the different faces. Let the specific free surface energy, σ, be plotted radially as a function of the direction at each surface point. This is the full curve of the two-dimensional plot in Figure 2-11. At each point of the surface construct planes perpendicular to the radius vector at that point, as illustrated by

* Equation (664), $(\epsilon_r' - t\eta_r' - \mu_1''\gamma' + p'')_s\delta N + \Sigma'(\sigma'l' \operatorname{cosec} \omega' - \sigma l' \cot \omega')\delta N = 0$ is an expression for the increase of energy in the whole system due to the growth of the crystal, and in which δN is the distance which the crystal grows on one side. In addition to the symbols already defined, t is the temperature, μ'' the chemical potential, γ' the density, p'' the pressure, l' the common edge and ω' the angle of intersection.

† This usual form of the Gibbs-Curie criterion is derived from fundamental concepts in the following way: Perpendicular distances, h, from a point within the crystal to the several faces of area, s, are erected. The volume of the polyhedron is then the sum of volumes of the pyramids, or $V = \frac{1}{3} \Sigma_1^i hs$. The Helmholtz surface-free energy is $A = \Sigma_1^i \sigma s$. If one face grows at the expense of another $V = \frac{1}{3} \Sigma_1^i (h ds + s\, dh)$, the conditions of constant volume and fixed values of h lead to: $\Sigma_1^i h\, ds = 0$. The minimum free energy required for equilibrium is stated by $dA = \Sigma_1^i \sigma\, ds = 0$, if the capillary constants, σ, are fixed.

Neither of these conditions is altered by a constant multiplier, M, so that

$$\Sigma_1^i (Mh - \sigma)\, ds = 0 \quad \text{or} \quad \sigma i/h_i = M.$$

In the case of actual finite crystals this criterion must be modified slightly on account of the energy contributions of edges and corners.[9, 65, 83]

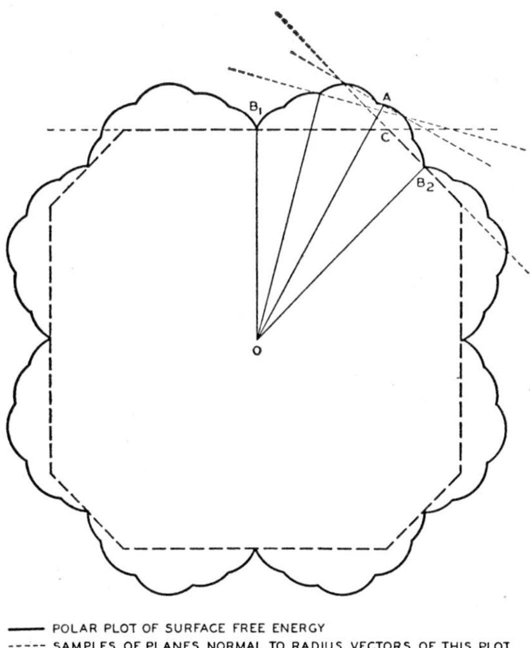

Figure 2-11. Typical polar plot of surface free energy for a crystal and the Wulff construction based on it.[58]

the dotted lines. Then the volume which can be reached from the origin without crossing any of the planes is geometrically similar to the shape which minimizes the surface free energy. The rigorous proof of this Wulff construction has been demonstrated by Liebmann,[104] von Laue,[179] and Kaishew.[74]

von Laue emphasizes that it does not suffice merely to have those faces which correspond to relative minimum surface energy. An absolute minimum is required: i.e., it is necessary to consider all possible combinations of faces and to find which of these relative minima is the smallest. The difficulties of analyzing and applying the Gibbs-Curie-Wulff concept to actual crystals are discussed by DeFay[32] and Herring.[58]

The firm thermodynamic basis of the Gibbs-Curie criterion has fostered much theoretical speculation, and a number of intriguing corollaries have been deduced. Viola,[177] for instance, postulates:

1. Growth of a crystal is proportional to the specific area of faces.
2. Normal growth of the faces of a stable crystal are proportional to their capillary constants.

3. The product of the growth rate and reticular density of different faces is a constant.
4. A transformation point always exists at a point of minimum surface tension between two polymorphic forms.
5. The surface tension is a minimum at a transformation point.

These are all straightforward deductions for stipulated conditions, but unfortunately actual examples are not numerous.

In a similar vein, Barillet and Choisnard[5] deduce that the interfacial tension between a solid and its solution increases regularly from undersaturation to supersaturation, and they offer observations on an NH_4Cl-oleic acid-water system in support thereof. However, it would seem that the necessary equilibrium conditions are hardly established in such an arrangement.

Stranski* and others[1, 55, 64, 65, 66] have applied the Kossel-Stranski theory of crystal growth (*vide infra*) to this important question of the equilibrium form of crystals, and restate the Gibbs-Curie criterion in terms of the work of separation of the atoms. The theory indicates that this energy should be constant for all faces when extended over the complete surface of the crystal. On this basis, the theoretical equilibrium form is calculated to be: a cube for NaCl, a rhombic dodecahedron for CsCl, an octahedron for CaF_2, a rhombohedron for $CaCO_3$ or $NaNO_3$, etc. In the majority of cases, the form observed in nature or found after slow and careful growth is that suggested by the theory, and exceptions find a ready explanation.

According to this Kossel-Stranski theory† the number of nearest and successively nearest neighbors of a particular lattice particle determine the bonding energy of the particle.[154, 155] Growth of the crystal will proceed by addition of a molecule to an uncompleted lattice row. This process is the *repeatable step* (*wiederholbarer Schritt*), and the lattice site that the molecule then occupies is the *half-crystal* growth position. The number of neighbors of a particle in the growth position is one-half those of a particle in the interior of the crystal. As far as the repeatable step is concerned there is no difference between the various lattice planes of a crystal. However, as one plane is completed a new one has to be started and this will occur at the middle rather than the edge of a face since the seed molecule will have more neighbors in the former location.

This is the situation in the case of homopolar crystals; surface nucleation at an edge will be preferred in heteropolar ones. If a lone particle, settling on a face to begin an entirely new layer, has a great number of closest neighbors, this face will grow fast normal to itself since new layers are nucleated easily. Thus, if the corresponding neighbor numbers are recorded

* Ref. A-38, p. 13.
† Ref. A-1 and A-18.

for the various lattice planes of a three-dimensional model, the faces may be arranged in order of increasing normal growth velocity or decreasing importance on the final crystal. It was in this way that the equilibrium forms mentioned above were deduced, and the reasoning has also been applied more recently to a number of other cases.[36]

A much older theory of crystal morphology is that of Bravais, who, about 1850, suggested that the order of decreasing importance of outer faces would be the same as the order of decreasing close-packing of the corresponding lattice planes or reticular density. In these close-packed planes the molecules form a dense aggregate and seemingly neutralize each other's bonds so that few free valencies are directed toward the outer space. Hence, a molecule starting a new face of this same type will be but loosely bound and the tendency to form a seed will be low. On the other hand, a less densely packed plane will consist of molecules less tightly knitted together, and will therefore have more residual valencies emanating from the crystal. A molecule about to start a new plane will then be close to the other molecules of this plane and will have a greater tendency to remain and form a seed. Since more rapidly growing planes are dissipated with respect to slower ones, the close-packed surfaces will prevail.

Each of these two theories has been developed with appropriate examples,[22b, 37, 183] but few objective surveys have been made. The mineralogist has made extensive use of the idea of Bravais. Wranglen[189] compared the two interpretations in the case of elements and other homopolar crystals and concluded that they are in fair agreement for simple structures, but that the Kossel-Stranski theory seems to correlate better, although it is more difficult to apply.

Berent[10] measured the contact angles of liquids on various faces of NaCl and KCl, and found them to be in accord with the dictates of Curie's theory. Pockels[127] criticized this work because of the uncertainty and lack of reproducibility of the measurements. Wells[183] finds that crystals of different shapes tend to a standard form when further growth is permitted, and Friedel,[46] as well as more recent work in Russia,[124] confirmed the Gibbs-Curie theory in the same way.

There are, of course, many physicochemical phenomena which indicate that various kinds of crystal surfaces differ appreciably in surface energy, chemical activity, evaporation rate, etc. Herring *et al.*[59] describe many of the more purely physical properties in this sense, while Gwathmey, Leidheiser, and Smith[53] present the chemical case. Tragert, and Robertson[167] ascertained galvanically that the close-packed octahedral plane of copper is the only one which established a reversible potential and that all other planes are metastable with respect to this configuration.

The contact angles of various liquids on the various faces of crystals of

NaCl, CaF_2, S, alums, and sucrose have been measured in the writer's laboratory,[35, 136, 143] and here again, in most cases, the most stable faces are those most extensive in area. Quantitative investigation of the Gibbs' criterion was not possible since the separate surface tension parameters could not be evaluated.

However, on the other side of the experimental picture, both Berthoud[11] and Valeton[172] completed investigations which appeared to discredit Curie's notions. Berthoud showed that the work involved in the formation of the different habits of a crystal separating from solution is nearly the same in all cases, so that the different forms have sensibly the same stability. Valeton held single crystals of different habit in their saturated solutions for months at a time and observed no change in form. The experiment has been repeated under carefully controlled conditions at the Bell Telephone Laboratories[181] using six different ethylenediamine crystals and the same conclusions were reached. Llemmlein[106] also discusses the experimental production of nearly ideal crystal forms, and Bliznahov[13] points out that adsorption can exert a profound effect on the formation of these equilibrium structures. It seems evident from these experiments that the ultimate form of large crystals is determined almost exclusively by kinetic rather than thermodynamic factors.[1, 55, 64, 66]

One of the primary deductions from the Curie relation is that the various faces of a crystal should have different solubilities according to their different capillary constants. This was observed by Ritzel[135] who reported that water dissolved the octahedral faces of a crystal of NaCl faster than the cubic faces, and that the relation was reversed in the presence of urea. However, Korbs[88] and Brunner and Tolloczko[21] had previously reported contrary results in the same systems.*

These contradictory observations are only a small part of the tremendous amount of work done on solution and growth in this as well as other systems. The main conclusion—as already intimated—appears to be that the Gibbs-Curie criterion is valid, in principle at least, for very small crystals, but not necessarily for large crystals ($>2\mu$).[A-14, A-17, 144, 150] The extenuating circumstances mentioned by Gibbs himself frequently appear to be more the rule than the exception, but nevertheless the criterion appears to remain an ideal law of nature. It is readily understandable that the reluctant formation of the ideal Curie form of a crystal from the nonequilibrium form may result from the lack of mobility in the crystal itself. The nucleating influence of the form already established is likewise more powerful than the

* The ratio of vapor pressures or solubilities of crystal faces differing by 100 ergs/cm^2 along an edge of 1 cm is estimated,[18] by the osmotic work equation, $\Delta F = RT \ln P_1/P_2$, to be only $1 + 10^{-8}$, at ordinary temperatures.

tendency to form nuclei of the more stable form. This growth itself is, of necessity, at a finite rate for the production of a crystal of reasonable size so that the applicability of any purely thermodynamic theory can be questioned. Without doubt, dynamic considerations[A-38] outweigh the thermodynamic factors.

Since investigations on NaCl have played such an important role in arriving at this conclusion and in formulating our current concepts of the equilibrium forms of crystals, they will be described here as a typical example of this development.

Growth and Dissolution of Ordinary Salt Crystals*

There exists a wealth of material upon the habit modifications which sodium chloride crystals display and the modifications induced by the presence of other solutes during growth. The first really comprehensive paper upon the subject was published by Retgers[134] in 1892. Retgers explains his interest in the subject and lists the effects of acids, bases, and salts upon crystal habit. His procedure consisted of crystallizing the solution on a microscope slide and then, if anything of interest appeared, recrystallizing upon a larger scale. He claims that he never found the rhombic dodecahedral or the tetrakishexahedral truncations which many other researchers claimed to be present. Moreover, other workers found some of his inactive ions to be active and vice versa. The explanation offered by Retgers is that there are many substances which cause small pyramids to appear on cubic faces, thus leading the unwary into believing that they see faces of octahedral or more complicated forms. However, the microscopic results of Retgers were found to be nonreproducible on a larger scale. The main results of his work were as follows:

1. Truncations of an octahedral nature, or cubo-octahedrons, were realized from solutions containing $CrCl_3$, $CdCl_2$, and urea.
2. He obtained cubo-octahedrons from solutions containing carnalite, acetamide, other amides, and alcohol.
3. Retgers noted that other salts increased the size and clarity of the crystals, but did not alter their habit.

In 1896, Orlov[120] conducted a large number of experiments along the lines of Retgers, but obtained notably different results. He was successful in obtaining octahedra and truncated cubes from solutions containing NaOH and HCl, and also obtained elongated cubes from HCl solutions.

In 1907 the results of another series of experiments were published by Korbs,[88] refuting certain of Retgers' results but supporting others. Korbs confirmed the action of the amides, alcohol, acetic acid, and pyridine, and

* Excerpted from Ref. 158.

the formation of tetrahexahedra in the presence of glycine. This latter observation was not substantiated by Sweeny.[158]

Ritzel,[135] in 1911, conducted experiments upon the rate of solution of halite crystals in water and observed that the octahedral faces had a higher dissolution rate than the cubic faces. In an undersaturated solution of salt containing 5 per cent urea, he found the rates of solution of both faces to be equal, but in solutions containing more than 5 per cent urea the cubic face had the lower rate of solution. Sometime later Le Blanc and von Elissafov[100] investigated the rates of dissolution and growth upon the various faces of salt and announced that while there was some small difference in the rates of dissolution, the rate of growth was the same for all faces. In the same year Poppe[128] published a more critical examination of the situation. By means of solutions of varying degrees of undersaturation he was able to show that for undersaturations of 0.5 to 1.0 per cent each type of face has a specific velocity of solution, but at undersaturations of 2 per cent or more the rates of solution of all the faces are equal.

In 1915 Schnorr[141] did a good deal of work with rock salt crystals in solutions containing urea. He reached several conclusions, the most important of which are:

1. When growth or solution take place in the presence of the same concentration of urea, sharp corners are formed upon dissolution on the poles of those faces which predominate in the grown crystal form (Goldschmidt and Wrights law[49] of the reciprocity of growth and solution).
2. The differences in rates of solution between different faces diminishes as the undersaturation increases.
3. In the majority of cases, the form of the final body depends on the form of the original body placed in solution.

After the first World War, Spangenberg[150] investigated the idea that the cause of habit modification was the formation of a complex between the salt and the foreign ions which were present. A salt solution rich in Hg^{++} ions yielded crystals showing the dodecahedral faces, or at least truncations of their form. Conductivity measurements also indicated the formation of the complex $[Na\ CO(NH_2)_2 \cdot H_2O]Cl$ in the presence of urea.

Schnorr later[83b] expanded his work on crystal growth of NaCl to include not only urea, but also artificial brine solutions very rich in $MgCl_2$. Most of his observations on growth from a solution were made upon ground spheres of rock salt suspended in the solution to be investigated. It was his custom to note the crystallographic regions where the new salt deposited upon the sphere, together with the perfection of the resultant face and the order in which the faces extinguished themselves through growth. Schnorr observed in the latter case that for pure salt solutions the order of extinction was (110), (210), and finally (111). In pure salt solutions, all crystals, whether ground or naturally faceted, finally attained the (100) form.

Schnorr observed further that: (1) When seed crystals were placed in solutions 2 per cent undersaturated, rounded (111) districts formed at the corners, while the edges between the faces remained sharp. (2) Pyramidal growths appeared upon (100) faces from solutions which were 1 per cent undersaturated. (There may be some connection between these growths and those observed much earlier by Retgers.) (3) By growing seeds from the brine solution mentioned above, he was able to obtain the (110) face without striations, whereas in the other solutions striations were always present when this face appeared.

From such observations Schnorr concluded that (1) the end form is independent of the starting form, and (1) it is possible to dissolve a natural combination of faces and then crystallize out the same combination provided the dissolution is stopped before the end form is attained.

At the same time, Neuhaus[117] also considered the geometric disappearance of faces on rock salt due to growth. He described the faces found in urea solutions and contrasted them with those found in pure salt solutions. He found that the (100) face is just as smooth in both solutions but in the urea solution the appearance is that of a rounded square with broad bands between the faces of the (100) form. The (111) faces are smooth, but rounded by the (110) faces, and show ditrigonal truncations. The zone girdles are different in the different solutions, the pure salt solution showing (100), (110), and (210) faces in a girdle isolating the (111) faces. In the urea-salt solutions, however, (111) and (110) faces form the girdle and isolate the (100) faces. As the concentration of urea increases, the growth of the (111) faces is slowed down and (210) and (110) faces become indistinguishable from one another. Neuhaus came to the conclusion that the complexity of a form was directly proportional to the speed at which the form tended to eliminate itself from the growing crystal.

In the 10 years following Schnorr and Neuhaus, the most important work specifically upon salt was accomplished by Yamamoto,[192] whose interest seems to have been the securing of large clear crystals of NaCl. His initial work was concerned with the catalysis of crystal growth by cations which were contained in the resultant crystal in appreciable amounts. He found that Mn^{++} ion gave the best results, while Pb^{++}, Sn^{++}, and Cd^{++} were somewhat less satisfactory. It is of interest to note that Yamamoto found that the Cu^{++} ion promoted the formation of nontransparent crystals while Retgers obtained big, clear cubes in the presence of the same impurity.

The most recent work done upon the modification of the crystal habit of

NaCl is that of Booth.[14] Booth studied the anomalous coprecipitation of tagged ions with NaCl. Pb^{++} and Cd^{++} ions behave alike in that they both inhibit and thicken the crystal layers, form oriented overgrowths on the (100) face, and slow down crystallization. Pb^{++} forms a (111) face on salt from acid solution, as does Bi^{+++} and to a lesser extent Mn^{++} and Zn^{++}. The acidity of the solution does not seem to affect the results obtained. Of the ions mentioned above, only the Cd^{++} was found to coprecipitate; the others seem to be adsorbed upon the (111) face due to a good fit between the adsorbed and the adsorbing planes.

POLYMORPHISM

Particular substances are by no means restricted to specific crystalline forms, or even to different forms in the same crystallographic system. Such multiplicity of forms is termed *polymorphism* in general or *allotropism* in the case of elements. In general, the number of forms which a material assumes is relatively few, although in principle there is no limit. One or two is most usual, although many more are known in numerous cases. For example, ten different polymorphs of tin tetraethyl have been recorded and six of lead tetraethyl,[151] while at least as many different allotropes of phosphorus have been reported from time to time. Fifteen are recorded for carborundum, and Mitchell[115] proposes that there is no limit to the number of possibilities. In fact, the wide variety of forms exhibited in this particular case has occasioned the designation of *polytypism* to distinguish from normal polymorphism.

Polytypism consists essentially of a multiplicity of forms which arise from variations in the sequence of stacking within the unit cell. It has been reported in a wide variety of minerals, cadmium iodide, and aliphatic compounds.[34] Polytypism is especially significant in the interpretation of growth patterns and spirals.[34, 176] Natural fats and oils[3] appear to be especially replete with a wide variety of different crystalline forms.

Two types of polymorphism are encountered in nature, reversible (*enantiomorphism*) and irreversible (*monotropism*). The phase diagrams of these two types are illustrated in Figure 2-12. In the first type the two forms are in reversible equilibrium at the transition point, which lies below the melting points. In the second type, form II is metastable with respect to form I, and the transition point lies above the melting points of both solids. The familiar pair of rhombic and monoclinic sulfur is a common example of dimorphic enantiomorphism, while white and red phosphorus form a monotropic system.

Partington[123] presents a thorough discussion of polymorphism, while Smits[149] has compiled an elaborate "Theory of Allotropy" for the case of

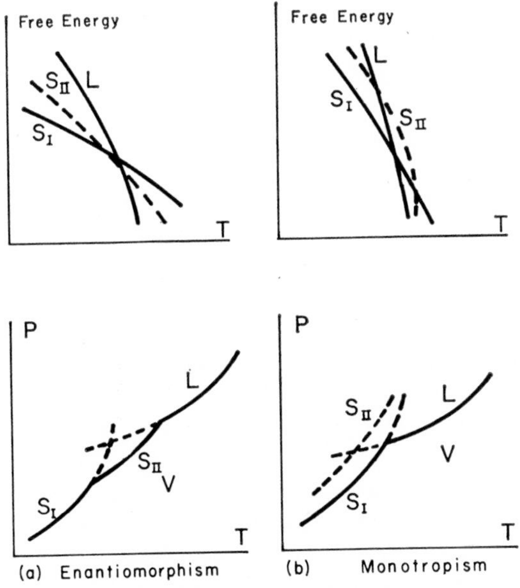

Figure 2-12. Polymorphism.

elementary substances. A complete catalogue of organic polymorphs is available in Deffet's[33] list. Tammann[159] paid particular attention to the rate of polymorphic change, a subject which has been considered more recently[56, 125, 151, 161, 169] in the light of later understandings of the thermodynamics and kinetics of phase transitions.

METASTABILITY

Kinds of Equilibria

It is necessary to recognize that various unique conditions of equilibrium exist in addition to the usual state of true or stable equilibrium.[20, 102] These modifications are those of unstable, metastable, and false equilibria. The state of true equilibrium is defined by the Gibbs' criterion of minimum free energy ($\delta G = 0$), while stable and unstable states are attended with free energy decreases and increases, respectively. The metastable state is one in which equilibrium persists with respect to all but one phase. It is time-independent and, therefore, stable. An unstable equilibrium, on the other hand, is an uncertain and unnatural process. False equilibrium is time-dependent and ordinary equilibrium laws do not apply.

La Mer[93] has illustrated the three cases of real equilibrium with the simple mechanical analogy of an ordinary brick in various arrangements on a plane

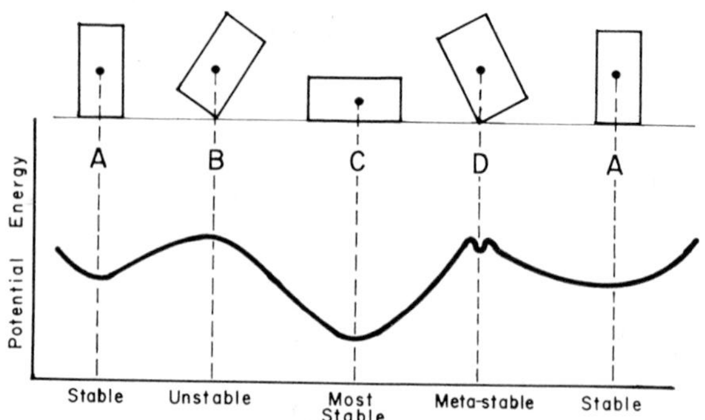

Figure 2-13. Stability. After LaMer.[93]

surface, shown in Figure 2-13. The stable states, A and C, are stable to small finite displacements and will resume their proper positions immediately upon removal of any disturbing force. The unstable configuration, B is, unique and will assume a new, more stable position upon the imposition of even an infinitesimal displacing force. The law of successive equilibria corresponds to this change when it occurs in steps to the next adjacent level in the potential energy curve.

Both configurations A and C are stable and rest at minima in the potential energy curve. C differs from A in being at the lowest level of all possible states, and therefore, represents the most stable of all conditions which may be assumed by this system. It is analogous to the absolute minimum of all minima, which specifies the equilibrium form of crystals.

The metastable state, D, arises from the bluntness of the contact edge. This gives rise to a region of stability which is defined by the degree of beveling, or by the heights of the surrounding barriers in the potential energy curve. The degree of disturbance which state D can survive is also defined in these same terms, and this state differs from that of the unstable state B in that the latter cannot withstand even an infinitesimal displacement.

The question of stability in chemical systems is regarded in terms of the free energy-composition relationships. The simplest case is that of a binary pair and is represented schematically in Figure 2-14(a). The chemical potential of each component, $\mu_n = \partial G/\partial N_n$, at an equilibrium state A is given by the intercept of the tangent at point A on the free energy-mole fraction diagram.

The free energy at point A is

$$G^A = N_1^A \mu_1^A + N_1^A \mu_2^A$$

and at any point along the line of tangency will be

$$G = N_1\mu_1^A + N_2\mu_2^A$$

Any particular phase along this line is in equilibrium with the state A, since $\delta G = 0$, whereas any situation above this line is metastable since $\delta G > 0$. This follows from the following consideration:

$$xy = x_0 - y_0 = G_x - (N_1^x\mu_1^A + N_2^x\mu_2^A)$$

or,

$$G_x > G_y$$

Similarly, any phase below the line is unstable with respect to A, since then $\delta G < 0$.

Figures 2-14(b) and (c) represent, schematically, very common cases. The free energy minima of the former enjoy a common tangent, which means the two compositions B and C are coexisting phases, such as an ordinary saturated solution and excess solute. In the latter case, all solutions on the curve between C and D are unstable with respect to B, while all

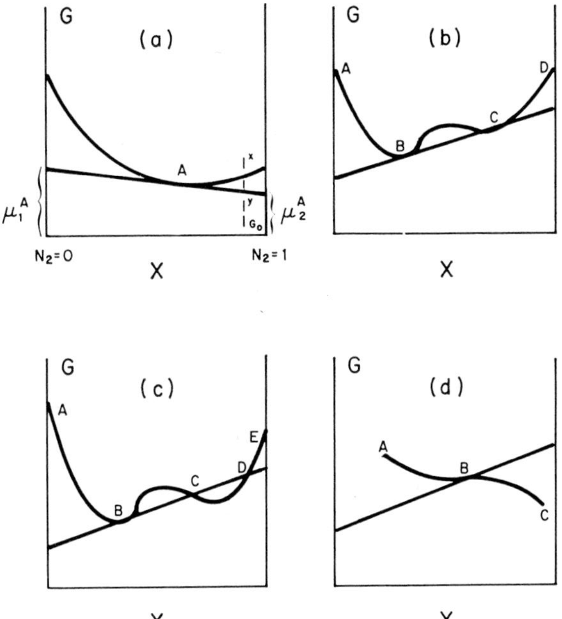

Figure 2-14. Free energy, G,–Composition, x, curves for binary systems.

along ABC and DE are stable because they lie on or above the tangent line. The phase B is thus stable to compositions on an equilibrium line of a convex nature, but unstable if this is concave. Since the maxima and minima of a continuous function appear alternately, so also we may expect stable and unstable equilibria of a body with one degree of freedom to occur likewise.[109]

Figure 2-14(d) represents the combination of these two cases through an inflected type of curve. Here, all homogeneous mixtures indicated by AB are stable with respect to B, while all along BC are unstable. Ordinary metastability is most frequently of the removed type shown in Figure 2-14(c) rather than that seen in (d). It is easy to understand the inhibition of transformation in the first case but not in the latter where the change would involve the formation of a phase differing only very slightly from the original.

The relationships in single-component systems are similar to the above representations with temperature replacing composition as the independent variable. Detailed considerations may be found in most modern physical chemistry texts, metallurgy monographs,[30] and other sources.[15, 23, 42, 101, 148, 180]

Direction of Metastability

While metastability is a real example of equilibrium in that it satisfies the general Gibbs' criterion of $\delta G = 0$, it is by no means perfectly reversible in the sense that it occurs with equal facility in either direction. There have been many claims (*vide infra*) that much less lag persists in rising temperature transitions than in the reverse—i.e., that vapors supercool more readily than their liquids superheat, that solids do not superheat or liquid-liquid pairs supersaturate, that low-temperature polymorphs change to high-temperature forms easier than the reverse, etc.

However, the only certain case of the unidirectional nature of metastability is that of solid-liquid transition. It is observed here that while supercooling of the liquid is quite easily effected it is ordinarily impossible to superheat the solid above its melting point. This is explicable on the basis that most solids consist of very small monocrystals and even single real crystals have a secondary structure. These discontinuities provide the focal points from which transition proceeds in a regular fashion. In fact, the transformation begins at these surfaces under conditions quite different from the usual macrothermodynamic specifications. Since this situation is significant for all subsequent considerations, we may very well now turn our attention to this subject of the Kelvin equation.

The Kelvin Equation

The Kelvin equation* is an essential ingredient of all quantitative theories of crystal formation. It was first deduced by Lord Kelvin[78] to express the variation, with size, of the vapor pressure of a liquid droplet. It was also implied in a general form by Gibbs at about the same time. Wollaston,[186] at a much earlier date, had observed that finely divided solids dissolved not only more rapidly but also to a greater extent.

If a spherical droplet of radius r is increased an infinitesimal amount dr by distillation of dn moles of liquid from a plane surface, the increase in surface is:

$$4\pi(r + dr)^2 - 4\pi r^2 = 8\pi r\, dr$$

The corresponding increase in surface free energy is $8\pi\sigma r\, dr$, where σ is the surface tension. The free energy involved in transferring the required dn moles from the plane surface to the droplet is $RT \ln P/P_\infty\, dn$, where P is the vapor pressure of the droplet and P_∞ that of the plane surface. At equilibrium these two changes must be equal:

$$8\pi r\, dr = RT \ln \frac{P}{P_\infty}\, dn$$

Now

$$dn = \frac{4\pi r^2}{v}\, dr$$

where v is the molar volume, whence

$$RT \ln \frac{P}{P_\infty} = \frac{2\sigma v}{v}$$

This original form of the Kelvin equation may be transformed immediately to the familiar Ostwald-Freundlich form expressing the enhanced solubility of fine particles, by applying the Raoult equation $P_i = P_i^0 X_i$ to the curved and plane surfaces, respectively. Here X_i is the mole fraction of the individual components of the solution, and in this case σ is the interfacial surface energy at the crystal-solution interface. If wetting is not complete at this boundary the normal component of the surface energy, $\sigma \cos \theta$. must be used in place of $\sigma \cdot \theta$ is the angle of wetting.

The $2\sigma/r$ of the above equation is in reality the excess pressure between

* This relation is known variously as the equation of "Kelvin" (W. Thomson), "Gibbs-Thomson," "Gibbs," "Ostwald-Freundlich," etc. The first two frequently imply the vapor-liquid situation, while the last often refer to the liquid-solid case.

the interior and exterior of a droplet, which when multiplied by the volume is nothing but the osmotic work $RT \ln P_A/P_B$ required to transfer a mole from the plane surface B to one of radius of curvature A: i.e., the Kelvin equation.

The basic equation for $(P_A - P_B)$ is derived in the following manner. The free energy of the system composed of the droplet of radius r and N_A moles in an environment of N_B moles is

$$G = N_A\mu_A + N_B\mu_B + 4\pi\sigma r^2$$

or the sum of bulk and surface free energies.
At equilibrium

$$dG = 0 = -\mu_A dN_B + \mu_B dN_B + 8\pi\sigma r\, dr$$

since

$$N_A + N_B = \text{constant}$$

Then,

$$\mu_B - \mu_A = -8\pi\sigma r \frac{dr}{dN_B}$$

If V_B is the volume of the droplet, $N_B V_B = \frac{4}{3}\pi r^3$

$$V_B = 4r^2 \frac{dr}{dN_B}, \quad \text{and} \quad \mu_B - \mu_A = -\frac{2\sigma V_B}{r}$$

Now $d\mu_A = V_A\, dP_A$ and $d\mu_B = V_B\, dp_B$, and since $V_A \approx V_B$,

$$P_A - P_B = \frac{2\sigma}{r}$$

The above considerations are for a spherical droplet. For a crystalline solid of definite geometric form, each face and its effective distance from some center point must be considered separately, and the whole assembly must, of course, satisfy Gibbs' condition of minimum surface energy. This leads (Ref. A-18, p. 87) to the Gibbs-Thomson equation in the form

$$\frac{kT}{2v} \ln \frac{P}{P_\infty} = \frac{\sigma_1}{r_1} = \cdots \frac{\sigma_i}{r_i}$$

where σ_i is the specific surface energy of the i face which is at a distance r_i from some central reference point; and P and P_∞ are the sublimation pressures of the finite and infinite size crystal, respectively. The $RT \ln P/P_\infty$ factor on the left is the chemical potential μ; and the criterion that this be constant throughout any system in equilibrium is, of course, tantamount to the Gibbs-Curie law for a polyhedron.

Stranski[153] has shown that one must reckon with the energy contributions of edges and corners since the former contributes significantly to the total surface energy when the particle is of such a size that the Thomson equation is descriptive of the properties. In this case it becomes

$$\frac{kT}{2v} \ln \frac{P}{P_\infty} = \frac{\sigma}{r} + \frac{x}{2r}$$

where x is the specific edge energy defined as the negative work required to separate the crystal faces at an edge divided by twice the length of the edge (since two boundaries are produced from the common edge). The specific corner energy is defined as half the work required to separate two crystal faces situated at a corner, but this does not contribute appreciably to the Kelvin equation.

The vapor pressure of ionized droplets has been investigated by Thomson.[164] In this case the electrical charge q opposes the surface tension according to the 4th power of the drop size, and

$$\ln \frac{P}{P_\infty} = \frac{V}{RT}\left(\frac{2\sigma}{r} - \frac{q^2}{8\pi r4}\right)$$

The effects of unit change are compared to uncharged H_2O droplets in Figure 1-14. It is evident that condensation is impossible upon charged water droplets if they are smaller than 0.63 mμ in radius, but above this size the charge assists condensation somewhat, relative to the uncharged case. There is no difference between positive and negative ions according to the equation, yet experimentally negative ions generally promote the condensation of supersaturated vapors better than the positive ions. This behavior has never been satisfactorily explained,[97] although many reasonable hypotheses have been advanced.[A-39, 16, 123]

Knapp[84] and, more recently, May and Kolthoff[111] have adapted the Kelvin equation to the molecular domain of small size and electrostatic charge, and modify the original equations to

$$\ln \frac{S}{S_\infty} = \frac{V}{RT}\left(\frac{2\sigma}{r} - \frac{q^2\delta}{4\pi D r^5}\right)$$

where δ is the distance between the double layers which carry a charge q, and D is the dielectric constant of the medium. Like Thomson's modification, this equation predicts that the solubility should increase with decreasing particle size but the effect is lessened by the charge, and that the solubility effect should approach zero for very small particles.

Still another modification of the original Kelvin equation is suggested by Kuhrt,[91] who takes into account the reduction in vapor pressure caused by the Brownian movement of the colloidal-like particles.

TABLE 2-5. VAPOR PRESSURE OF SMALL DROPLET OF WATER AT 20°C

r (cm)	p/Po
10^{-4}	1.001
10^{-5}	1.011
10^{-6}	1.114
10^{-7}	2.95

Direct experimental verification of Kelvin's equation is very difficult since the vapor pressure or solubility differences involved are very small. Calculated Table 2-5 illustrates this.

However, Thoma[163] has claimed verification of the vapor pressure form of the equation with an accuracy of 10 per cent. He measured the vapor pressure of various liquids contained in glass capillaries by means of an interferometer. Goodris and Kulikova[50] had also concluded the same from their measurements of the vapor pressure of small droplets of water, while Shereshefsky[145] observed vapor pressure lowering in capillaries to be much greater than that calculated by the Kelvin equation. Lashko and Petrenko[98] also discuss the limitations of the Gibbs-Thomson equation in this connection. In a later paper, Shereshefsky and Carter[145] ascertained the vapor pressure of water in capillaries of the order of microns in radius by equilibrating with the vapor over KCl solutions. They observed a regular increase in the ratio of r_{obs}/r_{calc} from 7 to 80 as the radius decreased from 9 to 3μ. The discrepancy may be reduced somewhat by assuming that there is an adsorbed film of stagnant liquid on the capillary walls, but the necessary connection ($\sim 4\mu$) is much larger than earlier estimates of 0.75[126] and 0.5–0.6,[188] and seems excessive even in the light of recognized long-range ordering forces in liquids.[36, 57, 96, 112]

Both the observed and the corrected discrepancies may be further corrected by assuming that the surface tension of droplets decreases with decreasing size. This possibility has been suggested by several workers in various connections[51, 110] and was analyzed critically in a comprehensive theoretical paper by the late Professor Tolman.[165] A number of theoretical[25, 62, 81, 85, 87] papers on surface tension and curvature have since stemmed from his momentous presentation. Tolman's fundamental equation in approximate form is:

$$\frac{\sigma}{\sigma_\infty} = \frac{r}{r + 2\delta}$$

where σ is the surface tension of a droplet of radius r; σ_∞ that of a plane surface; and δ a distance parameter of the Gibbs' surface of separation. If

σ is eliminated between this equation and the Kelvin equation we have

$$RT \ln \frac{P}{P_\infty} = \frac{2V\sigma_\infty}{r + 2\delta}$$

Values of about 2.1μ for δ are required to reconcile Shereshefsky and Carter's data[145] with their equation; but again these δ values seem excessively large when compared to the expected magnitude of the order of molecular diameters.

Tests of the Kelvin equation based on the rate of evaporation of small droplets lead to qualitative confirmation only. For this case the equation is written in the form

$$RT \frac{P - P_\infty}{P_\infty} = \frac{2\sigma V}{r}$$

which is valid if P is not very much different from P_∞. Since the rate of evaporation is essentially proportional to the pressure difference between the evaporating (small, concave) and condensing (large, plane) surfaces, we can expect an inverse proportionality between the rate of evaporation and the particle size. Lyalikov[108] observed this for Hg droplets, and from his data computed a surface tension of 454 ergs/cm^2. This is quite close to handbook values: i.e., 467.1 at 60°C.[95] Woodland and Mack,[188] and Shereshefsky and Steckler[145] found it necessary to assume that there is a halo of about 0.5 μ thickness surrounding droplets of n-butyl tartrate and n-butyl phthalate (0.5 to 2μ radius) in order to validate the Kelvin equation, but without this assumption the surface tension decreases with increasing curvature.[145]

The freezing and boiling behavior of liquids[90, 132, 133, 147] in fine capillaries and porous bodies are essentially in accord with the demands of the Kelvin equation.

The first really direct test of the Kelvin equation was that of LaMer and Gruen.[94] These workers equilibrated monodisperse aerosols of dioctylphthalate and oleic acid with solutions of the same in toluene and chloroform, respectively, and measured the growth under isopiestic conditions. This ingenious arrangement avoided the difficulty of measuring very small vapor pressure differences which plagued most of the previous investigations. Excellent quantitative confirmation of the Kelvin equation was realized. Stranski[A-39] also finds almost perfect agreement between modified theory and experiment, as illustrated in Figure 2-15.

The Kelvin equation is often called the Ostwald-Freundlich equation when applied to the case of enhanced solubility of fine powders. In this form it was first tested by Ostwald[121] and by Hulett.[70] Hulett found that the solubility of gypsum and $BaSO_4$ could be increased 20 and 80 per cent respectively by grinding to particles 0.1μ diameter. Dundon and Mack[39] repeated Hulett's experiments, employing conductivity methods, and found a similar (90 per cent) increase in the case of $BaSO_4$, but only a 4 to 12 per cent increase in the case of gypsum. They attributed Hulett's higher result to dehydration. Dundon and Mack also found appreciable increases (2 to 26 per cent) in the solubilities of fine particles (0.2 to 0.5μ) of PbI_2, Ag_2CrO_4, PbF_2, $SrSO_4$, and CaF_2. Using the Ostwald-Freundlich equation they computed surface energy values which are in the usual range allotted to solids.[173] They also found that the surface energy and molecular volume are inversely proportional according to this same equation, and they suggested a suppressing effect of charged ions on the solubility of fine particles.

May and Kolthoff have investigated the solubility of fine particles of lead chromate using both polarographic and amperometric methods of analysis. The instantaneous particle size was determined by dye adsorption and thorium B exchange. Freshly formed lead chromate exhibited enhanced solubilities of about 70 per cent but this fell quickly (in 20 minutes) to the normal value. In view of this rapid aging it is apparent that any exact test of the Ostwald-Freundlich equation by solubility determinations will be difficult. Qualitatively the observations are in agreement with the Knapp modification[84] of the basic equation. These workers also indicate that Balarev's[4] and Cohen and Blekkingh's[29] criticisms of Hulett's and Dundon's results are invalid.

Harbury[54] also emphasizes the experimental difficulties of testing the Kelvin equation by means of enhanced solubility of fine particles or depressed melting point. He considers it unsuited, even as a first approximation, and suggests retaining its significant theoretical features by substituting a "catch-all" factor, σ', for σ. This leads to some rationalization in connection with the interpretation of crystallization data.

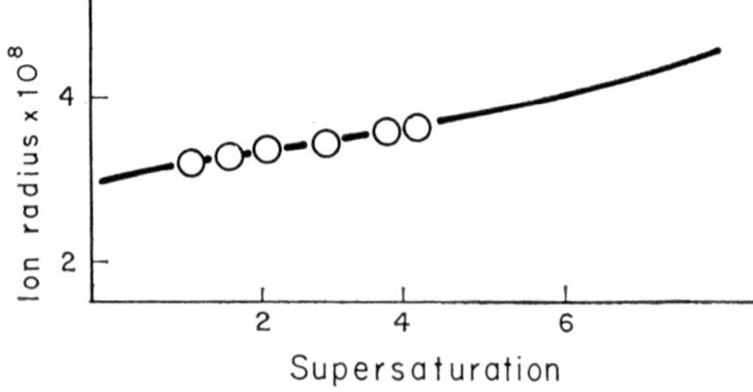

Figure 2-15. Variation of the radius of ions with the supersaturation.[178] Full line, theory; circles, experimental,

Van Hook and Kilmartin[175] have reported a transitory 4.3 per cent increase in the normal solubility of sucrose crystals when finely powdered material is added to syrup equilibrated with large crystals. These small crystals were prepared by very rapid precipitation with alcohol, and the total surface was evaluated by N_2 adsorption. This method of preparation eliminates the influence of any residual strain energy, and the area determination gives a truer measure of effective size than do microscopic methods. The interfacial tension calculated from the Kelvin equation (180 ergs/cm²) is in the usual accepted range (2 to 300). Equally agreeable values for the surface energy of solid NaCl are reported by Van Eeggeren and Benson[175] from determination of the heat of solution and enhanced solubility of NaCl smokes in ethyl alcohol.

Lastly, as still another test of the Kelvin equation, we expect a lowering in the melting point of solids when highly subdivided. This follows from the identity of the melting and solution processes indicated by inserting the Clausius-Clapeyron equation

$$\frac{\Delta P}{P} = \frac{\lambda}{R}\frac{\Delta T}{T^2}$$

in the approximate form of the Kelvin equation

$$RT\frac{\Delta P}{P} = \frac{2\sigma V}{r}$$

In this approximate form, $\Delta T/T = 2\sigma V/\lambda r$; λ is the heat of fusion, σ the solid-liquid interfacial tension, and ΔT the melting point lowering for a particle of radius r. Meissner[113] and Pablov[122] have reported such lowerings for finely divided stearic acid, tristearin, and azobenzene. Meissner observed a maximum lowering of 0.355°C in a layer 0.8μ thick. The expected lowering is about 0.1°C for particles with radius of 1μ.[76]

ENTROPY OF TRANSITION

Many of the thermodynamic equations of nucleation and growth involve entropy terms or may be readily cast into forms involving them. This is especially the case in those presentations couched in terms of the activated complex theory of reaction kinetics. It is, therefore, appropriate to consider entropy at this time in anticipation of its use. The transitions chiefly considered are those of 1-g and s-1 for single- and double-component systems.

Entropy of Vaporization

The Trouton rule is admittedly crude but is improved considerably by the modification introduced by Hildebrand.[61] This states that the entropy

Table 2-6. Entropy of Vaporization at Vapor Concentration of 0.005 mole l^{-1}

Normal Liquids		Metals	
Nitrogen	27.6 eu	Mercury	26.2
Oxygen	27.6	Cadmium	26.4
Chlorine	27.8	Zinc	26.4
Pentane	27.0	**Polar Liquids**	
Isopentane	27.4		
Hexane	27.2		
Carbon tetrachloride	27.0	Ammonia	32.4
Benzene	27.4	Water	32.0
Fluorobenzene	27.4	Ethyl alcohol	33.4
Stannic chloride	27.2		
Octane	27.6		
Bromonaphthalene	27.6		

of vaporization per mole is the same for all normal liquids if measured not at their boiling points as in Trouton's rule but at temperatures at which their vapors have equal concentrations. The improvement lies mostly with nonpolar liquids as is evident in Table 2-6. Differences have been turned to advantage by Hildebrand in interpreting the degree of perfection and regularity in the liquid state.

Actual vapor pressure data for inorganic compounds have been reviewed by Kelley,[77] and a comprehensive tabulation for inorganic and organic substances has been published by Stull.[157] Bailey[3] also considers these matters with particular reference to large molecules. These are only a few of the many contributions on this important function, which is of inestimable value in practical applications of liquid-vapor or solid-vapor transition theory.[41, 119]

Entropy of Melting

The entropy of transition in condensed systems is even more uncertain than that specified for vaporization by the Trouton rule. The corresponding Walden rule for melting is 2 to 3 e.u. for most elements, 5 to 7 e.u. for most inorganic compounds, and much greater and more variable values for many molecular compounds. Some particular values are illustrated in detail in Table 2-7. The values, in the case of the metals, are about the order of magnitude expected from the simple theory of the melting process, although there are exceptions. Kubaschewski[89] and Oriani[119] have rationalized these somewhat, in the case of metals, by considering the co-ordination numbers

TABLE 2-7. DATA REGARDING MELTING POINTS

	L_m (kcal mole^{-1})	T_m (°K)	ΔS_m (eu)	ΔS_m/ion or atom
Metals				
Na	0.63	371	1.70	—
Mg	1.16	923	1.26	—
Al	2.55	932	2.73	—
K	0.58	336	1.72	—
Cr	3.93	1823	2.15	—
Fe	3.56	1802	1.97	—
Cu	3.11	1357	2.29	—
Zn	1.60	692	2.32	—
Ag	2.70	1234	2.19	—
Pt	5.33	2028	2.63	—
Pb	1.22	601	2.03	—
Ga	1.34	303	4.42	—
Sb	4.77	903	5.39	—
Ionic Substances				
NaF	7.81	1265	6.19	3.1
NaCl	7.22	1073	6.72	3.4
KF	6.28	1133	5.53	2.8
KCl	6.41	1043	6.15	3.1
NH_4NO_3	1.539	442	3.46	1.7
Molecular Substances				
H_2	0.028	14	2.0	1.0
NO	0.551	110	5.02	2.5
H_2O	1.43	273	5.25	1.8
A	0.280	83	3.38	3.38
NH_3	1.84	198	9.30	2.4
N_2	0.218	63	3.46	1.7
CO	0.200	68	2.94	1.5
HCl	0.506	159	3.20	1.6
CO_2	1.99	217	9.13	3.1
CH_4	0.224	90	2.49	0.5
CCl_4	0.577	250	2.30	0.5
CH_3OH	0.525	176	2.93	0.5
C_2H_5OH	1.10	156	7.10	0.8
CH_3COOH	2.64	290	9.21	1.1
C_6H_6	2.35	278	8.45	0.7

and the disordering process of melting, while Pirsch[126] suggests the empirically corrected formula

$$\frac{\Delta H}{T - a} = k$$

for organic molecules, where a is a constant characteristic of the structure.

The higher entropies in the case of compounds are readily understood in the light of the greater disparity between the order in the liquid and solid states when the building units are not all identical. It would seem that some analog of the co-ordination number might rationalize the entropy change in this situation, and an immediate suggestion, in the case of ionic crystals, is the number of ions involved. If the values of ΔS for fusion are divided by the number of ions, values only slightly larger than 2.3 e.u. are obtained in many cases.

In the case of molecular compounds no simple counterpart of the co-ordination number is evident. The entropy per atom is, as expected, entirely unsatisfactory. Obviously the geometry of the molecule is significant for, as exemplified in the list, ΔS_m of symmetrical compounds, even of considerable size, is approximately the order of magnitude expected for the simplest case. However, the structure cannot account entirely for the entropy change of fusion since the molar value in a homologous series increases in an approximately linear manner for each regular increment to the chain length. This is illustrated in Table 2-8. The fact that each methylene group makes approximately the same contribution to the entropy of fusion as well as heat of fusion is highly significant. In the words of Ubbelohde,[170] it means that "in spite of the chemical links between these groups, each successive CH_2 group wobbles to some extent independently of its neighbors once the substance has melted." Melting a long-chain compound is envisioned by Garner *et al.*,[47] as a stepwise process wherein the molecule literally unwinds itself from the crystal face through rotation at successive carbon-to-carbon bonds, with one point of attachment being broken at a time.

The principal contribution to the entropy of melting is from the change in volume. If this is computed from the expansion and compressibility coefficients, the result is usually of the correct order of magnitude but somewhat less than the observed value. The difference is then allotted to the disordering process.[2, 40, 119, 131]

TABLE 2-8. ENTROPIES OF FUSION OF SOME HYDROCARBONS

	T_m (°K)	L_m (cal mole^{-1})	ΔS_m (eu)	ΔS_m/Carbon atom
CH_4	91.5	224	2.45	2.5
C_2H_6	101.4	668	6.57	3.3
C_4H_{10}	134	1050	7.85	2.0
C_5H_{12}	143.3	2000	13.9	2.8
C_6H_{14}	118	3110	17.5	2.9
C_8H_{18}	216	4930	22.8	2.9
$C_{18}H_{38}$	573.1	10000	33.3	1.8

The above tabulations demonstrate that the Walden rule for fusion is at best only a crude approximation, approached by simple elements and symmetrical compounds but varying widely for other compounds even when the widest selection of co-ordination numbers is applied in an attempt to realize fundamental entropy changes of the order of R cal/mole deg, the order of magnitude expected for a change from an ordered to a disordered state.

Entropy of Solution

The identification of the solution process with melting suggests a comparable situation insofar as the entropy of crystallization from solution is concerned. However, even wider discrepancies must be expected because of solvation effects. The unmixing effect alone may contribute as much as 1.4 eu.* This, together with solvation factors, leads us to expect generally higher entropy changes upon crystallization from solutions than from melts. This is illustrated in the Table 2-9. On the other hand, the entropies of polymorphic transitions are expected to be considerably lower than in fusion[67] (See Table 2-10).

The values in Table 2-9 have been selected mostly from Kelley's compilation.[77] The solubility values of ΔH were calculated according to the ideal solution law

$$\Delta H_{\text{sol}} = RT^2 \frac{d \ln m}{dT}$$

This is admittedly an approximation which needs correction according to the activity behavior of the systems involved, but unfortunately this information is not available for most of the systems listed.

The additional compilations in Table 2-11 of heat and entropy effects attending solution emphasize that any constancy of entropy of crystallization from solution, in analogy to the Trouton and Walden rules, is at best only the crudest approximation. This approximation is emphasized further by the fact that many cases of retrograde and exothermic solubility are known.

Whenever possible, directly determined data (e) of the heats of solution are the sources of the listed values. In other cases the results are computed (c) from solubility curves, corrected, wherever possible, for activity be-

* The unmixing effect may be estimated from the equation for the entropy of the mixing of an ideal binary solution: $\Delta S = -R \sum N \ln N$, and from which

$$\Delta S_{\max} = 1.38 \text{ eu.}$$

The value for a regular solution entails a very complicated computation[44, 60, 61, 187] but the final result is not much different from that for an ideal solution.

TABLE 2-9. ENTROPY OF FUSION FROM SOLUBILITY (*c*) IN BINARY SYSTEMS AND MEASURED DIRECTLY (*e*)[77]

Substance	T_m (°K)	Heat of Fusion (cal mole^{-1})		Entropy of Fusion (eu) (measured)	$\Delta S(c) - \Delta S(e)$
		c	*e*		
Al	931.7	2620	2550	2.74	+0.075
Al_2Br_6	370.6	5540	5520	14.62	+0.05
Al_2Cl_6	65.6	17700	16960	36.43	+1.59
Sb	903.1	4430	4770	5.28	−0.38
$SbCl_3$	346.5	3130	3030	8.74	+0.29
Bi	544.1	2560	2505	4.60	+0.10
Br_2	265.9	2580	2580	9.70	0.00
$Ba(NO_2)_3$	868	(5900)	—	(6.80)	—
CCl_4	249.1	640	644	2.59	−0.02
Cd	594	1480	1460	2.46	+0.03
Cl_2	238.4	1720	1615	6.77	+0.44
Co	1763	3840	3660	2.08	+0.10
H_2S	187.6	580	568.3	3.03	+0.06
Fe	1803	3720	3560	1.97	+0.09
FeS	1468	5400	4670	3.41	+0.50
$PbCl_2$	771	5310	5650	7.33	−0.44
Au	1336	2950	3030	2.27	−0.06
Mg	923	2160	1160	2.34	+1.08
Mn	1493	3650	3450	2.31	+0.07
KCl	1043	—	6410	6.15	—
$K_2Cr_2O_7$	671	8600	8700	13.07	−0.25
KNO_3	611	2910	2840	4.65	+0.11
$SiCl_4$	205.5	1920	1845	8.98	+0.37
$AgBr_4$	703	1300	2180	3.10	+0.17
$AgNO_3$	482	2550	2755	5.72	−0.42
Na_2CO_3	1127	7000	—	(6.21)	—
NaOH	595	2000	—	(3.36)	—

TABLE 2-10. ENTROPY OF SOME POLYMORPHIC CHANGES[167]

Substance	Transition	T_t (°K)	ΔH (kcal)	ΔS_t(eu)	T_f (°K)	ΔH_f (kcal)	ΔS_f (eu)
CO	h.c.p.*–f.c.c.	720	0.06	0.08	1768	3.8	2.1
Fe	b.c.c.–f.c.c.	1183	0.22	0.2	1808	3.7	2.0
Ti	h.c.p.–b.c.c.	1155	0.95	0.9	2073	3.8	1.8
Sn	gray-white	292	0.54	1.8	505	1.74	3.4
HgI_2	red-yellow	430	0.65	1.5	532	4.65	8.7

* h.c.p., hexagonal close-packing; f.c.c., face-centered cube; b.c.c., body-central cube.

TABLE 2-11. ΔS FOR CRYSTALLIZATION FROM SATURATED SOLUTIONS

Solute	Method	ΔS (eu)	Remarks
		Nonpolar Solutes	
p-Dibromobenzene	c	12.8	Alcohol, ether, benzene and bromobenzene solvents[146]
Naphthalene	c	13.8	Benzene solvent,[103] 60°C
Urea	c & e	8.9	Ref. 184
Sugar	c & e	3.5–13.5	0–60°C[174]
Various (28, mostly organic)	c	2.5–40	Ref. 152 (organic solvents)
Various	c		Ref. 182 (organic and aqueous solvents)
		Ionic-anhydrous[184]	
KCl	c & e	11.1	Aqueous solution
NaCl	c & e	1.2	
$Ba(NO_3)_2$	c & e	23.2	
$AgNO_3$	c	8.1	
$KClo_3$	c	29.4	
KNO_3	c	(17)	
$K_3Fe(CN)_6$	c	37.7	
KBr	e	11.1	
KI	e	8.7	
K_2SO_4	e	20–24	
NH_4Cl	e	12.2	
ZnI_2	e	5.35	
AgF§	e	11.7	
AgBr	e	67.3	
AgI	e	86.8	
AgCN	e	93.5	
TlF	e	31.9	
TlBr	e	4.7	
TlI	e	90.3	
Tl_2SO_4	e	24.6	
$TlClO_4$	c	40	
$(NH_4)H_2PO_4$	e	12.7	
Na_2HPO_4	e	74	
11-Amino acids	e	1.6 to 6.5	
$(NH_4)_2HPO_4$	e	6.8	
KH_2PO_4	e	13.2	
		Ionic-hydrated	
$Na_2CO_3 \cdot 10H_2O$	c & e	47.0	20°C Ref. 184
$NaOH \cdot H_2O$	c & e	8.7	Ref. 184
$ZnSO_4 \cdot 6\text{–}7H_2O$	e	9.8–15.7	5 to 25°C Ref. 48
$MgSO_4 \cdot 7H_2O$	c & e	17	
$LiNO_3 \cdot 3H_2O$	c	32.9	
$CuSO_4 \cdot 5H_2O$	e	8.65	
$BaCl_2 \cdot 2H_2O$	e	16.5	
$Li_2SO_4 \cdot H_2O$	e	14.6	
$Na_2SO_4 \cdot 10H_2O$	e	60–67	
$Na_2S_2O_3 \cdot 5H_2O$	e	26.1	
$Na_2CO_3 \cdot 10H_2O$	e	47.6	
$NiSO_4 \cdot 6H_2O$	e	12.9	

havior.[184] The agreement is generally quite good. Even a casual glance at the entropy charges reveals a tremendous variation, with no suggestion of rationalization, such as those based on the number of ions involved.[75, 99, 166, 171]

The list is not intended to be complete, but only representative. The *International Critical Tables* and Landolt-Börnstein's *Tabellen* are the sources of most of the data involved, while some additional values are included as noted. Water is the usual solvent and 25°C the temperature unless otherwise noted.

REFERENCES

1. Anshells, O. M., *Uchenye Zapiski*, No. 215 Ser. Geol. Nauk, **8,** 84 (1952), *C. A.*, **52,** (1932). *Acta. Cryst.*, **8,** 49, 521 (1955); **11,** 459 (1958).
2. Aranow, R. H., Witten, L., and Andrews, D. H., *J. Am. Chem. Soc.*, **62,** 812 (1958).
3. Bailey, A. E., "Melting and Solidification of Fats," New York, Interscience, 1950.
4. Balarev, D., *Kolloid Z.*, **96,** 19 (1941).
5. Barillet, F., and Choisnard, A., *Compt. Rend. 17th Congr. Chem. Ind. (Paris)*, 525 (1937); *C. A.*, **32,** 6925; *Bull. Soc. Franc. Mineral*, **61,** 297 (1938); *C. A.*, **33,** 4847.
6. Bates, F. J., and Associates, "Polarimetry, Saccharimetry and the Sugars," C440, U.S. National Bureau of Standards, Washington, D.C., Government Printing Office, 1942.
7. Baumhauer, A., *Z. Krist.*, **50,** 33 (1911); **55,** 249 (1915).
8. Behr, A., *J. Am. Chem. Soc.*, **4,** 11 (1882).
9. Benson, G. C., and Patterson, D., *J. Chem. Phys.*, **23,** 670 (1955).
10. Berent, Z. *Krist.*, **26,** 529 (1896).
11. Berthoud, A., *J. Chim. Phys.*, **10,** 624 (1912).
12. Blasdale, W. G., "Equilibrium in Saturated Salt Solution," New York, Reinhold Publishing Corporation, 1927.
13. Bliznakov, G., *Izvest. Bulgar. Akad. Nauk. Mat. Telsh. Fiz.*, **3,** 23 (1952); *C. A.*, **49,** 5923.
14. Booth, A. H., *Trans. Faraday Soc.*, **47,** 663 (1951).
15. Borelius, G., *Ann. Physik.*, **24,** 489 (1935); **28,** 507 (1937).
16. Bradley, R. S., *Quart. Rev.*, **5,** 316 (1951).
17. Bragg, W. L. "The Crystalline State," London, Bell, 1933.
18. Brandes, H., *Z. physik. Chem.*, **126,** 196 (1927).
19. Bravais, A., "On the Systems Formed by Points Regularly Distributed on a Plane or in Space," Paris, 1850, Engl. trans., Cryst. Soc. Am., 1950.
20. Bridgman, P. W., *Rev. Modern Phys.*, 20 (1935).
21. Brunner, L., and Tolloczko, S. T., *Akad. Wis. Krakau*, 594 (1903).
22. Buerger, M. J.,
    (a) *J. Appl. Phys.*, **17,** 909 (1950).
    (b) *Am. Mineralogist*, **32,** 593 (1947).
23. Buerger, M. J., in "Phase Transformations of Solids," New York, John Wiley & Sons, (1951).
24. Buff, F. P., *J. Chem. Phys.*, **19,** 1591 (1951).; **23,** 419 (1955).

25. Bunn, C. W., "Chemical Crystallography," Oxford, Clarendon Press, 1945.
26. Butuzov, V. P., *Obshchestva*, **85**, 395 (1956); *C. A.*, **51**, 3224.
27. Caspari, W. A., *J. Chem. Soc.* (*London*), **125**, 2382 (1924).
28. Cohen, E., "Piezochemistry and Problems of Chemical Morphism," New York, McGraw-Hill Co., 1926.
29. Cohen, E., and Blekkingh, *Z. physik. Chem.*, **186A**, 257 (1940).
30. Cottrell, A. H., "Theoretical Structural Metallurgy," New York, Longmans-Green, 1948.
31. Curie, P., *Bull. Soc. Mineral. de France*, **8**, 145 (1885).
32. DeFay, R., *J. Phys. et Radium*, **11**, 615 (1950).
33. Deffet, L., "Repertoire des Composes organiques polymorphes," Liege, Desoer (1942).
34. Dekeyser, W., and Amelincx, S., "Les Dislocations et La Croissance des Cristaux," Paris, Maisson, 1955.
35. DelGiudice, F., M.S. thesis, College of the Holy Cross, 1950.
36. Deryagin, *Z. Phys.*, **84**, 657 (1933).
37. Donnay, J. H. D., and Harker, D., *Am. Mineralogist*, **22**, 446 (1937).
38. Donnay, J. D. H., Nowacki, W., and Donnay, G., "Crystal Data," New York, Geol. Soc. America (1954).
39. Dundon, M. L., and Mack, E., *J. Am. Chem. Soc.*, **45**, 2479, 2650 (1923).
40. Dworkin, A. S., and Bredig, M. A., *J. Chem. Phys.*, **64**, 269 (1960).
41. Everett, D. H., *J. Chem. Soc.* (*London*), 2566 (1960).
42. Finck, J. L., "Thermodynamics from a Generalized Standpoint," Brooklyn, New York, Flatbush Publ., 1952.
43. Findlay, A., "The Phase Rule," p. 287, London, Longmans-Green & Co., 1931.
44. Fowler, R. H., "Statistical Thermodynamics," p. 354, Cambridge, University Press, 2nd Ed. 1949.
45. Frank, F. C., *Phil. Mag.*, **42**, 1014 (1951).
46. Friedel, G., *Bull. Soc. Handb. Min.*, **30**, 326 (1907).
47. Garner, W. E., Madden, F. C., and Rushbrooke, J. E., *J. Chem. Soc.*, (*London*), 2491–2502 (1926).
48. Giauque, W. F., Barieau, R. F., and Kunzler, J. F. *J. Am. Chem. Soc.*, **72**, 5686 (1950).
49. Goldschmidt V., and Wright, F. F., *Vabs. Min.*, **17**, 355 (1943); **18**, 335 (1904).
50. Goodris, and Kulikova, *J. Russ. Phys. Chem. Soc.*, **56**, 167 (1924).
51. Guggenheim, E. A., *Trans. Faraday Soc.*, **36**, 397 (1939).
52. Guinier, A., "X-ray Crystallography," Engl. trans., London, Hilger and Watts, Ltd. (1952).
53. Gwathmey, A. T., Leidheiser, H., and Smith, G. P., *Nat'l Advisory Comm. for Aeronautics*, Tech. Note #146 (1948).
54. Harbury, L., *J. Phys. Chem.*, **50**, 190 (1946); **51**, 382 (1947).
55. Hartman, P., and Perdok, W. G., *Proc. Kon. Ned. Akad. Wetenschap.*, **55B**, 134 (1952).
56. Hartshorne, N. H., Ref. A-38, p. 149; *J. Chem. Soc.* (*London*), 3705 (1955).
57. Henniker, J. C., *Rev. Mod. Phys.*, **21**, 322 (1949).
58. Herring, C., *Phys. Rev.*, **82**, 87 (1951).
59. Herring, C., and Nichols, *Rev. Modern Physics*, **21**, 187 (1949).
60. Hildebrand, J.,
    (a) *Anal. Chem.*, **24**, 720 (1952).
    (b) *Science* 90 (1939); *J. Chem. Phys.*, **20**, 1520 (1957).

61. Hildebrand, J. H., and Scott, R. L., "Soluiblity of Non Electrolytes," 3rd Ed. New York, Reinhold Publishing Corp., 1950.
62. Hill, T., *J. Phys. Chem.*, **56**, 526 (1962); *J. Am. Chem. Soc.*, **72**, 3923 (1950).
63. Hodgkin, D. C., and Pitt, G. J., *Ann. Repts. Prog. Chem.* (*London*), **47**, 432–69 (1951).
64. Honigmann, B., "Gleichgewichts und Wachstumsformen von Kristallen," Darmstadt, Steinkopf, 1958.
65. Honigmann, B., Moliere, K., and Stranski, I. N., *Ann. Phys.*, **1**, 181 (1947).
66. Honigmann, B., and Stranski, I. N., *Z. physik. Chem.*, **196**, 6 (1950); *Z. Electrochem.*, **56**, 338 (1952).
67. Hood, G., *J. Am. Chem. Soc.*, **75**, 6315 (1953).
68. Hougen, D. A., and Watson, K. M., "Chemical Process Principles," New York, John Wiley & Sons, 1947.
69. Hudson, C. S., *J. Am. Chem. Soc.*, **26**, 1065 (1905); *Z. physik. Chem.*, **50**, 273 (1904).
70. Hulett, G. A., *Z. physik. Chem.*, **37**, 385 (1901); *Z. anorg, Chem.*, **40**, 196 (1904).
71. "International Tabellen zur Bestimmung von Kristallstrukturen," Berlin, Borntraeger, 1935.
72. "International Tables of X-ray Crystallography," 3 Vols., Kynock Press, Birmingham 1952, 1959.
73. Jagodzinskl, H., "Handb. der Physik. VII. Crystal Physics," Berlin, Springer, 1955.
74. Kaishew, R., *Izvest. Bulgar. Acad. Naulk Otdel. Fiz. Math.* Tekh. Nauki, Ser. Fiz. **2**, 191–213 (1951) (German summary), **4**, 85 (1954); *C. A.* **51**, 3222.
75. Kapust, A. F., and Yatsimirsh, K. B., *Zhur. Fiz. Khim.*, **22**, 1271 (1948) C. A. **43**, 1242.
76. Kauzmann, W., *Chem. Rev.*, **43**, 253 (1958).
77. Kelley, K. K., *U.S. Bur. Mines*, Bull. **393** (1936).
78. Kelvin, Lord, *Phil. Mag.*, **42**, 448 (1881).
79. Kern, R., *Compt. rend.*, **236**, 830, 942 (1953); **240**, 324 (1955); *Bull. Soc. Franc. Min. et Crist.*, **78**, 461 (1955).
80. Kilmartin, E. J., and Van Hook, A., *Sugar*, **45**, #10 (1950).
81. Kirkwood, J. G., and Buff, F. P., *J. Chem. Phys.*, **17**, 338 (1949).
82. Klug, H., and Alexander, L. E., "X-ray Diffraction Procedures for Polycrystalline and Amorphous Materials," New York, John Wiley & Sons, 1954.
83. Knacke, O., and Stranski, I. N., *Naturwiss.* **26**, 385 (1952).
84. Knapp, L. F., *Trans. Faraday Soc.*, **17**, 457 (1922).
85. Koenig, F. U., *J. Chem. Phys.*, **18**, 444 (1950).
86. Kolthoff, I. M., *J. Am. Chem. Soc.* and *J. Phys. Chem.* (1934—to date).
87. Kondo, S., *J. Chem. Phys.*, **25**, 662 (1956).
88. Korbs, A., *Z. Krist.*, **43**, 451 (1907).
89. Kubaschewski, O., *Trans. Faraday Soc.*, **45**, 931 (1949).
90. Kuhn, W., *Helv. Chim. Acta*, **39**, 1071 (1956).
91. Kuhrt, E., *Naturwiss.*, **38**, 281 (1951); *Z. physik.*, **131**, 185 (1952); *C. A.*, **46**, 5386.
92. Lakhampal, M. L., and Puri, R. P., *Nature*, **172**, 917 (1953).
93. La Mer, V. K., *Ind. Eng. Chem.*, **44**, 1271 (1952).
94. La Mer, V. K., and Gruen, R., *Trans. Faraday Soc.*, **48**, 410 (1952).
95. Lange, N. A., "Handbook of Chemistry," 6th Ed., Sandusky, Ohio, 1946.
96. Langmuir, I., *J. Chem. Phys.*, **6**, 873 (1938).

97. Langsdorf, A. L., *Ind. Eng. Chem.*, **44**, 1299 (1952).
98. Lashko, N. F., and Petrenko, B. G., *Ukrain. Khim. Zhur.*, **11**, 270 (1936); *C. A.*, **31**, 4192.
99. Latimer, W. H., *Science*, **112**, 424 (1950); *J. Chem. Phys.*, **19**, 1139 (1951).
100. Le Blanc, M., and von Elissafov, C., *Chem. Zentr.*, **1**, 609–10 (1914).
101. Leontovich, M., *J. Exptl. Theoret. Phys.* (U.S.S.R.), **8**, 844 (1938).
102. Lewin, S., *J. Chem. Ed.*, **30**, 136 (1953).
103. Lewis, G. N., and Randall, M., "Thermodynamics," p. 299, New York, McGraw-Hill Book Co., 1923.
104. Liebmann, H., *Z. Krist.*, **53**, 171 (1914).
105. Lindenberg, W., *Neues Jahrb. Mineral. Abhandl.*, **89**, 149 (1956).
106. Llemmlein, G. G., *Doklady Akad Nauk. S.S.S.R.*, **98**, 973 (1954); *C. A.*, **49**, 5061.
107. Lonsdale, K., "Crystals and X-rays," New York, D. Van Nostrand Co., 1949; Royal Coll. Sci. J., **21**, 1–10 (1950).
108. Lyalikov, K. S., *Acta Phys. Chem.*, U.S.S.R., **12**, 43 (1940).
109. Macmillan, W. D., "Statics and Dynamics of a Particle," p. 137, New York, McGraw-Hill Book Co., 1927.
110. Martynov, B. J., *Zhur. Fiz. Khim.*, **23**, 278 (1949).
111. May, D. R., and Kolthoff, I. M., *J. Phys. Chem.*, **52**, 836 (1948).
112. McBain, J. W., "Adsorption of Gases by Solids," p. 444, London, 1932.
113. Meissner, *Z. Anorg. Chem.*, **110**, 169 (1920).
114. Miers, H., and Isaac, F., *Proc. Roy. Soc.* (*London*), **A82**, 184 (1909).
115. Mitchell, R. S., *J. Chem. Phys.*, **22**, 1977 (1954).
116. Muller, E., *Phys. Rev.*, **102**, 624 (1956); *J. Appl. Phys.*, **27**, 474 (1957).
117. Neuhaus, A., *Z. Krist.*, **68**, 48–54 (1928).
118. Newkirk, W. B., *Ind. Eng. Chem.* **28**, 760, (1936).
119. Oriani, R. A., *J. Chem. Phys.*, **19**, 93–7 (1951).
120. Orlov, P., *J. Russ. Chem. Soc.*, **28**, **I**, 715 (1896).
121. Ostwald, W., *Z. physik. Chem.*, **34**, 513 (1900).
122. Pablov, *Z. Krist.*, **6**, 37 (1910).
123. Partington, J. R., "Treatise of Physical Chemistry," London, Longmans-Green, 1952.
124. Petrov, D. A., and Bulskanova, A. A., *Izvest. Akad. Nauk U.S.S.R. Otdel. Khim. Nauk.*, 396–409 (1949); *C. A.*, **44**, 895.
125. "Phase Transformations in Solids," Cornell Symposium, 1948; New York, John Wiley & Sons, 1951.
126. Pirsch, J., *Mikrochem. Acta*, 992 (1956); *C. A.*, **50**, 11756.
127. Pockels, *Naturwis. Rundschau.*, **14**, 383 (1899).
128. Poppe, W., *Jahr. Min. Beil. Bd.*, **38**, 363 (1914).
129. Porter, M. H., and Speller, R. C., "Barkers's Index of Crystals," 3 vols., Cambridge, Heffer, 1951, 1956, 1957.
130. Pozdnyakov, P. G., *Kristallografiya*, **1**, 356 (1956); *C. A.*, **51**, 793.
131. Prigoyine, I., and DeFay, R., "Thermodynamique Chimique," Paris, Dunod (1946).
132. Puri, R. P., Sharma, L. R., and Lakhampal, M. L., *J. Phys. Chem.*, **58**, 389 (1954).
133. Reiss, H., and Wilson, I. B., *J. Coll. Sci.*, **3**, 551 (1948).
134. Retgers, J. W., *Z. physik. Chem.*, **9**, 267 (1892); **12**, 582 (1893).
135. Ritzel, A., *Z. Krist.*, **49**, 152 (1911).

136. Robertson, J. K., M.S. thesis, College of the Holy Cross, 1950.
137. Robertson, J. M., "Organic Crystals and Molecules," Ithaca, N.Y., Cornell U. Press, 1953.
138. Rochow, E., *Science*, 272 (Mar. 17, 1950).
139. Rooseboom, S., "Die heterogenen Gleichgewichte," Braunschweig, 1901 et. seq.
140. Rutgers, A. J., "Physical Chemistry," New York, Interscience, 1954.
141. Schnorr, W., *Z. Krist.*,
 (a) **54,** 289 (1915).
 (b) **68,** 1 (1928).
142. Schoenflies, A., "Theorie der Kristallstruktur," Berlin, 1932.
143. Schwendiger, R. B., M.S. thesis, College of the Holy Cross, 1950.
144. Semenchenko, V. K., *J. Phys. Chem. USSR*, **19,** 298, 350, 429 (1945).
145. Shereshefsky, J. L., *et al.*,
 (a) *J. Am. Chem. Soc.*, **50,** 2966 (1928).
 (b) *J. Am. Chem. Soc.*, **72,** 3682 (1950).
 (c) *J. Chem. Phys.*, **4,** 108 (1936).
146. Shroder, H., *Z. physik. Chem.*, **11,** 449 (1893).
147. Skapski, A. S., and Sill, R. C., *J. Chem. Phys.*, **24,** 644 (1956); **36,** 1350 (1957).
148. Slater, J. C., "Introduction to Chemical Physics," New York, McGraw-Hill Book Co., 1939.
149. Smits, A., "Die Theorie der Komplixitat und der Allotropie," Berlin, 1938, 2nd ed.; English trans. of 1st ed., New York, Longmans-Green, 1922.
150. Spangenberg, K., *Z. Krist.*, **59,** 375–80 (1920).
151. Stavely, L. A. K., *et al.*,
 (a) *J. Chem. Soc.* (*London*), 2290 (Sept., 1950).
 (b) 2572 (1951); *Trans. Faraday Soc.*, **52,** 26 (1956).
152. Steiner, L. E., "Chemical Thermodynamics," P. 293, New York, McGraw-Hill Book Co., 1948.
153. Stranski, I. N., *Z. Krist.*, **105,** 91 (1953).
154. Stranski, I. N., and Kaischew, R., *Z. Krist.*, **78A,** 373 (1931).
155. Stranski, I. N., Kaischew, R., and Krastanow, L., *Z. Krist.*, **88A,** 325 (1934).
156. "Structure Reports," N.V.A., Oosthoek Uitgevers Mij., Utrecht, Netherlands. Vol. 8 (1956) links up with Vol. 7 of the Strukturbericht, and subsequent volumes (vol 15 (1957)) continue the catalog of data. Vol. 14 (1959) contains a cumulative index for 1940–50.
157. Stull, D. R., *Ind. Eng. Chem.*, **39,** 517–550 (1947).
158. Sweeny, G. D. M., B.S. thesis, College of the Holly Cross, 1952.
159. Tamman, G., "States of Aggregation," New York, D. Van Nostrand Co., 1921.
160. Teeple, J. E., "The Industrial Development of Searles Lake Brines," Chemical Catalog Co., 1929.
161. Temperley, H. N. V., "Changes of State," New York, Interscience, 1956.
162. Thibault, N. W., *Am. Min.*, **29,** 327 (1944).
163. Thoma, *Z. physik.*, **64,** 224 (1930).
164. Thomson, J. J., "Conductivity of Electricity Through Gases," p. 149, (1903).
165. Tolman, R. C., *J. Chem. Phys.*, **16,** 788 (1948); **17,** 118, 333 (1949).
166. Topol, L. E., Mayer, S. W. and Ransom, L. D., *J. Am. Chem. Soc.*, **64,** 862 (1960).
167. Tragert, W. E., and Robertson, W. D., *J. Electrochem.*, **103,** 87 (1955).
168. Turnbull, D., "Solid State Physics," Vol. 3, p. 246, New York, Academic Press, 1956.

169. Turnbull, D., and Cohen, M. H., *J. Chem. Phys.*, **29,** 1049 (1958).
170. Ubbelohde, A. R., *Sci. J. Roy. Col.. Sci.*, **15,** 40–50 (1945).
171. Ubbelohde, A. R., *Quart. Rev.*, **IV,** #4 (1950).
172. Valeton, J. J. P., *K. Sachs. Ges. Wies. math-physik Klasse*, Leipzig, **67,** 1 (1915); *Phys. Z.*, **21,** 606 (1920).
173. Van Hook, A., and Kilmartin, E. J., *Z. Elektrochem.*, **56,** 302 (1952).
174. van't Hoff, J. H., "Zur Bildung der Ozeanis Chem. Salzlagerungen," Braunschweig, 1908.
175. Van Eeggeren, F., and Benson, G. G., Can. J. Chem., **35,** 1130 (1957); *C. A.*, **52,** 13398.
176. Verma, A. R., "Crystal Growth and Dislocations," New York, Academic Press, (1953).
177. Viola, C., *Atti. R. Acad. Lincei*, **V, 27,** 107–112 (1918), *C. A.*, **13,** 3046; *Compt. rend.*, **167,** 342 (1918), *C. A.*, **12,** 2413.
178. Volmer, M., *Ann. Phys.*, **24,** 719 (1935).
179. von Laue, M., *Z. Krist.*, **105,** 134 (1943).
180. von Rashevsky, N., *Z. Physik.*, **54,** 736 (1939).
181. Walker, A. C., Private communication, Nov. 16, 1949.
182. Weissberger, A., "Techniques of Organic Chemistry," I, Chap 3, p. 113, New York, Interscience, 1945.
183. Wells, A. F., *Phil. Mag.*, **37,** 184, 217, 605 (1946); Annual Reports Chem. Soc., **43,** 62 (1947).
184. Williamson, A. T., *Trans. Faraday Soc.*, **40,** 42 (1944).
185. Wilson, A. J. C., "X-Ray Optics. The Diffraction of X-Rays by Finite and Imperfect Crystals," New York, John Wiley & Sons, 1949.
186. Wollaston, *Phil. Trans.*, **103,** 57 (1813).
187. Wood, S. E., *J. Chem. Phys.*, **15,** 358 (1949).
188. Woodland, L. D. J., and Mack, E., *J. Am. Chem. Soc.*, **55,** 3149 (1933).
189. Wranglen, G., *Acta Chem. Scand.*, **9,** 661 (1955).
190. Wulff, G., *Z. Krist.*, **34,** 449 (1901).
191. Wyckoff, R., "Crystal Data," 5 vols., New York, Interscience, 1948—to date.
192. Yamamoto, T., *Bull. Inst. Phys. Chem. Research (Tokyo)*, **10,** 52–60 (1931).

Chapter 3

MODERN THEORIES

GENERAL

The adjustment of any metastable state involves two consecutive steps: (1) surmounting the energy barrier which defines this condition, and (2) subsequent passage to a state of lower energy and greater stability. In the cases of supercooled liquids and supersaturated solutions, these two general steps are tantamount to nucleation and growth, respectively. Historically, these two steps were considered to be independent of each other, nucleation being the more difficult and the slower.

This distinction appears reasonable on the simple kinetic grounds represented by the general equation

$$k = k_o \, e^{-E/RT}$$

where k is the specific reaction rate constant, and E the activation energy or barrier to reaction. This equation may be written in terms of the activated complex theory as

$$k = \frac{RT}{Nh} e^{\Delta S^*/R} \cdot e^{-\Delta H^*/RT}$$

where R is the gas constant, N is Avogadro's number, h is Planck's constant, and ΔS^* and ΔH^* are the entropy and enthalpy of the activation processes, respectively. It is not unreasonable to expect that the latter will be of the same order of magnitude for both nucleation and growth processes, but the entropy or orientation function involved in marshalling the initial nucleus must be considerably greater than that entailed in the extension of an already ordered base. Since the entropies of activation for such processes are negative, the relative rate of change in nucleation will be less than that of growth, according to the disparity in values.

This distinction between nucleation and growth is evident in most of the early theories and experimental studies of transition phenomena. Early works may be classified quite clearly as dealing independently with one or the other of these two processes, and very few considered the simultaneous processes of nucleus generation and subsequent growth. A logical connection

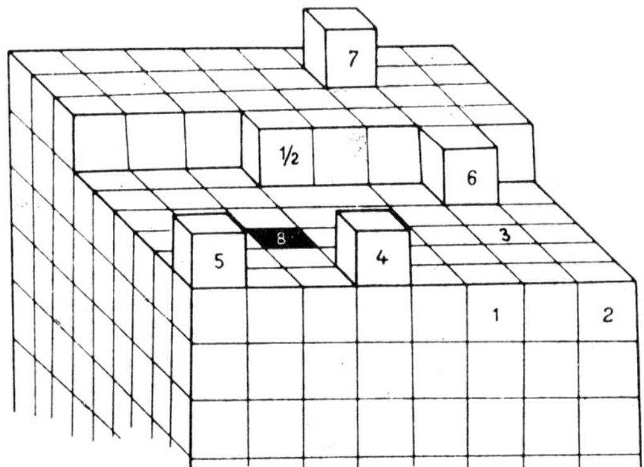

Figure 3-1. Kossel's crystal model.[136]

1) edge 2) corner 3) surface 4) edge adsorbed molecule 5) corner adsorbed molecule 6) edge position or step 7) surface adsorbed molecule or center 8) surface hole ½) kink or repeatable step.

between the two became apparent with Kossel's detailed consideration of the mechanism of crystal growth.[136]

The model idealized in Figure 3-1 is visualized for this purpose. Many of the possible positions at which individual building units can become incorporated in the crystal lattice are pictured here, and the equilibrium problem consists of calculating the most probable. There are actually more positions possible than those represented in the figure, but those indicated are the more important ones. Stranski[213a] has listed 27 for the simple cubic heteropolar crystal, together with the energy corresponding to each. Those positions involving the most work of separation will be the most stable or, conversely, will be those favored in the reverse process of crystal building. The most favored of all positions is that designated by position (½), and growth will proceed by successive addition in these positions until the row is completed. This exhausts the most likely position; then the next preferred position adjacent to the extremities of the completed step will serve as the starting point for a new strip. Kossel rated the relative importance in NaCl of kink, edge and center as 0.8738, 0.1807, and 0.0662, respectively. The crystal-building process then consists essentially of the laying down of successive strips and the advance of these strips across the uncompleted surface. When each layer is completed the necessity of starting a new step arises; the difficulty of starting this by the establishment of a kink is greatest at the center of a face and least at a corner of a simple ionic crystal. Just the reverse is true in the case of nonpolar crystals. These periodic interruptions of the regular addition of growth units constitute the surface or two-dimensional nucleation which is necessary for growth, according to the ideas of Kossel, Volmer, Stranski and others. However, this sporadic process is largely obviated by a more recent propostion of Frank.

The model also allows calculations of the preferred or equilibrium forms of crystals according to the different energy changes involved in growth in different directions. It suffices to indicate at this time that this atomic model suggests the unification of nucleation and growth ideas, since the rate of addition of new material to a growing surface will clearly be a function of the frequency of surface nucleation, the step height, and its rate of advance.

Many restrictions on this oversimplified picture are immediately evident upon consideration of the consecutive requirements in any heterogeneous reaction.[83] These are, in order:

1. Transport from the medium to the growing environment
2. Adsorption on the surface
3. Orientation in the surface
4. Desorption of products
5. Dissipation of products

In phase transitions the last two steps consist essentially of the dissipation of the heat of transition, which may become significant if the rate of growth of the new phase is rapid. At this stage, only the first three steps will be considered.

It is obviously necessary for building material to be available continuously in the immediate neighborhood of any site that grows without interruption. The original supply becomes depleted in the very early stages of construction, and new material must be withdrawn from the surrounding medium. This movement is the basis of the several diffusion theories of growth proposed by Nernst, Berthoud, Valeton, and others.

A growth unit is not necessarily disposed to immediate incorporation in the growing base once it has arrived on location by diffusion, (1) because it may evaporate or diffuse away, and (2) because it may not have settled at a favorable point. In the latter instance it must migrate to a more favorable point of attachment. Considerations of this requirement are the central theme of the adsorption theories of growth of Kossel, Volmer, Brandes, etc. Even when immediately at a preferred point of growth, the molecule must be maneuvered or "jockeyed" into the final correct position on the growing lattice. This final requirement accounts in good measure for the entropy factor.

Should any one of the three consecutive steps outlined be much slower than the other two, the over-all rate of growth will occur at approximately that velocity. Many theories of growth have evolved and have been tested under these conditions. Becker, Döring, and others, however, have considered situations in which two or more of these processes occur with comparable speeds. The net result is sometimes complicated and has not been worked out in detail in all cases.

Chronologically, the first definitive theory of crystal growth was the purely thermodynamic proposal of Curie (1885),[52] which was based upon the fundamental ideas of Gibbs. These were endorsed and extended by Wulff[250] in 1901, and experimentally by Marc somewhat later.[152] Berthoud[22] in 1912 and Valeton[234] in 1915, following Gibbs' own comments, recognized that kinetic factors must prevail over thermodynamic ones in determining the actual habit of a crystal, and adapted the diffusion theory of Nernst, Noyes, and Whitney[168] in modified form to fit their observations.

Volmer's first paper[239] on the adsorptive processes involved in crystallization was presented in 1921, and his subsequent theoretical and experimental considerations are discussed in full in his book[A-18], published in 1939. Haber in 1922 and Brandes in 1927 also considered these same factors, and since that time a host of workers[16, 67, 130, 136, 208] have thoroughly explored the thermodynamic and kinetic features of the process in the greatest detail.

The latest ideas of Burton, Cabrera, and Frank of the Bristol school have stimulated another spurt of both theoretical and experimental papers on the general subject of the mechanism of crystal growth.[13] This lively state of both theoretical and practical investigations is indicated by the number of[A-37 to 45] recent symposia listed in Appendix A.

NUCLEATION

Elements of Theory

It was realized at an early date[92, 120, 178a] that the Gibbs-Thomson equation was sufficient to explain the reality of metastability. Qualitatively, the incipient new phase would have an enhanced vapor pressure or solubility when first formed because of its minute size. It would, therefore, immediately disappear rather than grow to a larger size. Quantitatively,

$$r = \frac{2\,\sigma M}{dRT \ln \alpha}$$

where α, expresses the supersolubility as a pressure or concentration ratio, d is the density, and r the radius of an isotropic nucleus in equilibrium with the supercooled or supersaturated state. This equation may be coupled with the general kinetic equation

$$V = k\, e^{-W/RT}$$

in order to express the rate of initiation (V) of the imminent transformation. Here k is a frequency factor, and W the minimum energy required to form the nucleus. The constant k may be evaluated in several ways but the more important consideration in this elementary exposition is the activation energy W. This is the net work of forming the surface of the initiating germ and that required to form its bulk without any surface: namely,

$$W = W_s - W_N$$

The former contribution is σA, σ being the interfacial tension and A the area. If the new particle is taken to be a sphere, its volume is $v = \frac{4}{3}\pi r^3$ and area $A = 4\pi r^2$.

The net work of transferring an infinitesimal amount of fluid from the homogeneous medium to the surface requires a free energy expenditure of σdA, which is just equal to the product of the volume transferred across the pressure gradient p: namely, $p\ dv = \sigma dA$. The pressure difference within and without the curved surface is, thus, $p = 2\sigma/r$, since $dv/dA = r/2$. The surface work term is $2\sigma v/r$, and

$$W = \sigma A - \frac{2\sigma}{r} \cdot \frac{1}{3} rA = \frac{1}{3} \sigma A = \frac{1}{3} \sigma W_s$$

The work of nucleation is thus one-third the work of forming its own surface, or $W = \frac{4}{3}\pi r^2 \sigma$. For the critical nucleus (*vide infra*) which is one just exceeding the size specified by the Gibbs-Thomson equation

$$W = \frac{16\pi M^2 \sigma^3}{3\ d^2 R^2 T^2 \ln^2 \alpha}$$

whence the basic equation for the rate of formation of spherical critical nuclei becomes

$$v = k \exp\left[-\frac{16\pi M^2 \sigma^3}{3\ d^2 R^3 T^3 \ln^2 \alpha}\right]$$

This expression demands an almost explosive increase in the rate of nucleation as α exceeds definite real values. This requirement is in keeping with observation (Figure 3-2).

The basic equation must be modified for different forms and varieties of nuclei, and the pre-exponential factor remains to be evaluated. These modifications will be considered in detail in a later section. Satisfactory agreement is realized in cases of nucleation from vapors, but only fair or qualitative comparisons result for condensed systems.

Growth

The first serious theories dealing with growth of crystals were those of Gibbs, Curie, and Wulff and were entirely thermodynamic in nature.

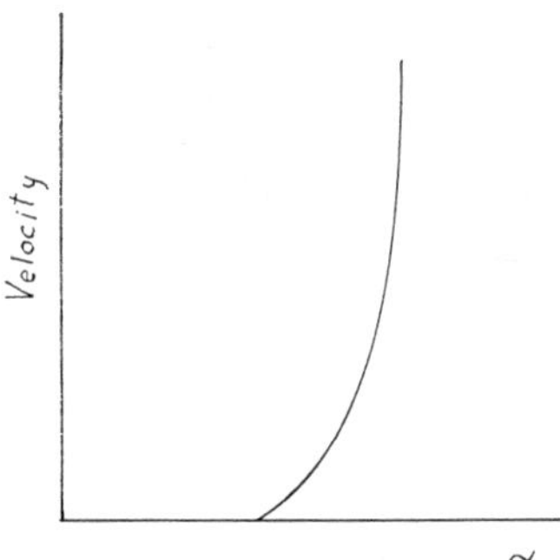

Figure 3-2. Velocity of nucleation *vs.* supersaturation or supercooling, α.

These theories dealt essentially with the question of equilibrium form and morphology and not at all with considerations of the rate at which the actual crystal might be produced. Gibbs, however, appreciated the possibility that kinetic factors might prevail over surface-energy factors alone, and that while the latter factors probably dominate in the initiation of crystallization, they would probably become insignificant in the extension or growth thereof.

The Nernst-Noyes-Whitney theory of heterogeneous reactions was formulated in 1897 to account for dissolution phenomena and was immediately applied to the presumed reciprocal process of growth. This theory postulated the establishment of a film of saturated mother liquor on the surface of the immersed crystal. This condition was maintained by diffusion of material to or from the solid surface according to whether the surrounding solution was oversaturated or undersaturated. The rate of transfer of material in this strategic step was the controlling kinetic factor. The theory was eminently successful in explaining observed dissolution data when uncomplicated by chemical reaction, but was at once realized to be inadequate when confronted with crystallographic and growth-rate data. It was modified accordingly by Berthoud, Valeton, Friedel, and others, but even so was again found to be unsatisfactory by Spangenberg. His chief objection rested upon the incontrovertible fact that the habit of crystals is quite sensitive to conditions of growth such as supersaturation, temperature, and impurities.

The diverse experiments of Marc and his school at this time (1908) suggested that the condition at the interface of a growing crystal is better described in terms of an adsorbed layer than the more general implication of a saturated fluid film. Growth occurs at a measurable rate by addition to the substrate lattice of molecules from this layer, and the abstracted molecules are replaced from the surrounding solution. Foreign substances which are adsorbed but not incorporated into the lattice impede crystallization as a result of the irreversible interference they create. Such were the beginnings of the so-called adsorption-layer theories of growth of Volmer, Brandes, etc. Most of the recent speculations about the detailed mechanism of growth originated from such considerations.

If, as demonstrated by Volmer, the mobility in the adsorbed state is high, the rate of growth will be determined by the rate at which molecules impinge upon the surface of the growing crystal and the concentration of critical nuclei capable of continued growth. Volmer[239c] first analyzed this situation for liquid droplets growing from vapor in the following way:

The chemical potential for the system involving embryos of n molecules will be

$$\Sigma G = (\mu_l - \mu_g)n + \sigma n^{2/3}$$

where μ_l and μ_g refer to the chemical potential per molecule in the liquid (l) and gaseous (g) phases, respectively, and σ is a term proportional to the surface-free energy. The maximum of this expression, corresponding to the formation of critical nuclei, is

$$n^* = \frac{2}{3} \frac{\sigma}{(\mu_g - \mu_l)}$$

and the number of these critical nuclei is approximately

$$N^* = N \exp\left[-\frac{1}{3}\frac{\sigma n^{*2/3}}{kT}\right]$$

When these critical nuclei continue to grow by addition of the molecules which strike their surfaces, the velocity of condensation will be

$$Q = N^* n^* \cdot 4r\pi^{*2}\beta$$

where β is the rate of collision per unit area, and is $\beta = p/\sqrt{2\pi mkT}$ according to kinetic theory. The accommodation coefficient was taken to be unity. The spherical shape assumed for the liquid droplet is tantamount to

$$\sigma n^{*2/3} = 4\pi\sigma r^{*2}$$

and

$$n^* = \tfrac{4}{3}\pi r^{*2} v_l$$

where σ is now the $l - g$ interfacial tension, and v_l the specific volume. The velocity of condensation then becomes

$$Q = N \cdot 4\pi r^{*2} \frac{p}{\sqrt{2\pi mkT}} \cdot \exp\left[-\frac{4}{3}\frac{\pi\sigma r^{*2}}{kT}\right]$$

This simplified thermodynamic treatment was soon improved by Farkas,[67] and then considered in a statistical way by Stranski and Kaischew,[36, 122, 2131] both arriving at essentially the same result. Becker and Döring[16, 36] rejected the thermodynamic approach because of the dynamic nature of the phenomenon concerned, and analyzed the problem in a purely kinetic way (see next section). Their result, as given by Frenkel[A-4] and others,[12, 253] is

$$Q = N \cdot 2\pi r^{*2} \frac{p}{kT} \sqrt{\frac{1}{3} \frac{\mu_g - \mu_l}{m}} \cdot n^* \cdot \exp\left[-\frac{4\pi\sigma r^{*2}}{3kT}\right]$$

The main forms of these several growth equations are generally in accord with experimental observations, but detailed comparison and application are still incomplete.

In the case of condensed systems, the collisional factor involves transport by molecular diffusion,[192] and Becker[15] proposed the following over-all equation for the nucleation rate:

$$J = c \cdot e^{-u/kT} \cdot e^{-A(T)/kT}$$

u is the activation energy of diffusion, and $A(T)$ the work required to form the surface of the nucleus. If these nuclei grow as spheres, the velocity of crystallization will be:

$$Q = c \exp\left[-\frac{1}{kT}\left(u - \frac{4}{3}\pi r^{*2}\sigma\right)\right] = c \exp\left[-\frac{1}{kT}\left[u + \frac{4}{3}\pi\sigma\left(\frac{2v\,\sigma T}{\lambda(T_o - T)}\right)^2\right]\right]$$

when the Gibbs-Thomson and Clausius-Clapeyron equations are inserted. c is a constant, v the molar volume and λ the latent heat of transition. Since $e^{-u/kT}$ decreases with lowering temperature or increasing supersaturation, while $e^{-[A(T)/kT]}$ behaves conversely, the rate curves for both nucleation and growth will pass through maxima, as observed by Tammann. The sharpness of the transition stage will depend upon the parameters involved in each case. This pattern is illustrated in Figure 3-3.

SOME DETAILS OF NUCLEATION THEORY WITH TESTS

The Simplest Case

The total free energy of a nucleus composed of n ultimate units consists chiefly of bulk and surface components. If μ is the chemical potential of the individual units with respect to the saturated condition, O the area of the new phase, and σ the interfacial energy, the free energy of the formation of the nucleus will be

$$\Delta G = n\mu + O\sigma$$

This combination does not include any strain contributions;[71] if these were

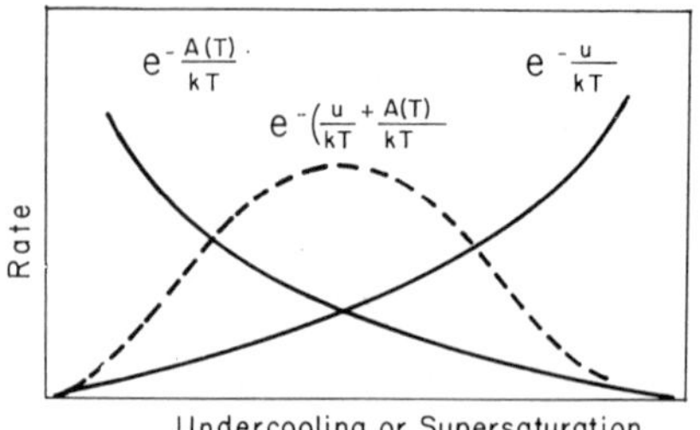

Figure 3-3. Composition of the growth curve.

present another term of the form nC would be added where C represents the unit strain energy. When the nucleus is taken to be a sphere of radius r, its volume and area are $\frac{4}{3}\pi r^3$ and $4\pi r^2$, respectively. $n = \frac{4}{3}(\pi r^3/v)$, where v is the volume of the individual molecules which are assumed to compact entirely upon forming the embryo. A general equation

$$\Delta G = n\mu + bn^{2/3}$$

may be written, where shape and surface-tension factors are collected together in the b term. The equilibrium condition of $\partial\Delta G/\partial n = 0$ is satisfied by $n^* = -(2b/3\mu)^3$. This indicates that the free energy change first increases as the embryo grows by aggregation of molecules, but soon reaches a limit, after which a decrease ensues. The maximum, n^*, corresponds to the critical nucleus and to the point of spontaneous adjustment of the metastable state. A particle smaller than the critical size (frequently designated a "germ" of "embryo") will disappear by evaporation or dissolution, whereas a nucleus above this size is stable and will continue to grow. The critical condition may be formulated more explicitly in the following way for the spherical particle:

The interaction of molecules to form a germ in a homogeneous system may be represented by the equations:

$$A_1 + A_1 \rightleftarrows A_2$$

$$A_1 + A_2 \rightleftarrows A_3$$

$$A_1 + A_3 \rightleftarrows A_4$$

$$\vdots$$

$$A_1 + A_{n-1} \rightleftarrows A_n$$

or, when this succession of reactions is in a state of reversible equilibrium,

$$nA \rightleftarrows A_n$$

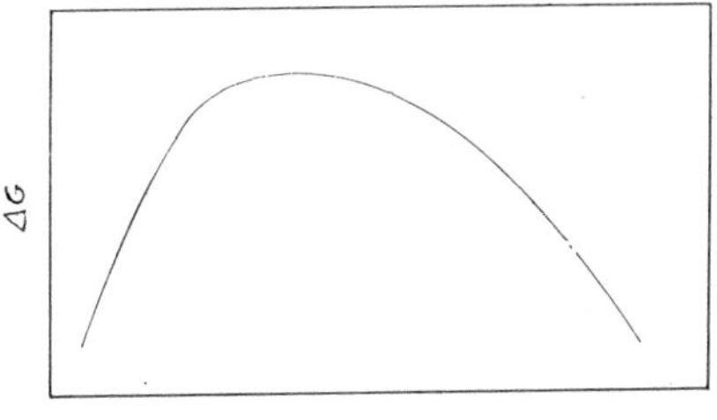

Figure 3-4. Free energy *vs.* size of particle.

The bulk free energy per molecule for this system is

$$\mu = kT \ln A_n/A^n$$

or

$$\mu = kT \ln \alpha$$

when the ratio of true thermodynamic concentrations, A, is expressed as the supersaturation, α. The total free energy of the nucleus consists of this part and a surface contribution, so that

$$\Delta G = \frac{4}{3}\frac{\pi r^3}{v}\cdot kT \ln \alpha + 4\pi r^2 \sigma$$

Figure 3-4 expresses the form of this equation. The size of the critical nucleus is found by maximizing this expression with respect to r, and is

$$r^* = \frac{2\sigma v}{\mu} = \frac{2\sigma v}{kT \ln \alpha}$$

The free energy change involved in this nucleation step is, accordingly,

$$\Delta G^* = \frac{4\pi r^{*2}\sigma}{3} = \frac{\sigma O}{3} = \frac{n\mu}{2} = \frac{16\pi\sigma^3 v^2}{3\mu^2}$$

and the rate of forming these critical nuclei at this energy level

$$J = c\cdot\exp\left[-\frac{16\pi\sigma^3 v^2}{3k^3T^3 \ln^2 \alpha}\right]$$

This equation has been tested most amply by Volmer and Flood[239d] for the condensation of supercooled vapors. Table 3-1 shows that the agreement between theory and experiment is good.

Similar good agreement was observed by Flood[73] for mixed vapors of ethyl alcohol and water. The basic theory for such polycomponent systems is outlined by Volmer[A-18] and extended by Reiss.[192] Stranski and his co-

TABLE 3-1. CRITICAL SUPERSATURATIONS[239d]

Vapor	Supercooling (deg C)		n^* molecules	r^* (Å)
	Obs.	Calc.		
Water, 275.2°K	4.2	4.2	80	8.9
Water, 261.0	5.0	5.0	72	8.0
Methanol, 270°	3.0	1.8	32	7.9
Ethanol, 273°	2.3	2.3	128	14.2
n-Propanol, 270°	3.0	3.2	115	15.0
i-Propanol, 265°	2.8	2.9	119	15.2
n-Butanol, 270°	4.6	4.5	72	13.6
Ethyl acetate, 242°	8.6–12.3	10.4	40	11.4

workers continue the study of the influence of ions on the condensation of many vapors, and this work and many other related contributions are collected together in the *Proceedings of the Conference on Interfacial Tension and Nucleation* held at Boston University in 1951.[A-38, A-39, A-40] A great many of the investigations in this field are focused on the behavior of water vapor under all possible homogeneous and heterogeneous conditions. These, of course, are significant for the understanding and interpretation of natural precipitation phenomena, which particular application will be presented in a later section.

The pre-exponential term in the above equations is a frequency factor, and has been considered by Farkas,[67] Becker and Döring,[16] Zeldovich,[262] Frenkel,[A-4] and others.[192] In the case of gas condensing to liquid, Becker and Döring assumed quasi-equilibrium conditions and considered the rate of formation of nuclei to be large compared to their rate of evaporation. With a constant accommodation coefficient, a, which expresses the rate of these two processes, the value of the frequency term becomes

$$\frac{\sqrt{2}\, aN^{3/2}}{\sqrt{\pi}\, R^2}\left(\frac{p_\infty}{T}\right)^2 \frac{\sqrt{\sigma M}}{\rho}\, \alpha^2$$

where N is Avogadro's number, p_∞ is the equilibrium vapor pressure at temperature T, and ρ is the gas density. The numerical value of this expression exclusive of the α^2 term is approximately 10^{25} and remains quite insensitive to ordinary changes in conditions. This means that the $\ln^2\alpha$ term in the exponential part of the nucleation-rate equation dominates in practically all circumstances, and this is illustrated in Figure 3-5 and Table 3-2.

The diagrams and table demonstrate the explosive nature of nucleation between $\alpha = 4$ and 5, and are a vivid illustration of the metastable limit

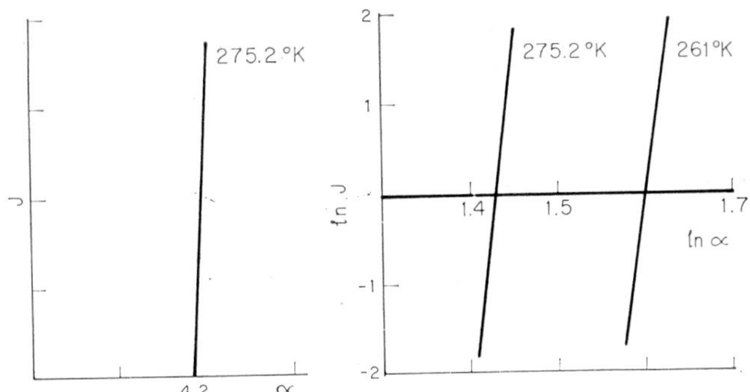

Figure 3-5. Nucleation of water vapor as function of supersaturation ratio.[184]

TABLE 3-2. SENSITIVENESS OF NUCLEATION RATE OF WATER VAPOR TO SUPERSATURATION

α	1.1	2	3	4	5
$\Delta G^*/2.3\ hT$	5000	94	37	24	12
J	—	10^{-69}	10^{-12}	10	10^{13}
t	—	10^{62}y.	10^{3}y.	10^{-1}sec.	10^{-13}sec.

t = time for appearance of first droplet in 1 ml.

of Ostwald. The intercepts of the curves on the $J = 1$ axis may be interpreted as the appearance of the first nucleus which then triggers a multiplicity of additional centers of growth. This suggestion intimates the powerful catalytic activity of appropriate foreign bodies, which has been considered in detail by Volmer,[A-18] Pound,[185] Turnbull,[230] Bradley,[31] and others.[101]

Bradley[A-23] has summarized the Becker and Döring analysis of nucleation from the vapor phase as follows:

"The energy $\Delta u(n)$ required to vaporize a nucleus containing n molecules may be writtein in the form

$$\Delta u(n) = nW - f\gamma n^{2/3}$$

where W is the heat of vaporization per molecule, γ the surface free energy, and f a shape factor. The energy required to transfer dn molecules from one nucleus to the vapor will be

$$d\Delta u(n) = dn(W - \tfrac{2}{3}f\gamma n^{-1/3}) = dn \cdot W(n)$$

where $W(n) = W - \tfrac{2}{3}f\gamma n^{-1/3}$. For simplicity n is assumed to take the values unity upwards, although, of course, these equations cannot in fact be applied in the region of low values of n.

"Let us suppose that nucleu can grow as a result of molecular collisions from the vapor, and that they can also decrease their size by evaporation. Let $q(n)$ and $a(n)$ be, respectively, the rate of evaporation and condensation in molecules per second on a nucleus containing n molecules of which $s(n)$ molecules are in the surface. Then

$$q(n) = s(n)\nu e^{-W(n)/kT}$$

where ν is the vibration frequency of a surface molecule for vibrations perpendicular to the surface, and the expression for the vacuum rate is used because the drops are very small. For such drops evaporation is not governed by diffusion.[30] Similarly,

$$a(n) = s(n)\nu\alpha e^{-W/kT}$$

since at an equilibrium pressure p_∞ the rates of evaporation and condensation are equal for a patch of plane surface containing $s(n)$ molecules, so that the rate of condensation is given by

$$s(n)\nu e^{-W/kT}$$

It follows that at pressure p the rate of condensation on such a patch is given by

$$\frac{p}{p_\infty} \cdot s(n)\nu e^{-W/kT}$$

and this must also be the rate of condensation on the curved surface. It should be noted that the expression for $q(n)$ contains $W(n)$ since this is the activation energy for the loss of a molecule from a nucleus containing n molecules, whereas the equation for $a(n)$ contains W, since the rate of evaporation from a plane surface determines the saturation vapor pressure, which is a function of W.

"The actual problem of the formation of nuclei may be replaced by the easier but less real problem of a system of nuclei in a stationary state, i.e., the concentration of nuclei of any size remains constant, so that $I(n) = I(n+1) = I$ for all values of n, where $I(n)$ is the net rate of formation per second per cm^3 of nuclei containing n molecules, from nuclei containing $(n-1)$ molecules;

$$\frac{dz(n)}{dt} = I(n) - I(n+1) = 0$$

for the stationary state, where $Z(n)$ is the concentration per cm^3 of nuclei containing n molecules.

"In order to keep up the steady flow of nuclei it will be necessary to remove those nuclei which have grown well past the critical size, say those containing N molecules, and replace them by an equivalent quantity of vapor. The choice of N is immaterial, so that

$$I(n) = z(n-1)a(n-1) - z(n)q(n)$$

and

$$I(n+1) = z(n)a(n) - z(n+1)q(n+1)$$

The usual bulk and surface components of the free energy of formation of a nucleus of n molecules,

$$\Delta G(n) = -nkT \ln \alpha + f\gamma n^{2/3}$$

suggest the definition of a function $\phi(n)$ by the relation

$$\begin{aligned} a(n)\phi(n) &= z(1)a(1)\alpha^n e^{-f\gamma n^{2/3}/kT} \\ &= z(1)a(1)e^{-[\Delta G(n)/kT]} \end{aligned}$$

so that

$$q(n)\phi(n) = z(1)a(1)\alpha^{n-1} \exp\left[-\frac{f\gamma(n^{2/3} - \frac{2}{3}n^{-1/3})}{kT}\right]$$

since the ratio of $a(n)/q(n)$ is

$$\alpha e^{-\frac{zf\gamma n^{-1/3}}{3kT}}$$

Now if n is sufficiently large

$$\begin{aligned} n^{2/3} - \frac{2}{3}n^{-1/3} &= n^{2/3}\left[1 - \frac{2}{3n}\right] \\ &\approx n^{2/3}\left(1 - \frac{1}{n}\right)^{2/3} \\ &\approx (n-1)^{2/3} \end{aligned}$$

Hence

$$q(n)\phi(n) \approx a(n-1)\phi(n-1)$$

and

$$\begin{aligned} \frac{I}{a(n-1)\phi(n-1)} &= \frac{z(n-1)}{\phi(n-1)} - \frac{z(n)}{\phi(n)} \\ &= -\frac{dz(n)/\phi(n)}{dn} \end{aligned}$$

Then

$$I \int_1^N \frac{dn}{a(n-1)\phi(n-1)} = -\left[\frac{z(n)}{\phi(n)}\right]_1^N$$

since I is a constant, independent of n.

"Now $Z(n)$ is by definition zero, since nuclei of this size are removed. and $\phi(1) = z(1)e^{-}\Delta G(1)/kT = z(1)$ since no energy is needed to form a nucleus of one molecule from single molecules. Hence

$$I \int_1^N \frac{dn}{a(n-1)\phi(n-1)} = 1$$

and

$$I = z(1)a(1) \bigg/ \int_1^N e^{\Delta G(n)/kT}$$

when $n - 1$ is replaced by n, as an approximation.

"Since $G(n)$ has a maximum at $n = n_c$, $e^{\Delta G(n)/kT}$ will also have a very sharp maximum at this point and it suffices to replace $\Delta G(n)$ by the first two terms of the Taylor series

$$\Delta G(n) = \Delta G(n_c) + \frac{1}{2}\xi^2 \left[\frac{d^2\Delta G(n)}{d\xi^2}\right]_{n=n_c}$$

where for convenience the origin has been transferred to $n = n_c$ and where $\xi = n - n_c$. Now

$$\left[\frac{d^2\Delta G(n)}{d\xi^2}\right]_{\xi=0} = -\frac{2}{9} f\gamma n_c^{-4/3}$$

so that

$$\int_1^N e^{\Delta G(n)/kT} \cdot dn \approx e^{[\Delta G(n_c)/kT]} \int_{-\infty}^{+\infty} \exp\left[-\frac{\xi^2 f\gamma n_c^{-4/3}}{9kT}\right] \cdot d\xi$$
$$\approx \left[\frac{9\pi kT n_c^{4/3}}{f\gamma}\right]^{1/2} e^{\Delta G(n_c)/kT}$$

where the limits $\pm\infty$ are permitted owing to the sharpness of the maximum. The precise value of N is obviously immaterial, whence

$$I = z(1)a(1)\left[\frac{f\gamma}{9\pi kT n_c^{4/3}}\right]^{1/2} \exp\left[-\frac{\Delta G_{\max}}{kT}\right]$$
$$= \frac{Z(1)a(1)}{n_c}\left[\frac{\Delta G_{\max}}{(3\pi kT)}\right]^{1/2} \cdot \exp\left[-\frac{4}{27}\left(\frac{f\gamma}{RT}\right)^3 \cdot \frac{1}{\ln^2 \alpha}\right]$$

which is Becker and Döring's equation.

"For $Z(1)a(1)$ we can write the well-known expression for the collision frequency per cm³ per second between molecules. It is hardly necessary to emphasize that this final equation is not exact. It will be noted that the nuclear current I is very sensitive to the value of α, so that, although nucleation proceeds at any value of $\alpha > 1$, geological times would be needed to obtain a visible nucleation unless α reaches a quasi-critical value, in agreement with observation with the Wilson cloud chamber."

Nonspherical Nuclei

When the separating nucleus is not isotropic the free energy contribution of the surfaces is defined by a term $\sum^n \sigma_n O_n$, and is restricted in geometric form by the Gibbs-Wulff condition. The size of the critical nucleus in terms of the length of the normal, from the h face to the center of the crystal then becomes

$$r_h = \frac{2\sigma_h v}{\mu}$$

where the particular surface free energy of each face replaces the isotropic value. The free energy of nucleation is

$$\Delta G^* = \frac{4\pi^2 \sum^h a_h \sigma_h}{3\mu^2} = \frac{4 \sum^h a^3 \sigma^3}{27\mu^2}$$

where a_h is the shape factor for the h face, μ the chemical potential with respect to the equilibrium crystal, and $v = \frac{1}{3} \sum^h ar^3$.

Since little is known about the surface free energies of different faces of crystals, this expression is often approximated by that of an equivalent sphere, for which the shape factor is 4π. This gives immediately the previous equation with the $^{16}/_3$ factor.

Condensed Systems

In the case of condensed systems, such as nucleation from melts, solutions, or in solids, the free energy of formation is, as before

$$\Delta G^* = \frac{16\pi\sigma^3 v^2}{3\mu^2}$$

when the nucleus is considered to be a sphere. Since

$$\frac{d\mu}{dT} = -\Delta S^*$$

the chemical potential with respect to the separating phase is

* Hoffman[105] adds a T/T_o factor to this expression, where T and T_o are the actual and equilibrium temperatures, respectively.

$$\mu = -\int_{T_o}^{T} \Delta s \, dT$$

or approximately $\Delta S(T_o - T)$. Thus,

$$\Delta G^* = \frac{16\pi\sigma^3 v^2}{3(\Delta S)^2(T_o - T)^2}$$

which develops the significance of the entropy of the transition concerned.

Dunning[63] develops a similar equation for the anisotropic solid, as well as indicating the absolute reaction rate theory[83] form. Turnbull,[230b] Stavely and Thomas,[211] Van Hook and Bruno,[A-37] Pines,[183] Hirano,[103] and Cagle and Eyring[41] also apply the transition state theory to three-dimensional nucleation and indicate the modifications necessary for transport contributions. These assume the usual form of additional $e^{-Q/kT}$ factors, where the Q's are activation energies of the various steps involved.

The Eyring theory[83] gives, for the rate of nucleation

$$J = \frac{RT}{h} e^{-\Delta G^*/RT}$$

Since the limit of metastability will obviously correspond to $J = 1$, we have

$$\ln \frac{RT}{h} = \frac{16\pi\sigma^3 v^2 T_o^2}{3RT(\Delta H)^2(T_o - T)^2}$$

where T_o signifies the equilibrium transition temperature, and T_c the actual temperature—namely, the metastable limit. Taking the limit of supercooling of water to be $T_c = -38.0$°C, Fisher, Holloman and Turnbull[71] compute that $\sigma = 32.8$ ergs/cm and also the following values of J at different temperatures:

T(°C)	−33	−34	−35	−36	−37	−38	−39	−40	−41	−42	−43
log J	−10.89	−8.33	−5.98	−3.82	−1.84	0	+1.70	+3.27	+4.74	+6.10	+7.3

The explosive onset of nucleation at a fairly critical temperature is again evident.

Turnbull[230c] has applied this analysis to the supercooling of many metals and finds interfacial energies which are about one-half the heat of fusion.* It was necessary to observe the limit of supercooling in small droplets of liquids in order to isolate and eliminate the effects of ever-present foreign nuclei—a difficult, if not impossible, requirement under ordinary bulk conditions.[A-37, 193] Some of Turnbull's results are summarized in Table 3-3.

* Jackson and Chalmers[114] arrive at this same ratio from theory of solidification which is based on the geometry and crystallography of the interface.

TABLE 3-3. SUBCOOLING DATA[230b]

Substance	Crystal Structure	Max. Subcooling (°C)		$\frac{\Delta T}{T_o}$	σ (ergs/cm²)	σ_g (cal/g-atom)	$\frac{\sigma_g}{\Delta H_f}$
		Large Samples	Small Particles				
Mercury	Hexagonal	14	46	0.197	21.6	262	0.47
Water	Hexagonal	36.8	39	0.143	32.8	471	0.33
Gallium	Orthorhombic	55	76	0.250	57	592	0.455
Tin	Tetragonal	31	110	0.218	61.3	806	0.453
Bismuth	Rhombohedral	30	90	0.165	55.5	841	0.336
Lead	FC cubic	—	80	0.133	34.0	488	0.394
Silver	FC cubic	—	227	0.184	128	1260	0.466
Germanium	Diamond	—	219	0.178	153	1790	0.352
Gold	FC cubic	—	221	0.166	133	1320	0.436
Copper	FC cubic	—	236	0.174	189	1410	0.453
Nickel	FC cubic	—	319	0.185	261	1895	0.452
Palladium	FC cubic	—	330	0.181	213	1890	0.459
Platinum	FC cubic	—	370	0.182	245	2185	0.465

Pound[184] also found remarkably good agreement with elementary nucleation-rate theory when mercury and tin droplets were dispersed in oil and separated from each other by protective coatings of oxides, soaps, or salts. In the case of Sn droplets, 2.5 to 5.0 μ diameter, the interfacial tension computed from the rate of nucleation was 58.5 ± 1 ergs/cm at 115°C, close to that observed by Turnbull[230b] (52.5). The critical nucleus for homogeneous nucleation was calculated to be 11.4 to 11.8 Å in radius. This would contain about 250 atoms of Sn. The pre-exponential factor was computed to be 3×10^{34}, but the agreement with the theoretical value of 3×10^{35} from the activated complex theory was regarded as fortuitous.

In the case of systems of more than one component, the effect of concentration on the chemical potential must be taken into account. Dunning[63] outlines this calculation for a binary system, such as an ordinary crystallizing solution, in the following way: If the mole fraction of the nucleus is x_2 and that of the mother liquor x_1 when the original composition was x, the decrease in free energy upon nucleation, neglecting surface energy, will be

$$\Delta G = \left(1 - \frac{n}{N}\right) G(x_1) + \frac{n}{N} G(x_2) - G(x)$$

where the G's are the corresponding free energies, n the number of molecules in the nucleus, and N Avogadro's number. When $n \ll N$, $x - x_1$ is small and

$$G(x_1) = G(x) - \left(\frac{\partial G}{\partial x}\right)_x (x - x_1)$$

where $(\partial G/\partial x)_x$ is the slope of the free energy curve at x. Then

$$Nx = (N - n)x_1 + nX_2$$

or

$$x - x_1 = \frac{n(x_2 - x)}{N - n}$$

and

$$\Delta G_1 = -\frac{n}{N}\left[G(x) - G(x_2) + (x_2 - x)\left(\frac{\partial G}{\partial x}\right)_x\right]$$

When the surface free energy is added to this expression and the condition of spherical nucleus formation evaluated by maximizing,

$$\Delta G^* = \frac{16\pi\sigma^3 N^2[x_2 v_B - (1 - x_2)v_A]^2}{3\left[G(x) - G(x_2) + (x_2 - x_1)\left(\frac{\partial G}{\partial x}\right)_x\right]^2}$$

where v_B and v_A are the molecular volumes of the two components. Becker[69] has applied the same reasoning to the case of alloys, estimating the free energy change due to composition from bond energy interactions, and obtains

$$\Delta G^* = zV(x - x_2)^2 n^{2/3}$$

Here

$$V = V_{AB} - \tfrac{1}{2}(V_{AA} - V_{BB})$$

where V_{AB} is the AB bond energy, etc. Borelius[27] considered that nuclei would appear and persist when $\partial^2 E/\partial x^2$ was positive, but would disappear when negative. This is confirmed by experiments on the Au-Pt system, but so is Becker's theory.[27]

Dunning and Shipman[64] and VanHook and Bruno[A-37] have investigated the nucleation of strong sucrose syrups and find essential agreement with the demands of the Volmer theory for this process. Figure 3-6 compares the results at 25°C. Interfacial energies of about 5 ergs/cm were calculated from these results, and the energy of activation for the nucleation process was found to be 10 kcal. mole^{-1} or less, according to the temperature. The intercepts of the Arrhenius plots lead to entropy values 5 to 14 times the theoretical, so that steric factors involved in forming the nucleus must be very restrictive. This same sort of discrepancy (i.e., 10^3 rather than 10^{33} for the pre-exponential factor) is also reported by Preckshot and Brown[A-38] for the nucleation of quiet supersaturated KCl solutions.

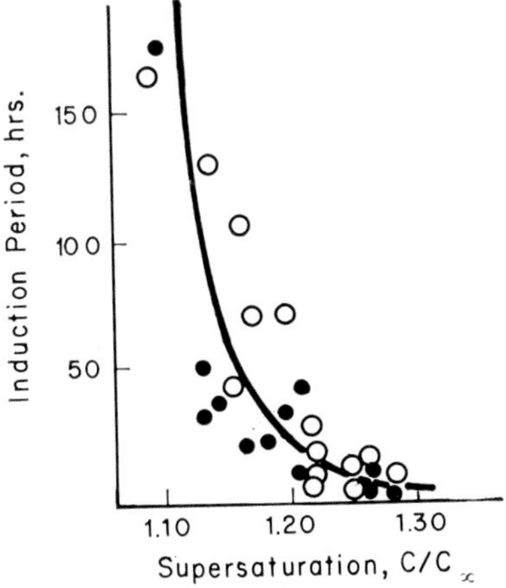

Figure 3-6. Nucleation of sugar syrups.[64]
● Dunning and Shipman,[64] 25°C.
○ Van Hook and Bruno, [A-37] 25°C.

The size of the critical nucleus of sucrose turns out to be equivalent to a sphere of about 20Å radius, which would contain 80 to 100 molecules. This is comparable to the collections estimated in many simple and condensed systems, but considerably larger than those estimated in the precipitation of slightly soluble salts, and smaller than some of the estimates of the photographic latent image.[116] In the former case, Christiansen and Nielsen[46] apply straightforward kinetic reasoning and steady-state conditions to the nucleation problem. The rate of production of nuclei is described by

$$\frac{d_c}{dt} = \lambda C^p$$

where c is the concentration of nuclei, C that of the ions in solution, and λ and p constants, the latter being the number of ions required to form the critical nucleus. The relative nucleation rate

$$\frac{dx}{dt} = \frac{1}{C_o}\frac{dc}{dt}$$

becomes λC_o^{p-1} when the nucleation does not effectively change the initial concentration. This is observed to be the case in the precipitation of many slightly soluble salts, and the well-defined induction period, t_f, is then represented by

$$\lambda t_f = C_o^{1-p}$$

This equation enables an estimate of p, which is found to be 8 in the case of $BaSO_4$, 6 for Ag_2CrO_4, 3 for CaF_2, etc.[45] These are total number of ions, so that the equivalent molecular units would be 4, 2, and 3, respectively. LaMer states, "This new attack on the size of the nucleus merits further refinement and extension to new systems." This suggestion has been followed in many papers on the subject,[25, 34, 50, 55, 61, 62, 94, 144, 172, 177, 230a, 236a] but Turnbull[230d] feels that heterogeneous nucleation prevails in most of these situations.

Amsler and Scherrer[5] have investigated spontaneous nucleus formation in aqueous and alcoholic solutions of KCl, KBr, and KI, and found good qualitative agreement with the Volmer theory, but concluded that too many factors are involved for a close quantitative test. Dehlinger and Wertz[56] data for aqueous alum solutions also belied the quantitative aspects of this theory,[86] although Neumann and Niess[170] found the comparison satisfactory. Essential accord has also been found in other homogeneous systems: e.g., cyclonite (1,3,5-trinitro-1,3,5-azocyclohexane) from nitric acid[A-37] and acetone-water,[65] $KClO_3$ and Na soaps from water,[210] and a wide variety of inorganic salts and organic acids from water and other solvents.[28, 85] The effects of added or foreign crystals ("seeds") in different solutions have been reported by Volmer and Weber,[239e] Stranski and co-workers,[213b] and Vonnegut.[240]

Nucleation in solids has been reviewed recently by Jacobs and Tompkins,[115] and by Smoluchowski,[207] while Hartshorne and his co-workers[96] continue their very intensive investigations of the rates of transformation of the polymorphs of S, CBr_4, HgI_2, *o*-nitroaniline, etc.

The Critical Nucleus

The physical reality of the critical nucleus was first demonstrated by Ostwald.[119, 178b] For this purpose he inoculated supercooled salol and supersaturated sodium chlorate solutions with progressively smaller and smaller parent material. These graded sizes were obtained by continuous grinding with an inert diluent such as lactose. Assuming there was a regular diminution in size as grinding proceeded, the minimum effective particle was determined to be 10^{-7} to 10^{-8} g for salol. This is equivalent to a sphere several microns in diameter and containing 10^{13} molecules or more. This is considerably larger than the size of the critical nucleus calculated from the metastable limit, but the experimental method must be admitted to be highly uncertain.

Other experimental verifications[A-37, 100, 124, 149, 158, 178c, 182] of the critical nucleus are subject to the same quantitative uncertainties, so that the best estimates of the critical size are probably the computed ones. This frequently turns out to be about 10Å in radius, and containing usually less than 100 molecules for vapor-liquid systems and somewhat more in condensed systems. This result is comparable to the limit set by equating the bulk energy of the separating molecules to the surface energy, namely

$$\frac{4}{3}\pi r^3 \rho L = 4\pi r^2 \sigma, \quad \text{or} \quad r = \frac{3\sigma}{\rho L}$$

where r is the radius of a sphere, ρ the density, σ the specific surface energy, and L the heat of the transition involved. Since this conidtion represents the limit of formation of an intact body, it will thereby define the critical nucleus. For liquid-solid transitions, σ is usually[A-40] about 100 ergs/cm and L usually less than 100 cal/g. These typical values give the representative result of 10Å for the radius. The L term in the case of vapor-liquid transformations would be 4 to 10 times greater, and with everything else the same, a smaller nucleus would be required. This is an intimation of Ostwald's Law of Stages, according to which unstable forms appear in successive order. We have already seen (Chapter I) that pronounced exceptions occur since kinetic factors usually prevail. Such considerations have been examined by Volmer,[A-18] Stranski and Totomanow,[214d] and Bradley.[A-13]

Tolman[228] has pointed out that the surface tension of droplets should depend upon size, decreasing with the radius of curvature r according to the relation

$$\frac{\sigma}{\sigma_\infty} = \frac{r}{r + 2\delta}$$

where σ and σ_∞ are the surface tensions for the curved and plane surfaces, respectively, while δ is a parameter expressing the displacement of the surface of tension from the surface of discontinuity. It is approximately a molecular diameter. This expression requires a 25 per cent reduction in the conventional surface-tension value when volumes the size of critical nuclei are concerned, and therefore a reduction in the energy barrier to nucleation and consequently some facilitation of the nucleation process. However, the theory[17, 42, 127, 131, 134, 143, 155] and experimentation in this regard are not so well defined as to be able to justify the correction at this time.[A-39, 230d]

Two-dimensional Nuclei and Frank's Theory

The foregoing considerations all refer to the three-dimensional nucleation which is required for the appearance of a new phase from a homogeneous medium and must be modified for the two-dimensional counterpart presumed necessary for the continued growth of a perfect solid body. The following simplified treatment presented by Mott[164] contains the essential features and results of the more elaborate considerations of Volmer, Stranski, and others.

If the nucleus is circular, with radius r, its energy will be

$$W = -\pi r^2 w + 2\pi r\sigma$$

where w is the free energy per unit area gained upon condensation on the surface, and σ the energy per unit length of edge. The maximum of this energy is

$$W^* = \frac{\pi\sigma^2}{w} \quad \text{at} \quad r^* = \frac{\sigma}{w}$$

The likelihood of forming this critical nucleus per unit time and per unit area is then

$$Ze^{-\pi\sigma^2/wkT}$$

where Z is the collision frequency of vapor or solute per unit time on a unit area.

Now, the free energy of condensation on the nucleus will be given by

$$w = \frac{kT}{a^2} \ln \frac{n}{N - n}$$

where n is the number of molecules in the nucleus, N the total number of available sites, and a^2 the area occupied by one molecule. For $n \ll N$, this is

$$w = \frac{kT}{a^2} \ln \frac{n}{N} = \frac{kT}{a^2} \ln \alpha$$

where α is the relative supersaturation. Since the rate of nucleation is the controlling step, the rate of growth will be

$$z \exp\left[-\frac{\pi a^2\sigma^2}{(kT)^2 \ln \alpha}\right]$$

and growth will continue only if $\ln \alpha$ is greater than 1.

Burton and Cabrera[A-37] and Burton, Cabrera, and Frank[38a] have examined this equation very critically and find that even noncircular nuclei do not change the essential features greatly. Their final result for the rate of formation of two-dimensional nuclei is

$$z \frac{s}{s_0} \exp\left[-\frac{\phi^2}{(kT)^2 \ln \alpha}\right]$$

where Z is the rate at which fresh molecules arrive at the surface, s the surface of the crystal and s_o the area per molecule in the surface layer, and

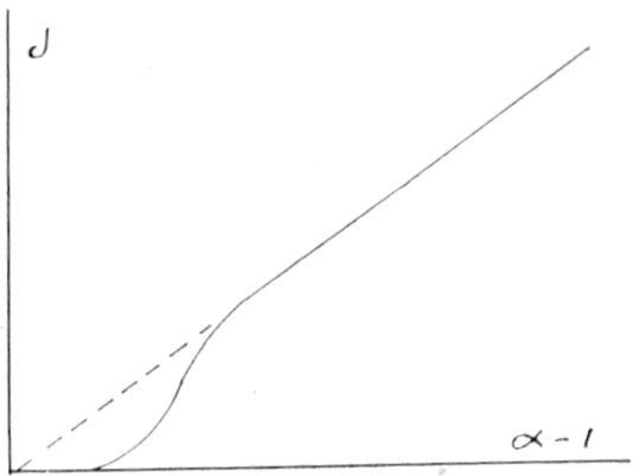

Figure 3-7. Rate of growth, J, as a function of degree of supersaturation, α[A-37, p. 45]

ϕ is the nearest neighbor binding energy ($\frac{1}{2}\phi = \sigma a$). This form is the same as that deduced by Becker and Döring[16] in 1935 for rectangular nuclei. The shape of the rate curve is represented in Figure 3-7. With reasonable values of the parameters involved, Frank estimates that supersaturations of at least 25 per cent or more are required for the two-dimensional nucleation of a solid growing in vapor. Burton *et al.*[38a] compute even higher critical values. Above these limits the growth rate should become linear in terms of supersaturation, since a nucleus for continued growth will always be assured.

The growth then depends only upon the rate of arrival of the molecules which are to be incorporated into the crystal lattice. The nucleation number will fall off rapidly below the critical level, and hence the observed growth rate should deviate markedly from linearity—a behavior reminiscent of the Christiansen-Lindemann account of monomolecular gas kinetics. Strickland-Constable[A-37] has shown that a strictly linear law would be realized only as the net difference between a process of evaporation or solution and deposition when these two processes advance independently. A nonlinear law results when the two are connected as in a nucleation process.

The first and most significant experimental investigation of this two-dimensional hypothesis for growth was that of Volmer and Schultze[239f] who measured the rates of growth of mercury droplets and phosphorus, naphthalene, and iodine crystals at very low supersaturations. Measurable rates were realized with the first three materials at all positive supercoolings, but were observed to cease at small supersaturations in the last instance. This was interpreted as indicative of growth by a two-dimensional growth mechanism, even though the critical point of about 1 per cent oversaturation was considerably less than the 20 per cent which had been estimated as the upper limit The approximately linear results with the other two solids were considered to be due to unusual conditions of condensation and adsorption. Figures 3-8, 3-9, and 3-10, and the corresponding Tables 3-4, 3-5, and 3-6

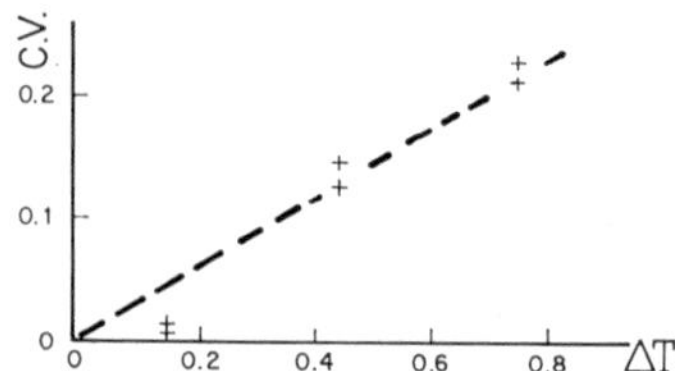

Figure 3-8. Condensation velocity of iodine vapor[239f] (Table 3-4).

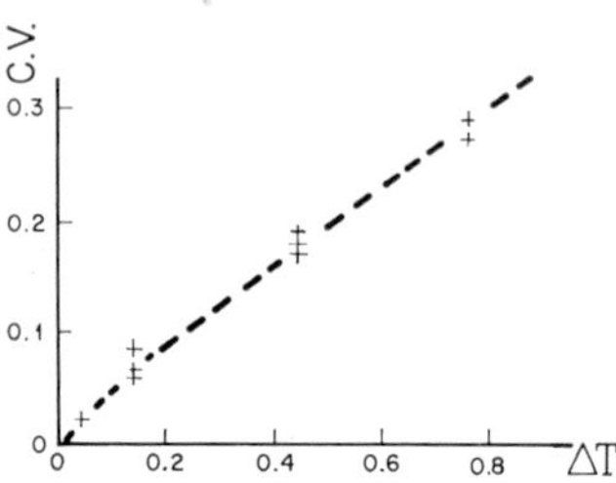

Figure 3-9. Condensation velocity of naphthalene vapor[239f] (Table 3–5).

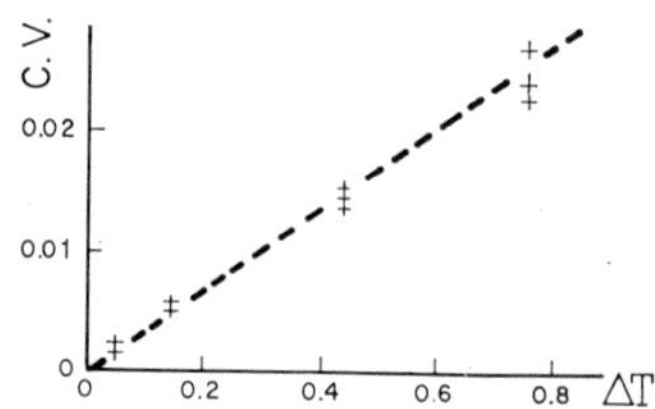

Figure 3-10. Condensation velocity of phosphorus vapor[239f] (Table 3–6).

are typical results of Volmer and Schultze for iodine, naphthalene, and phosphorus.

Honigmann[107b] has summarized the literature concerned with the rates of growth of crystals from vapor, but until his later investigations[107c] on the development of hexamethylenetetramine crystals none was suited for quantitative inquiry at low supersaturations. Honigmann found that the growth of nearly perfect crystals proceeded quadratically in terms of low values of supersaturation, while imperfect crystals grew linearly, Figure 3-11. Hillig[A-45] reports similar results for the growth of ice crystals, and Neumann[170] for solid potassium from vapor. (See Chapter 4.)

The signal importance of the iodine results and their original implication of a critical oversaturation for growth led the author to repeat Volmer and Schultze's experiments exactly as performed originally. In the first[60] trials, flamed U-tubes were filled directly by distilling in redistilled iodine. Most of the results duplicated Volmer and Schultze very well. However, the last

TABLE 3-4. CONDENSATION VELOCITY OF IODINE VAPOR[239f]

Supercooling (°C)	C.V. (mm/hr)	
	Face I	Face II
0.037	<0.00001	<0.00001
0.15	0.0033	0.005
0.45	0.14	0.13
0.76	0.22	0.21

TABLE 3-5. CONDENSATION VELOCITY OF NAPHTHALENE VAPOR[239f]

Supercooling (°C)	C.V. (mm/hr)		
	Face I	Face II	Face III
0.037	0.014	0.013	0.014
0.15	0.08	0.065	0.07
0.45	0.185	0.18	0.175
0.76	0.28	0.29	0.28

TABLE 3-6. CONDENSATION VELOCITY OF PHOSPHORUS VAPOR[239f]

Supercooling (°C)	C.V. (mm/hr)		
	Face I	Face II	Face III
0.15	0.0063	0.006	0.006
0.76	0.030	0.025	0.030
0.037	0.0016	0.0017	0.0016
0.15	0.0050	0.0040	0.0047

set of determinations in a sequence of 0.45–0.15–0.77° supercooling was fitted better by a linear relationship than the otherwise more suited higher order of about 2. It was also noted that the crystallization velocity of any particular crystal decreased as growth progressed, and that this was accentuated at lesser supercoolings.

Pahl,[180] working at very high growth gradients (48° supercooling), had noted that air, H_2, and CO_2 exerted pronounced effects on the growth rates of iodine dendrites, and for this reason greater care was taken in the preparation of another tube.[165] The iodine was repeatedly redistilled over P_2O_5 before being admitted to the tube which had previously been baked. It was then flushed further while redistilling from arm to arm. The results realized with this tube were much steadier, and drifting was largely elim-

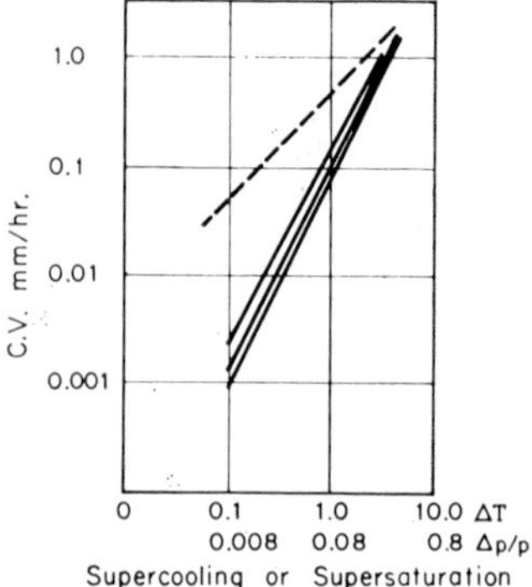

Figure 3-11. Crystallization velocity of hexamethylenetetramine single crystals, from vapor.[107b,c]

—— Mean values (Nearly perfect crystals; slope ~2).
-- Maximum values (Imperfect crystals; slope ~1).

inated. However, the values at the highest supercooling were considerably less than before. Three typical runs are depicted in Figure 3-12. After the last run, approximately 1 mm of ordinary laboratory air was admitted to the tube. At this point growth at the highest ΔT was virtually arrested, and subsequent evaporation was greatly impeded, too. It was also noted that the habit of the crystallites formed in the presence of this air was different.

Obviously, this particular critical experiment requires further intensive study. It may be pertinent to point out in this connection that some uncertainty exists regarding the magnitude of the accommodation coefficient of solids.[212] In the case of iodine, Volmer[A-18] cites a value of 0.056 at 40°C, increasing normally to 0.21 at 70°C, but Stern and Gregory[212] find a decreasing change from -56 to $+35$°C, with a value of about 0.01 at 0°C. Pahl finds $\alpha = 0.16$ at 15°C and cites Alty's value of ~1 at liquid air temperature.

Bradley and Drury[31] have also more recently repeated the Volmer and Schultze iodine experiment and find no evidence for a critical supersaturation of growth down to very low values of supersaturation. The growth rate was found to be parabolic in this region and so was that for the cubic form of CBr_4. However, the monoclinic form exhibited a linear rate curve to supersaturations as low as 0.004.

While the two-dimensional theory of growth nucleation was developed for and applied to solids growing in ideal gas nutrients, the same essential features may be expected to apply in condensed systems.[29] In this case, Nitschmann[174] measured the growth rates of salt cubes in saline solutions

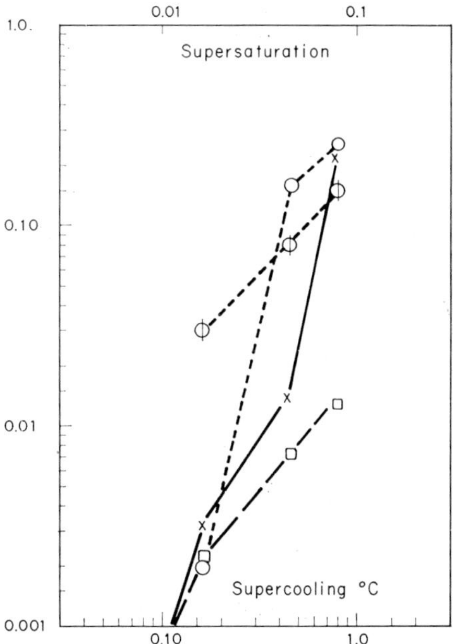

Figure 3-12. Growth rate of iodine single crystals from vapor. Typical runs: × Volmer and Schultze[239f] (slope ~2); ○ and ∅ Bogucki[60] (slope ~2 and ~1, respectively; □ Murphy[165] (slope ~1).

which were supersaturated by the evaporation of water. When the cubes were free of vicinal faces growth did not occur unless the supersaturation was at least 0.045 per cent. Fresh crystals, however, continued to grow in this solution until completely exhausted. This was taken to confirm Volmer and Stranski's hypothesis of the necessity of a critical supersaturation for growth in a liquid system. Analogous instances are known to the chemist, such as gypsum and calcite in water. The solubility of these substances when determined from oversaturation is invariably greater than when equilibrium is approached from below.[69, 109, 229] The discrepancy in these cases is readily understood in view of the complications due to solvation and extremely slow attainment of equilibrium

Interruptions of growth and even suspension thereof are not uncommon in crystal-growing experiments and have been reported by a number of workers.[A-37, 51, 139, 163, 215, 251] Booth and Buckley,[26] in particular, emphasize that even slight amounts of impurities may accumulate and impede or even arrest further growth. This possibility was indicated in Nitschmann's experiments where the supersaturated conditions were produced by evaporation of water using a stream of air. The critical values were higher as the rate of flow was increased, suggesting a "poisoning" effect. This is illustrated by the following figures from his paper (Ref. 174, p. 290).

1. air/hr	−1.47	2.01	1.57	2.01	2.14	1.08	1.22
Crit.O'sat. %	−0.0098	0.0155	0.0192	0.0204	0.0379	0.0081	0.0154

In another direction, Frank[75d] has pointed out that Haward's[98] molecular beam experiments are in astonishingly straightforward agreement with the theory of surface nucleation, although this may be questioned.[107d] In these experiments, Haward observed no appreciable growth or evaporation from a film of HgI_2 at 22.9°C unless the beam of the same material with which the film was bombarded was at least 40 per cent over- or undersaturated, respectively. Even a greater excess, or deficit, was required with anthracene. However, Sears and Cahn[201c] show that molecular beam results cannot always be interpreted as indicating critical values for nucleation since the adsorbate temperature may be higher than that of the substrate.

Another indication of two-dimensional nucleation is to be found in the growth experiments of Marcelin.[153] In these early observations on the layer-like growth of *p*-toluidine from solution, the thickening of the crystal appeared to progress in a stepwise fashion. From the change in interference colors each layer was estimated to be approximately one molecule thick (although recent observations on many other substances reveal much thicker layers), and the delays between successive additions are presumably caused by the slower two-dimensional nucleation required for the initiation of each new step.[230b] Similar growth patterns in the electrodeposition of cadmium and zinc have been reported by Volmer.[239g] The relation between layer growth and surface nucleation is discussed in detail by Bunn and Emmett[37b] and others.[A-37, 19]

The above references indicate the reality of two-dimensional nuclei, and in iodine, the most significant case, the observed threshold is considerably less than even the most liberal theoretical estimate. In fact, the discrepancy between theory and experiment for the rate of growth of a crystal at low supersaturations might be $e^{3,100}$ or more, surely in the words of Burton,[40] "one of the largest ever recorded." Obviously, many additional or different kinds of nuclei for growth would be necessary to reconcile this disagreement.[38a]

This apparent impassé was resolved by F. C. Frank at the Bristol Symposium on Crystal Growth in 1949.[A-37] At that time Frank proposed that if a crystal contained a dislocation which was self-perpetuating, the need for surface nucleation would be largely[189] but not entirely[40] circumvented, and the crystal would grow continuously even at very low supersaturations. The screw dislocation and various modifications meet this specification, and the simplest form is shown as a block model in Figure 3-13.

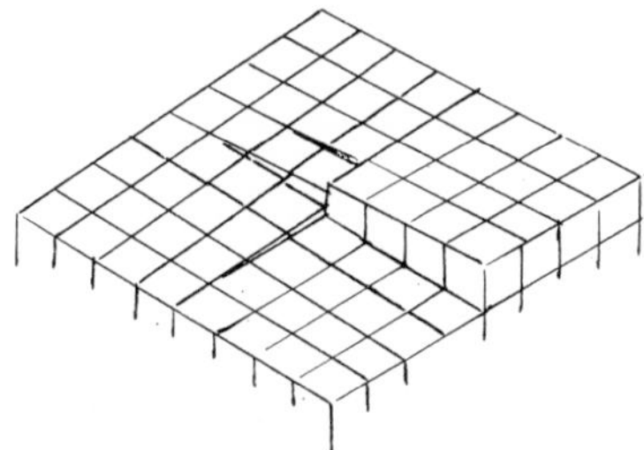

Figure 3-13. The end of a screw dislocation.

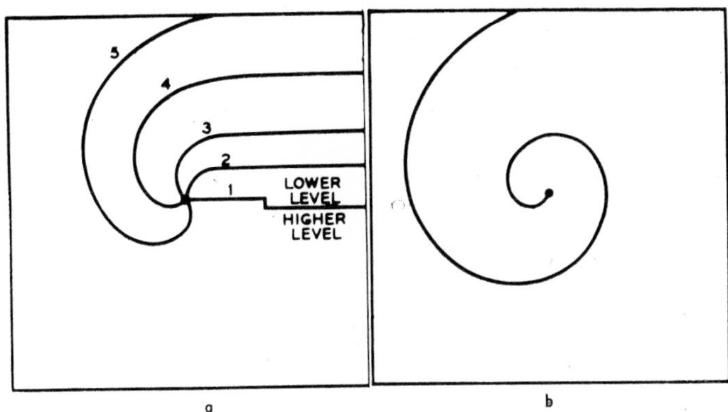

Figure 3-14. Growth spiral resulting from growth on the wall due to a screw dislocation.[204]

When an atom diffuses over the surface of a crystal such as represented in Figure 3-13, it will become attached at the top step formed by the two planes. The crystal surface becomes essentially a helical ramp (simulating a lock-washer) arranged in the direction of a right- or left-handed screw. After completing one entire layer the dislocation will still be present, but one layer higher. The atoms will attach themselves all along the step at about the same rate but the angular velocity near the center will be much greater. This can be seen in Figure 3-14, which represents the top view of a spiral dislocation. Line 1 is the flaw as shown in Figure 3-13. As this line grows by the addition of atoms, it assumes position 2, and 3, 4, 5, etc. This progress continues until the form in Figure 3-14(b) is generated. The actual shape of the spiral will depend upon the rate of growth and the crystal itself. Since a step is always present in the crystal, the need for two-dimensional nucleation is absent and the crystal continues to grow at supersaturations below those otherwise required.

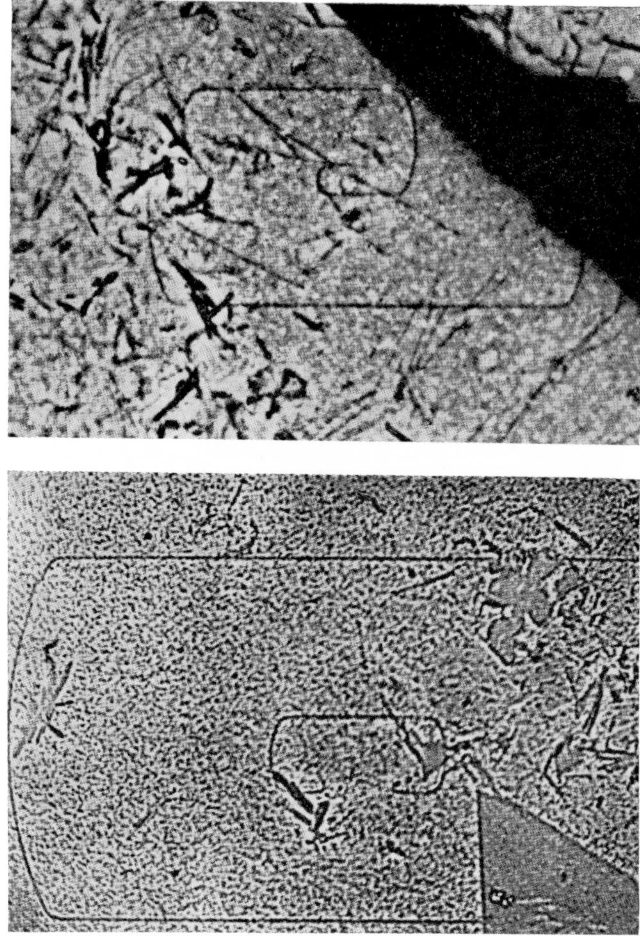

Figure 3-15. Step markings on the surface of natural beryl crystals. 540× and 690×, respectively. Photographs by J. Griffin.[38b, 89]

The immediate reaction to Frank's suggestion was a diligent search for the occurrence of the spirals predicated to be formed on the surface. While J. Griffin reported at this same conference (A-37, p. 192) that his interferometric examination of the surfaces of beryl crystals had not revealed the presence of spirals of the Frank type, this opinion was soon revised by the photographs reproduced in Figure 3-15. Since then the search for growth spirals has been extensive, and they have been found in almost all cases examined with sufficient care. They are, for instance, quite common on the

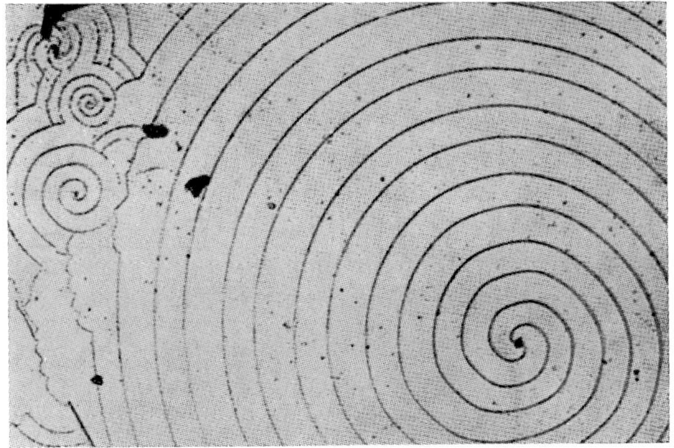

Figure 3-16. Spirals on silicon carbide.[A-3]

basal faces of ordinary silicon carbide crystals and can be observed under even ordinary reflected light at low magnification. Incidentally, these spirals on silicon carbide have been recognized by the metallographer as structural features for some time. Figure 3-16 illustrates only a single case of the many hundreds recorded by Verma,[A-17] Dekeyser and Amelinckx,[A-3] and others.[A-3, 33, 112] The current literature is replete with reports of their occurrence on both synthetic and natural crystals.

Frank also investigated the quantitative aspects of these spirals and their influence on growth rate.[75] The screw dislocation replaces the two-dimensional nucleus, provided that the distance between pairs of dislocations, or between a dislocation and a boundary, exceeds the diameter of the critical nucleus of the surface-nucleation theory. The limiting case is a crystal whose faces are only twice as wide as the critical nucleus. The distance between the turns of the spiral will then assume special significance, for below it the theoretical rate of growth will be determined essentially by a nucleation mechanism and will exhibit a parabolic dependence on supersaturation, while above it the nucleus is in effect ever-present and a linear relationship will exist.[104]

The rate of advance of a curved step in the crystal will be given by[75]

$$v = v_0 \left(1 - \frac{\rho_c}{\rho}\right)$$

where ρ is the radius of curvature of the advancing step, and ρ_c that of the critical nucleus; v_o is the rate of advance for a straight step and is given by

$$v_o = 2(\alpha - 1)x_s z_v \beta$$

where z_v is the frequency of arrival of vapor molecules at the surface, β a factor which is unity in simple cases, $(\alpha - 1)$, the supersaturation, and x_s the average distance a molecule wanders on the crystal surface from the time it arrives until it evaporates. Volmer[A-18] had shown that the chief supply of accreting molecules is by migration over the surface of the crystal rather than by direct impingement at the point of growth so that molecules travel considerable distances on the surface before evaporation. They thus have considerable opportunity for being incorporated into the growing lattice, once adsorbed on the surface. For ordinary cases

$$x_s = ae^{\phi/kT} \sim 4 \times 10^2 a$$

where a is the interatomic distance, and ϕ the nearest neighbor interaction enery.

The curved step advances at a velocity v_o over the greater part of its length, but more slowly near its origin. The spiral developed in this way is defined by the approximate equation

$$\frac{\rho}{\rho_c} = 2\left(\theta - \frac{v_0 \tau}{2\rho_c}\right) > 0$$

where θ is an orientation factor, and τ the number of turns of the spiral passing a fixed point in unit time. The rate of growth of the crystal is the quantity

$$t = \frac{v_o}{4\pi\rho_c(1 + 3^{-1/2})}$$

multiplied by the step height. Since v_o is directly proportional to the supersaturation, while ρ_c is inversely proportional to it, the steady-state growth rate is proportional to the square of the concentration. A more detailed analysis[75c] gives essentially the same pattern of a transition from a parabolic growth law at relatively low supersaturations to a linear law at high concentrations.

Crude theoretical estimates of the parameters involved in the more elaborate equation for I_2[75d] suggest that the transition from a parabolic to a linear growth curve should occur at about 10 per cent supersaturation, as shown in Figure 3-17. This is taken to be in satisfactory agreement with the observations of Volmer and Schultze, and also suggests that the absence of deviations in the cases of naphthalene and phosphorus is due to excessively large values of x_s.

This remarkable ratification of Volmer and Schultze's observations has recently been strengthened by the experiment of Sears[201] on the rate of evaporation of *p*-toluidine. This obverse of growth also proceeds from a

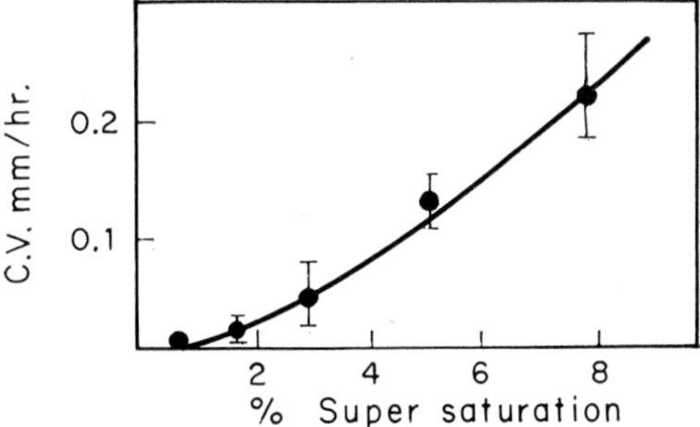

Figure 3-17. Growth rate of I_2 crystals from vapor.[239f] Mean value and range of scatter shown for seven crystal faces (omitting one anomalously slow-growing face).

dislocation,[108] so that the rate should diminish from linearity as the undersaturation is diminished. Kozlovski[138] also reports that the dissolution of 2-methylnaphthalene in ethyl alcohol is analogous to growth and evaporation for the solid-liquid transition, and, with Lemmlein,[148] finds common features of growth from the vapor, melt, and solution.

Figure 3-18, from Sears, illustrates schematically the expected situation for evaporation and growth while Figure 3-19 indicates that *p*-toluidine evaporates hardly at all at undersaturation ratios of 0.90 to 0.48, while at 0.35 the single point is at 3×10^{-6} cm/sec. The growth of this material from vapor has also been studied by Lemmlein[148] and Dukova and Chirnov.[44] Marshall and Gunn suggest tentatively that ice crystals do not grow at vapor densities below an excess of 0.066 gM^{-3}.

Neumann and co-workers[170] find that the critical oversaturation for growth of K crystals from vapor is considerably greater than that for I_2, yet smaller than expected by theory. Sears[201] suggests that this may be due to strongly adsorbed layers of oxide.

Additional quantitative information on growth in condensed systems at low supersaturations has also recently become available. Morris and Strickland-Constable[163] find that the LCV (linear crystallization velocity) of benzophenone at supercoolings of 0.1 to 1.5°C may be represented by a basically linear low whose constant of proportionality changes discontinuously, or by a higher order relationship which applies only statistically because of the pronounced variation of individual values. From the vapor quantitative considerations do not appear to lead to any compelling acceptance of Frank's theory, although the curves are of the right shape. Jantsch[117] also finds that the LCV of melts is determined by kinks at supercoolings less than 3°C, while two-dimensional nucleation prevails at higher subcoolings.[141] With phenyl salicylate melts, Danilov and Malkin[53] ob-

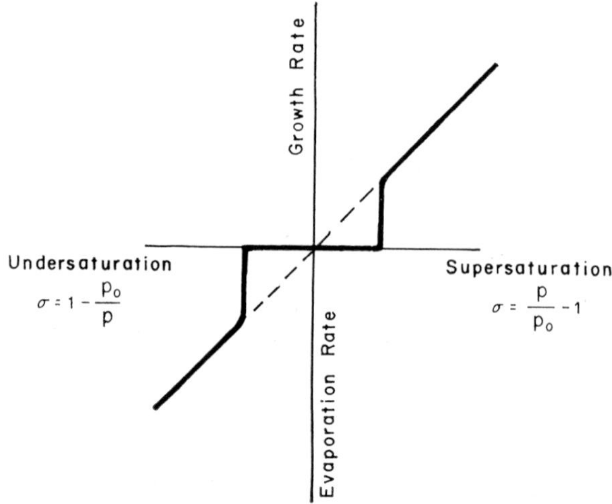

Figure 3-18. Theoretical growth and evaporation rate of a perfect crystal.[201b]

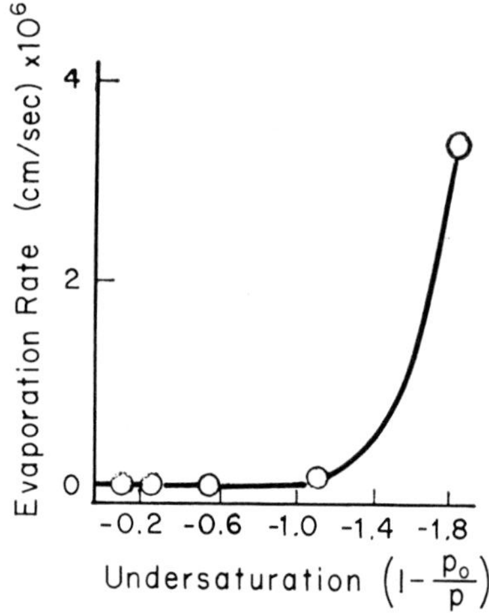

Figure 3-19. Evaporation rate of a perfect face of *p*-toluidine.[201b]

served no measurable growth until supercooled 1.6°C, after which the growth accelerated very rapidly.

Hartshorne's extensive investigations on polymorphism[96] include careful considerations of the rates of transformation of cubic to monoclinic CBr_4 and β to α-sulfur just below their transition points. He concludes that neither the linear law nor a two-dimensional nucleation mechanism applies. The data are not inconsistent with the requirements of dislocation theory, although this conclusion must be treated with considerable reserve in view of the scatter of the observations.

In solutions, Komarova and Figurovski[133] report that the growth rates of crystals of potassium alum, KCl, KI, K_2SO_4, $Na_2CO_3 \cdot 10H_2O$, NH_4Cl, $Pb(NO_3)_2$, and $Ca(SO_4) \cdot 5H_2O$ are linear over appreciable ranges of supersaturation at 20 and 25°, but approach zero at small but finite levels in most cases. These effective critical oversaturations for growth are, respectively, 0, 0.01, 0.018, 0.2, 0.44, 0.086, 0, and 0.26. The writer[236b] has not detected any such thresholds of growth in the case of growing sucrose crystals, where reliable and consistent measurements were made to supersaturation ratios as low as 1.001 and even lower. Taylor[222] also found that small sugar crystals erode and heal themselves within at least 0.1°C of saturation (supersaturation $\sim$1.001), and one crystal grew or dissolved within 0.04° (0 = 1.0005) when observed over sufficiently long periods. Smythe,[206] however, found that the growth rate of sugar solutions was linear only above supersaturations of 3 to 9 per cent, according to the temperature. Below this level, the indices of the growth curves were between 1.4 and 2.0. It is to be noted that growth spirals on these crystals—a direct indication of Frank's mechanism—were not observed until recently[1] when a barrier to growth at very low supersaturations was also reported.

Booth and Buckley's studies[26] on the growth of ethylenediamine tartrate crystals from aqueous solutions emphasize the experimental difficulties of clearly selecting between a linear and a quadratic law of growth and designating the existence of a critical oversaturation level for this growth. Even slight amounts of impurities exert a tremendous influence on the growth rate. Figure 3-20 is reproduced from their papers.

In summary, then, it may be inferred from growth and evaporation studies that a dislocation mechanism is most likely, especially in view of confirmation by direct observation[142, 230e] applicability in catalysis theory,[9] usefulness in explaining dye adsorption and poisoning phenomena,[247] whisker growth,[201, 244] etc.[39, 201, 189] Their significance for crystal growth has been endorsed by most workers in the field, with, however, some note of caution from Buckley[35] and others.[A-19, A-42, 138, 145]

Heterogeneous Nucleation

The catalytic effect of foreign bodies in nucleating metastable systems is well known and obviously results from the reduction in free energy of formation of the critical nucleus. Volmer (Ref. A-18, p. 100) showed that the free energy change on a wetted surface ($\Delta G'$) is given by

$$\Delta G' = \Delta G \left[\frac{(2 + \cos \theta)(1 - \cos \theta)^2}{4} \right]$$

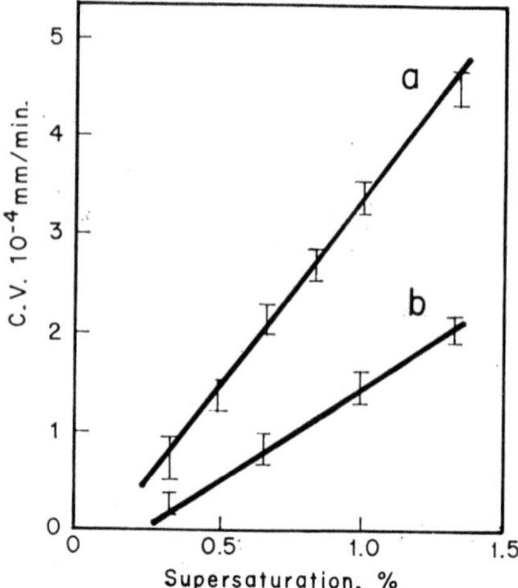

Figure 3-20. Rate of growth of ethylene diamine d-tartrate single crystals in the presence of slight amounts of impurities.[26] (a) Pure solution, 42°C. After Booth and Buckley.

with respect to the homogeneous change (ΔG). θ is the angle of wetting, and when this is complete, $\theta = 0$ and $\Delta G' = 0$; the foreign body is an effective seed! This basic principle has been elaborated in great detail by Turnbull[230c, f] and Frank and Van der Merwe[75b] and tested experimentally by Twomey.[231] Not only ordinary catalytic effects but also those of strain and oriented overgrowths may be accounted for in this way.[113, 186, 230] Table 3-7 illustrates the effectiveness of a few solids in promoting the formation of ice crystals from supercooled clouds. The closeness of the lattice constants of AgI and ice presumably accounts for the high efficiency in this case. It has frequently been assumed[37, 196, 216, 224] that the correspondence in this fit—or misfit—of lattice distances must be less than a definite limit for overgrowth and nucleation, but the considerable latitude which is observed in many epitactic systems suggests that factors other than this distance alone must be involved. Hume-Rothery,[110] for instance, suggested a 15 per cent tolerance, but this has had to be extended upward in many instances.[245]

Time Lag in Nucleation

The ordinary Gibbs-Kossel-Stranski-Volmer theory of nucleation assumes steady-state conditions, but there may be situations where these conditions do not prevail. There may be a delay in the appearance of the critical nucleus and this will be considerable in very viscous systems or

TABLE 3-7. SUPERCOOLING CORRESPONDING TO MAXIMUM TEMPERATURE AT WHICH VARIOUS SUBSTANCES CATALYZE FORMATION OF ICE NUCLEI[230f]

Substance	ΔT(°C)
Silver iodide	2.5 ± 0.1
Lake Albany clay	11 ± 1
Volcanic ash	16 ± 1
Cryolite	20 ± 1
Topaz	23 ± 1

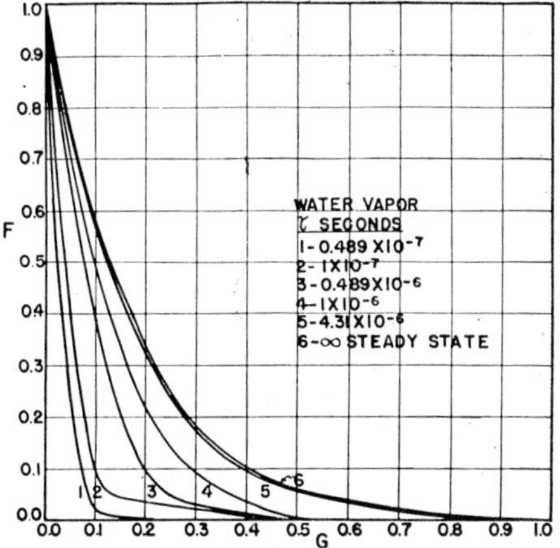

Figure 3-21. Influence of effective time lag (τ) on embryo concentration (F) in the self-nucleation of water vapor.[188] The nondimensional quantity G represents the embryo size.

where low accommodation coefficients are involved.[49] There exists, as it were, a time lag in the growth of potential nuclei (embryos, or germs) to critical-size clusters, such as illustrated in Figure 3-21.

This delay in nucleation may become acute in the condensation of water vapor. It is a cogent factor for consideration in the design and operation of hypersonic wind tunnels, when the liquefaction of the constituents of air itself is possible. This application has been considered by Probstein,[188] Kantrowitz,[123] and others.[68, 248, 249] In the case of sugar syrups, Dunning[63] estimates that about 100 hr may elapse before the nucleation process at 0°C approaches a steady state. Turnbull[230g] demonstrates that the induction period characteristic of solid reactions arises from the slow rate of diffusion in these systems,[253b] while Frisch[77] has recently suggested that the time-lag phenomenon is equivalent to the "memory" effect[20] so often associated with phase transitions, particularly by older writers.

SOME DETAILS OF GROWTH THEORIES AND TESTS

Diffusion Theories

Noyes and Whitney[175] observed that the rate of dissolution of cylinders of benzoic acid and lead chloride in water could be represented very well by the first-order equation

$$\frac{dC}{dt} = k(C_s - C)$$

where C is the instantaneous concentration at time t, and C_s the solubility. This result was generalized by Nernst[168] in a theory of heterogeneous reactions which assumed that equilibration at the interface was instantaneous. When the area A is in contact with volume V at concentration C, Fick's law gives for the rate of diffusion

$$\pm \frac{dC}{dt} = \frac{DA}{V} \frac{dC}{dy}$$

where dC/dy is the concentration gradient normal to the surface, and D the diffusion coefficient of the solute. The $\pm$ sign applies for growth of crystal or dissolution, respectively. The gradient across the interface of thickness δ is $(C - C_s)/\delta$, whence

$$\pm \frac{dC}{dt} = \frac{DA}{V\delta} (C - C_s)$$

or, the specific rate constant in the original Noyes-Whitney expression is

$$k = \frac{DA}{V\delta}$$

The observed monomolecularity of dissolution and many growth processes at first suggested the general applicability of this simple diffusion mechanism,[43] but more detailed considerations of the various factors involved soon indicated that this was by no means the universal situation. Even in the case of dissolution, where transport away from the boundary usually controls, unlikely thicknesses of the saturated film are computed. These may amount to as much as 20 to 50 μ in some cases, and are much thicker than the film usually conceived for the adsorption layer around a solid immersed in a liquid. However, the similarity of computed values is consistent with the view that the rates of reaction may be determined by the process of diffusion.[23, 162]

In the case of growth of crystals diffusion will control if the actual incorporation of building units into the crystal lattice is rapid. This is often the case with ionic crystals where the bond energies and forces are high, but with homopolar crystals and weaker interactions the surface reaction itself may be slower and thus prevail in the kinetics of growth. Many instances of these extreme cases are known, and probably many more are intermediate in nature.[81, 194] These latter situations correspond to the case of two or more consecutive reactions proceeding at comparable rates.

In these cases the concentration at the reaction site will assume a value, C_i, between that of the bulk solution C and the solubility C_s. The loss of material from this intermediate film by growth will be

$$-\frac{dC_i}{dt} = k_G(C_i - C_s)$$

while it will be replaced by diffusion at a rate given by

$$+\frac{dC_i}{dt} = k_D(C - C_i)$$

These two processes proceed at an equal rate in the steady state, so that

$$C_i = \frac{k_D C + k_G C_S}{k_D + k_G}$$

or the rate of growth in terms of depletion of the solution will be

$$-\frac{dC}{dt} = +\frac{dC_i}{dt} = \frac{k_G k_D}{k_G + k_D}(C - C_S)$$

The contributions of diffusion and growth may be resolved by means of temperature coefficients, but the computation has been completed in only a few cases. Sucrose and citric acid are examples where growth factors prevail at ordinary temperatures (see Chapter 6), but these give way, in the former case, to transport considerations as the temperature is increased.

Berthoud[22] was the first to make the suggestion of an intermediate concentration in the surface layer, and Valeton[233] used this same concept to explain the different growth rates of the various faces of a crystal. It was necessary, for this purpose, to assign different values of C_i to the several faces, since otherwise the crystal would not maintain its proper form but would grow isometrically as a sphere. This preservation of habit is one of the chief objections to the straightforward Nernst idea, and the fact that habit often changes according to the supersaturation also vitiates modifications of the Berthoud type.[A-1, 18, 160]

The inadequacy of the Noyes-Whitney-Nernst theory in many cases of crystallization was demonstrated by Marc[152] in extensive studies of the rate of growth in seeded solutions of K_2SO_4, $K_2Cr_2O_7$, $AgC_2H_3O_2$, KNO_3, alums, etc., chiefly by means of conductivity changes. Growth was shown to differ from dissolution (to which it should be equivalent according to the diffusion theory) in the following ways: (1) It is relatively much slower and easily measured; (2) The velocity of growth is independent of the rate of stirring if this is sufficiently vigorous; (3) The growth rate is not necessarily unimolecular. In some cases (*e.g.*, K_2SO_4) it changes, according to the temperature, from the basic monomolecular form with a 10-degree coefficient of about 1.5 (diffusion-controlled) to a bimolecular form with a temperature coefficient of about 2 per 10 degrees; (4) When a supersaturated solution is inoculated with seed crystals, there is initially a very rapid addition of material to this base, after which the normal velocity is established. This suggested to Marc that there was a preliminary adsorption with subsequent incorporation into the space lattice from this adsorbed layer; (5) Many substances when adsorbed considerably reduce the rate of growth, yet do not influence the rate of solution. Figure 1-20 shows the effects of 0.03 g of quinoline yellow in 100 ml potassium sulfate solutions of equivalent over- and undersaturations, respectively. Only those dyestuffs which color the crystals inhibit the velocity of growth. Bismark brown, ponceau red, quinoline yellow, etc., all color K_2SO_4 and retard its crystallization, but methylene blue is not adsorbed by this salt and therefore exerts no effect on the velocity of growth.

Marc's main observations and conclusions were confirmed and extended by Gapon[78] and others.[111, 118, 147, 209] However, considerable variability was observed in the initial behavior of adjusting solutions and actually an induction period rather than an initial acceleration was observed in the case of less soluble materials such as $PbSO_4$, $CaSO_4$, barium succinate, etc. This autocatalytic period has been ascribed to nuclei generation and multiplication (see p. 176) by a host of workers. Wagner[242] also criticized Marc's evaluation of the area term in his kinetic expressions and suggested that the true growing area may be very much greater than that estimated by Marc. This increase could be the result of imperfections, flaws, etc. in the seed material, or strained nuclei generated in the early part of the crystallization. These possibilities have been amplified in many later investigations.[A-37, 10, 90, 132, 223]

Adsorption Theories

Marc's suggestion of the role of adsorption in crystallization was immediately applied by Freundlich[76] to explain the influence of impurities upon the crystallization velocity of supercooled melts. He utilized the data of von Pickhardt[241] and of Padua and Galeati[179] and postulated that the adsorbed molecules impeded growth by preferential occupancy of lattice sites. This is in harmony with the straightforward crystallographic analysis of Valeton[233] concerning the arrangement of ions on a heteropolar lattice frame. In NaCl, for instance, the regular planes are occupied alternately by Na^+ and Cl^- ions, whereas the octahedral planes consist of one kind of ion and are stacked in order of alternate charge. These planes attract opposite charges much more strongly than do the cubic ones, and thus grow more rapidly and in time vanish. When urea, for instance, is preferentially adsorbed upon the octahedral faces, these same faces will eventually develop as their rate of growth is diminished.

In the case of melts it was assumed that the relative lowering of the crystallization velocity, $(v_o - v)/v_o$, would be proportional to the amount of adsorbed solute a. This would be given by the usual Freundlich adsorption equation, $a = a_o c^{1/n}$, where a_o and n are constants, and c the concentration of solute impurity in the melt or solution. The relative lowering of the C.V. would then be

$$\frac{v_o - v}{v_0} kc^{1/n}$$

The propriety of this equation is illustrated in Table 3-8. The value of $1/n$ is 0.4645, which is within the usual limits of 0.2 to 0.6. Tammann[221] had explained these same effects as due to the lowering of the melting point by the dissolved solute, but Freundlich (Ref. 76b, p. 329) indicated that this was wholly inadequate. Niggli[173] and Nacken[166] had also previously shown that Tammann's emphasis on the varying temperature of the growing interface as the result of the interplay of the heat of crystallization and its dissipation was unwarranted.[A-37, 151]

The above single example substantiating the simple adsorption hypothesis can be multiplied by many others;[24, 48, 80, 82] yet Freundlich[76] points out that "it would certainly be incorrect to ascribe the influence of foreign substances

TABLE 3-8. RELATIVE DEPRESSION OF THE CRYSTALLIZATION VELOCITY OF BENZOPHENONE BY CATECHOL[76b]

c = Mole Ratio Catechol to Benzophenone	$\frac{C_o - C}{C_o}$	
	Obs.	Calc.
0.0025	0.50	0.505
0.01	0.435	0.423
0.02	0.365	0.358
0.04	0.261	0.268
0.08	0.134	0.143

upon the crystallization velocity entirely to adsorption."[A-37, 58, 82] Walton and Brann[243] also showed that interaction (i.e., solvation) between the ingredients of a melt or solution was often more significant than orthodox adsorption, while Reinders,[190] as well as Ritzel,[195] pointed out the irreversible nature of adsorption during growth, and showed that growth may be impeded even without adsorption. The extensive observations in this field are reviewed by France,[74] Buckley,[A-1, 35] Wells,[246] and Whetstone.[247]

Volmer,[A-18, 239a, b] in 1921, began his studies on the kinetics of crystallization with a detailed consideration of the adsorbed state which was presumed to precede the actual incorporation of the building units into the crystal lattice. The Langmuir equation for the mass of gas m condensing on unit surface of solid per second was employed:

$$m = \frac{\alpha}{\sqrt{2\pi R}} \sqrt{\frac{M}{T}} (p_D - p_K)$$

where α is the accommodation coefficient, p_D the pressure, and p_K the equilibrium vapor pressure. The rate of growth normal to the surface v was then written in the approximate form

$$v \approx \frac{\alpha}{S} \frac{1}{\sqrt{2\pi R}} \sqrt{\frac{M}{T}} p_D, \qquad p_D \gg p_K$$

to account for the growth of mercury droplets on a glass plate at $-63°C$ when the vapor was supplied from liquid mercury at $-10°C$. S was a shape factor. Soon after cooling, single crystal flakes appeared whose thickness was at most only about one ten-thousandth of the diameter of the hexagonal face of the platelet. The thickness increased only after the leaflets had grown considerably to a diameter of 300 μ or more. The high accommodation coefficient of mercury (0.9 to 1.0) over this temperature interval required that but few atoms were reflected from the face.

The maximum value of v would be 2.5×10^{-7} cm sec^{-1} according to the p_D value at $-10°$, or 3×10^{-5}/min since growth occurs on two opposite faces. Actually, the observed increase in breadth was about 3×10^{-2} cm min^{-1}, or 1000 times the calculated growth. The condensing atoms were, therefore, not immediately incorporated into the lattice framework at the point of arrival, but must have been mustered to this point from the surrounding terrain in prompt fashion. Volmer visualized the newly arrived molecules as wandering quite freely over the surface of the crystal until they either (1) evaporated, (2) were attracted to and attached at a point of growth (a "kink"), or (3) formed with other molecules a nucleus for a new lattice layer in the case of an already filled surface. The importance of the second factor was greater the smaller the exposed area, and factor (3) assumed relatively greater significance as the leaflets increased in size. This concept of high surface mobility was most significant for the development of growth-rate theories since it emphasized the requirement of some sort of nucleating mechanism for the continuous growth of a crystal. The orientation of the building units within the mobile monolayer would dictate the form the growth would assume (equilibrium form, *vide infra*), as well as the starting point of each successive layer.

Volmer, with Adhikari,[239h] and with Moll,[239i] soon observed similar high radial growth rates that indicated high surface mobility in the growth of benzophenone and phthalic anhydride crystallites. For this purpose, a glass plate was covered with benzophenone which was then cleared from the edge for a short distance. Liquid mercury was allowed to drip upon this edge and while the drops never came into contact with the benzophenone the weight of this material on the plate actually decreased. In another experiment, a jet of mercury droplets was allowed to impinge upon a benzophenone crystal. The tip of the crystal diminished in size even when at a considerable distance from the stream of vapor and droplets. The same result was realized with salol; in this case, the loss of film was observed by interference patterns.

The rapid migration of silver and iodine over quartz, mica, and diamond faces has also been observed.[97, 239j] In still another type of experiment,[200, 202] one side of a tungsten plate, ZnO crystal or similar surface would be coated with elemental Ba, K, or radioactive Ag, for example. The rapid migration over the surface could then be determined or even directly observed in the field emission[14] and electron microscopes.[99, 203] The rate of this surface diffusion is much greater than that estimated by the ordinary volume diffusion laws[3, 47, 93, 169] and is also temperature dependent with activation energies of 10 to 20 kcal/mole.

Having established the ready availability of building units at almost any point in the growing surface, Volmer next examined the actual incorporation of these units into the crystal lattice. The model employed was that of Kossel.[136] (Figure 3-22.) The main conclusion was that the construction process consists essentially of the continued addition of the repeatable step and the main forces involved are those of the half-crystal. This result has already been outlined but will be repeated here in somewhat more detail for the case of a heteropolar crystal.

If e_o is the charge on each of two adjacent and oppositely charged ions and δ their distance apart in the crystal lattice, the energy of the pair is ρ_o^2/δ. In a crystal of the simple cubic type illustrated in Figure 3-22, the energy involved in placing an appropriate ion next to the one in position 1 would be equivalent to unity but the next one added to the row would have

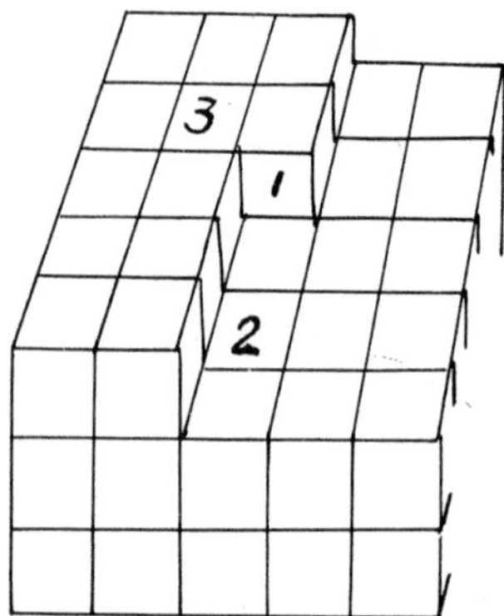

Figure 3-22. Kossel's simple cubic model.

the same charge as the central ion and would thus contribute a relative energy of $-\frac{1}{2}$ to the row energy. The next in turn would amount to $+\frac{1}{3}$, etc., so that the row energy, A_1 would be

$$A_1 = \frac{e_0^2}{\delta}\left(1 - \frac{1}{2} + \frac{1}{3} - \frac{1}{4} + \cdots\right) = \frac{e_0^2}{\delta}\ln 2 \approx 0.693\,\frac{e_0^2}{\delta}$$

The corresponding energies for addition after the completion of a row and surface are, respectively:

$$A_2 = \frac{e_o^2}{\delta}\left[1 - 2\left(\frac{1}{\sqrt{1^2+1^2}} - \frac{1}{\sqrt{2^2+1^2}} + \frac{1}{\sqrt{3^2+1^2}}\cdots\right)\right] \approx 0.124\,\frac{e_o^2}{\epsilon}$$

$$A_3 = \frac{e_o^2}{\delta}\left[\frac{1}{v_2} - 2\left(\frac{1}{\sqrt{2+1^2}} - \frac{1}{\sqrt{2+2^2}} + \frac{1}{\sqrt{2+3^2}}\cdots\right)\right] \approx 0.028\,\frac{e_o^2}{\delta}$$

The preferred order is $A_1 > A_2 > A_3$, but the order is just reversed in the case of homopolar crystals, when the surface, edge and corner are the preferred sites, in that order. This difference arises from the fact that the forces fall off much more quickly in homopolar crystals than in heteropolar ones so that only the first neighbors need be accounted for in the first case.[136]

In Stranski's model,[213] the n units in the side of a cubic framework are considered. All of the $6n^3$ faces of the cube are in contact except the $6n^2$ units on the surface. If ϕ is the binding energy for each pair of faces, the average binding energy for each unit will be

$$\frac{1}{2}\,\frac{6n^3 - 6n^2}{n^3}\,\phi = 3\phi\left(1 - \frac{1}{n}\right)$$

If the crystal extends infinitely, 3ϕ (the heat of vaporization) is the work of detaching the unit from the cube. Now, if the addition of a new layer on one face is considered, the first unit, say at a corner, involves an amount of energy ϕ. The next along the edge includes 2ϕ, and there are $2(m - 1)$ positions if the layer covers only m^2 and the n^2 units in the surface. The remainder all have a work of 3ϕ associated with them. This, again, is the *repeatable step* of Kossel.

The lattice energy of this repeatable step was resolved by Kossel into three component parts: $\phi_0 = \phi' + \phi'' + \phi'''$, ϕ' and ϕ'' are the two directional components parallel to the growing surface while ϕ''' is that normal to this surface. This last is the energy needed to start a new layer (or, essentially, two-dimensional nucleation), while a new row would require $\phi'' + \phi'''$ and the continuation of a row the sum of all three, or ϕ_0. In the case of a simple ionic crystal

$$\phi' = 0.6931 \frac{e_o^2}{\delta}, \qquad \phi'' = 0.1144 \frac{e_o^2}{\delta} \quad \text{and} \quad \phi''' = 0.0662 \frac{e_o^2}{\delta}$$

whence

$$\phi_0 = 0.8737 \frac{e_o^2}{\delta}$$

This is, then, the energy of the repeatable step, or that of addition within the surface of the plane. At the edge

$$\phi_0 = 0.0903 \frac{e_o^2}{\delta}$$

while at a corner

$$\phi_0 = 0.2470 \frac{e_o^2}{\delta}$$

Thus, as before, the points at which growth would be expected to ensue appear in the order: corner, edge, and mid-point, in the case of the simple cubic ionic model.

The total separation energy for a whole plane in this simple model would be the sum of the energies required for the corners, edges, and face: namely,

$$\phi + 4(m - 1)\phi + (m - 1)^2 \cdot 3\phi = 3\phi m^2 - 2\phi m$$

For a row added to an incomplete plane it would be $3\phi m(m - 1)$. The difference amounts to the extension of two faces of the cube by an amount r^2m, where r is the side of the unit cubelet. Two new steps of equal area will have been added, producing a new surface $4mr^2$, with corresponding energy $4mr^2\sigma$. This is to be identified with the surface binding energy $2m\sigma$, whence $2\sigma = \phi/r^2$. The extra energy, $2m\phi$, must be supplied by fluctuations, and is equivalent to the two-dimensional nucleation required for sustained growth.

Volmer and Marder's application[239k] of this model to the linear crystallization velocity of a crystal was essentially thermodynamic in nature, while Stranski and Kaischew[214e] employed a statistical-kinetic approach. Both expressed the rate of growth v as

$$v = K \cdot e^{-U/kT} \cdot e^{-A/kT}$$

where U is the activation energy of diffusion and A that of nucleation. In the case of melts, A depends upon the supercooling according to the expression

$$A = \frac{wM\sigma^2 T_s}{2d\,\delta Q_s(T_s - T)}$$

where T_s is the equilibrium melting temperature, Q_s the heat of fusion, w a shape factor, σ the edge free energy, and δ the distance between the crystal planes normal to the direction of growth. Collecting most of these parameters into a constant term B, the velocity of growth becomes

$$v = K \exp\left[-\left(\frac{U}{kT} + \frac{B}{(T_s - T)T}\right)\right]$$

where $(T_s - T)$ represents the supercooling.

Volmer and Marder's test of this equation with supercooled glycerine is illustrated in Figure 3-23. The dotted line represents the experimental results while the full lines are calculated with different empirical values in the theoretical expression. Stranski and Kaischew[213e] find a slightly better comparison on the basis of their improved treatment.

The general features of this Volmer-Stranski theory of growth are also confirmed in the crystallization of *o*-chloronitrobenzene from the melt[140] and of cyclonite from solution.[A-37] However, the pre-exponential factor in the latter case is found to differ greatly from the theoretical value—i.e., 10^2 instead of $10^{26\text{-}27}$. Experiments such as these constitute a broad confirmation of the proposed theories, but at the same time indicate that important dynamic features have been incompletely accounted for. In fact, the theoretical demand for periodic two-dimensional nucleation constitutes a considerable barrier to growth, and it seems remarkable that crystals even continue to grow at all. The obvious explanation is, of course, that actual crystals are not the ideal bodies postulated in the theory, and growth continues monotonously at finite rates because of ever-present and self-perpetuating flaws and/or defects.

Stranski and Totomanow[A-18, 213d,f] have also rationalized Ostwald's law of successive equilibrium on the basis of their considerations of the frequency of nucleation. Modifications with the smaller densities have smaller

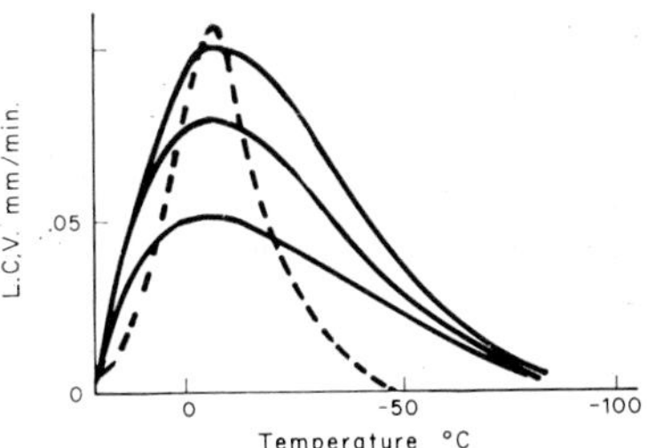

Figure 3-23. Volmer and Marder's test of the linear crystallization velocity equation.

specific surface energy. These are normally the forms stable at higher temperatures, so that they must have the greater frequency of nucleation. Ubbelohde[232] invokes entropy fluctuations to explain the same pattern. Many of the features of the growth of metals during electrocrystallization[70, 150, 237] have also been satisfactorily explained in similar ways. The work of Stranski and his students continues and is reviewed in several publications.[121, 130, 214g] The significant theoretical ideas have been supported by most investigators,[146, 210, 230d] although some project very serious objections.[8, 11, 86, 88, 125, 128, 176]

Recapitulation of Theories

The amazing feature of the adsorption theories of growth is that growth would probably be arrested at finite levels of supersaturation, or at least greatly impeded, by the need for some kind of surface nucleation. There is no theoretical reason to deny this requirement in the construction of perfect crystals; but since real crystals are probably never ideal we can expect this specification to be greatly mollified in actuality. Frank and his co-workers[75] at Bristol have already indicated how a simple edge dislocation can serve as a sort of self-perpetuating center of growth and the application of this proposal to the growth of real crystals has already been outlined in a previous section.

This impression of the present status of crystal-growth theories was one of the most significant conclusions of the Bristol symposium[A-37] in 1949, another being that a dynamic theory for conditions of rapid growth is most needed. Present theoretical considerations are still based very largely on equilibrium conditions, which may be approached in cases of very slow growth but certainly do not prevail when growth rates are high and high index faces develop.[A-37, A-39, 32, 80, 127, 220]

Layer and Dendritic Growth

The Kossel model suggests that the corners, edges, and faces of heteropolar crystals are, in order, the preferred building sites and thereby dictate the equilibrium form of a crystal. The order is just reversed for a homopolar crystal. The preferred order of positions also suggests that a crystal should develop from these particular points, and while the corners and regions of small radii of curvature are usually regarded as the most vulnerable points of solid bodies in many respects,[54, 95, 205] this is not necessarily the case in the development by growth.

Wherever the start, it follows, from the principle of a hierarchy of positions on the face of a crystal, that growth will proceed until the layer is completed because the energy yield of the repeatable step is greater than that of starting a new layer. The start of a new layer constitutes an interruption in the otherwise smooth and regular course of events, so that the addition of successive layers will occur in a periodic fashion. Straumanis[214] found such periodicity in the development of growth layers of solid metals from vapors and interpreted it according to the Kossel-Stranski model of growth.[A-37, 226] Gorbunova[87] also observed periodic cathode potential changes while a single crystalline face developed on the end of a wire.

Growth layers themselves were perceived by Marcelin,[153] who studied the growth of *m*-toluidine from alcoholic solution and observed that the thin plates which formed exhibited interference colors which maintained uniform tints as they spread across the face of the crystal. It was calculated that the layers were 3 molecules thick. Volmer[33, 91] observed similar thin layers on the surface of growing PbI_2 crystals, and Kowarski[137] on *p*-toluidine. The layers seemed to form on the edges of faces and spread inward in irregular patterns. Thin layers only a few molecules thick spread faster than thick ones. The steps on potassium alum growing in the presence of safranine are clearly evident, according to Alekseeva.[2]

Berg[19] observed the layer growth of crystals when confined between two heavily silvered optical flats, as also did Bunn and Emmett[37a, b] and Humphrey-Owen.[111] The cell was illuminated with parallel light and the fringes which formed indicated the concentration gradients at the growing interface.[59, 91] Similar optical arrangements hav been used by Tolansky[227] and Sultan.[218] The results of these workers are essentially those summarized by Bunn and Emmett as follows:

1. Layers very often start, not from edges or corners of crystals, but from the centers of faces, spreading outward toward the edges.
2. The thickness of the layers on many crystals increases as the layers approach the edges of the crystal faces.
3. The boundaries of the layers are often irregular, especially when growth is rapid; but as growth slows down there is a tendency to regularity of shape, the actual shape conforming to the symmetry of the crystal face.

4. Dissolved impurities may strongly influence the thickness and the shape of the layers, the effect being highly specific.
5. Thick layers have been seen only on crystals of certain ionic or polar substances; they have not been seen, under the experimental conditions used, on crystals of nonpolar substances.*

Figure 3-24 reveals the pattern of Fizeau fringes observed in these experiments, while Figure 3-25 is a plot of the concentration gradients observed about the several faces. These observations have been confirmed qualitatively by Ames, Cottrell, and Sampson,[4] Booth,[26] Kreuger and Miller[134] and others,[7, 66, 171] but not by Goldsztaub and Kern[84] and Egli.[A-42]

The fact that the supersaturation is greater at the corner than at the center in the case of ionic crystals—the only type on which these measurements were made—leads one to expect the formation of new nuclei there. This is in accord with the theoretical expectation but not with the actual microscopic observations of the British group of crystallographers. Berg[19] interprets his concentration distribution curves to signify that less solute arrives at each unit area of edge than at the center and therefore surface migration occurs from the center toward the edge. The accumulation of excess solute at the center when these operations are not in balance is likely to result in the formation of nuclei there. Buckley (A-1, p. 281) cites Haygood's explanation on the basis of adsorbed solvent molecules on the surface of the crystal. This may be stronger at the corner and edge, so that addition of molecules or ions would occur more readily at the center of a face than at a boundary. Frank[A-37] notes that dislocations would occur preferentially at face centers and one would expect growth layers to originate there.

Layerwise growth may be associated with equilibrium or quasi-equilibrium conditions, and when the rate of addition of accreting units is high we may expect aberrations of this smooth pattern of development. One of the most prevalent forms generated in such cases is that of dendrites, a typical example of which is illustrated in Figure 3-26.

Dendrites occur most commonly in the crystallization of metals and heteropolar compounds, but appear also in other classes especially when the rate of growth is high. By this same token dendrites and other forms occur frequently in industrially produced bulk crystals of all kinds. An outstanding feature of dendritic growth is that it is more likely to occur during the early part of the growth cycle. This behavior is especially prominent with metals. Uniformity of environment and the presence of impurities are also important factors in the formation of dendrites.[79, 129] These tree-like forms are favored in quiescent media, as exemplified by the exaggeration of frost

* Layerwise growth of sucrose crystals has since been reported.[1, 187, 236c]

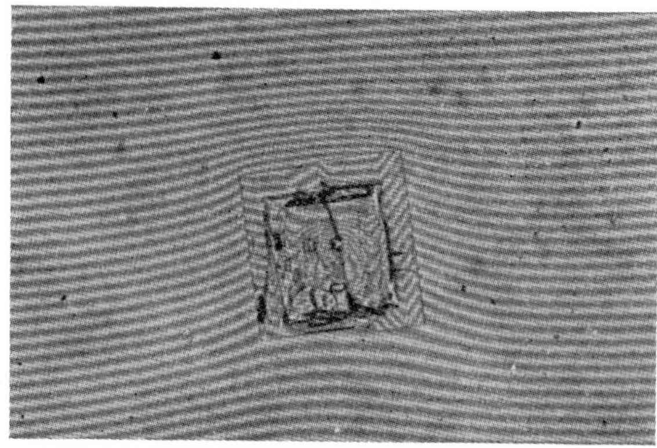

Figure 3-24. Crystal of sodium chlorate growing in thin layer of solution between nearly parallel half-silvered mirrors, illuminated by parallel monochromatic light.[37b]

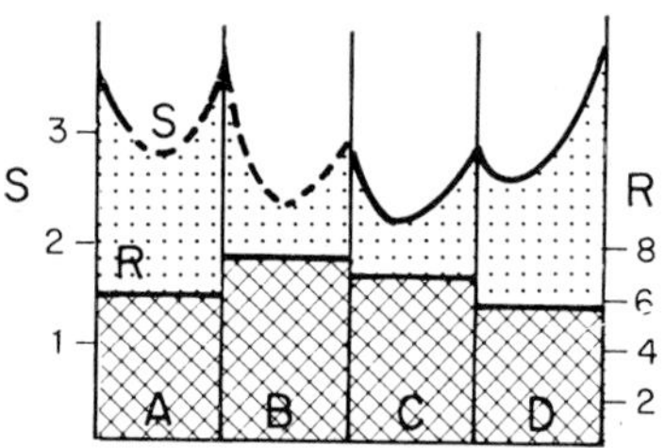

Figure 3-25. Supersaturation (S, in g/100 cc) and rate of growth (R, in cm/sec $\times 10^6$) of four faces of $NaClO_2$.[37b]

crystals during cold, still nights. The effects of these conditions suggest that it is not just growth rate alone that determines the occurrence of dendritic crystals, but probably the dynamic conditions within the nutrient medium.[6, 102, 126, 159, 198, 199] Their development early in the total growth may be correlated with these same conditions, or with the fact that the initial rate of growth of crystals is usually greater than normal because of strain, imperfections, or irregularities. The early dendritic superstructure is then frequently consolidated or filled in as growth continues.

Miers[161] accounted for dendrite formation, as realized in the evaporation of droplets of solutions, with the usual supersolubility concept. When the rate of concentration by evaporation exceeded the rate of withdrawal of solute by growth, the labile limit was reached nonuniformly along the crystal surface. The crystal then advanced more rapidly in these regions of higher concentration. This behavior would occur according to crystallographic and geometric restrictions so that a dendritic structure would result. This is illustrated in idealized form in Figure 3-27.

Figure 3-26. Some typical snow crystals.

Vogel's theory[238] of dendrite formation was based on the fact that the heat of crystallization will be dissipated more rapidly from a corner than from an edge and face, in turn. Accordingly, growth will be stimulated at these points and will become a "run-away" process in which points become sharper, spines longer, and acute angles sharper.

Papapetrou[181] combined the features of a transport problem with the limitations of the Kossel-Stranski model to arrive at essentially the same conclusion: namely, that growth would be enhanced at certain regions in the growing interface. Critical concentrations will exist for the formation of definite types—e.g., needles, side branches, etc.—somewhat in the sequence indicated in Figure 3-28. This conclusion finds some substantiation in the various boundary values which are ascertained for the formation of different types of ice crystals grown from vapor. In Table 3-9, ($\rho - \rho_{ice}$) is the supersaturation in the vapor as g.m^{-3} at temperatures from -6 to -20°C.

Buckley (A-1, p. 281) and Matz (A-11, p. 94) state that artificial snowflakes are needles or irregular when grown at rates of 0.5 mm/hr; plates at

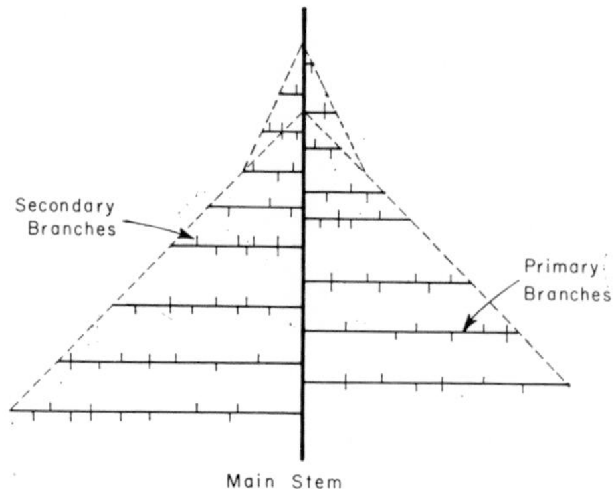

Figure 3-27. Branching in dendritic growth, After Papapetrou.[106]

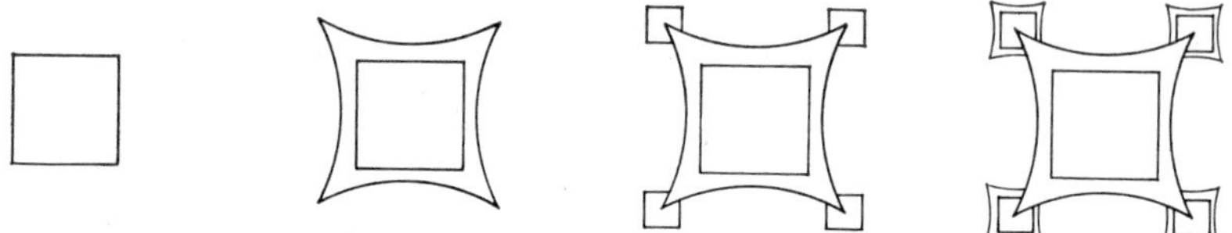

Figure 3-28. Development of a KCl dendrite, After Papapetrou.[106]

Table 3-9. Supersaturation and Habit of Ice Crystals[A-42]

Habit	ρ-ρ_{ice}	
	Latest Values	Earlier Values
Dendrites	0.150	0.194
Plates	0.138	0.182
Columns	0.117	0.161
Needles	0.066	0.111
No growth		

0.7; dendrites at 1.3; and ferns at 4.6. The manifold varieties of snow crystals have been recorded in many sketches and photographs, and one of the most beautiful collections of both natural and artificial flakes is that of Nakaya.[167] It seems that the life history of a snow flake is reflected in its habit and, therefore, atmospheric conditions during growth might be inferred from the morphology.[276b, c]

Mason and Ludlam[156, 157] imply the importance of diffusional and other factors in dendrite formation of snow flakes when they specify a correlation factor $Rd/D \gg 1$ for dendrites, and $\ll 1$ for polyhedral growth. R is the linear growth rate, d the diameter of the crystallite, and D the diffusion coefficient. Salli[197] finds a similar correlation in terms d and x, the thickness of the crystal-medium interface. If $x \ll d$, polyhedra form, but dendrites appear when $x \gg d$. The latter condition prevails in very viscous systems.

In aqueous solutions of heteropolar substances, Yamamoto[252] finds that there are critical growth rates above which skeletal rather than compact forms are produced. This critical rate is usually lower for large faces and thus makes the growth of good large crystals difficult. The critical level is often raised by even slight amounts of impurities, which thus serve as promotors or beneficiators. Cations are often more effective than anions or organic substances. Egli[A-37, A-42] and others[21, 26, 135, 219, 225, 226] have investigated these effects in some detail, spurred on by the improvements offered in the production of good, large, single crystals.

REFERENCES

1. Albon, N., and Dunning, W. J., *Nature,* **180,** 1348 (1957), *Acta Cryst.,* **12,** 219; **13,** 495 (1960).
2. Alekseeva, N. P., *Kristallografiga,* **4,** 92 (1955); *C.A.,* **52,** 31.
3. Alty, T., and Clark, A. R., *Trans. Faraday Soc.,* **31,** 648 (1935).
4. Ames, J., Cottrell, T. L., and Sampson, A. M. B., *Trans. Faraday Soc.,* **46,** 938 (1950).
5. Amsler, J., and Scherrer, P., *Helv. Phys. Acta.,* **14,** 318 (1941).
6. Anastasiadis, E., *Neue Hutte,* **2,** 425 (1957); *C.A.,* **52,** 825.
7. Anderson, N. G. and Dawson, I. M., *Proc. Roy. Soc. (London),* **A218,** 255 (1953).
8. Andronikashvili, E., *Acta Physicochim. URSS,* **6,** 689 (1937); *C.A.,* **32,** 4025.
9. Anon., *Chem. and Eng. News,* 2634, June 25 (1951).
10. Balarev, D., *Kolloid Beihefte,* **32,** 205 (1931), **37,** 180 (1933), **50,** 1 (1939).
11. Balarev, D., *Zeit. Min. Geol.,* 187 (A1942); *C.A.,* **38,** 5706.
12. Barnard, A. J., *Proc. Roy. Soc. (London),* **220A,** 132 (1953).
13. Bauer, E., *Z. Electrochem.,* **110,** 372 (1958).
14. Becker, J. A., *Ind. Eng. Chem., News Ed.,* 1387 (1952).
15. Becker, R., *Ann. Physik.,* **32,** 128 (1938).
16. Becker, R. R., and Döring, W., *Ann. Physik.,* **24,** 719 (1935).
17. Benson, G. C., and Shuttleworth, R., *J. Chem. Phys.,* **19,** 130 (1951).
18. Bentivoglio, M., *Proc. Roy. Soc. (London),* **115,** 58 (1927).
19. Berg, W. F., *Proc. Roy. Soc. (London),* **A164,** 79 (1938).
20. Bernal, J. D., *Nature,* **185,** 70 (1960).
21. Bertanza, L. and Martelli, G., *Nuovo cimento,* **1,** 324 (1955); *C.A.,* **491,** 4405.
22. Berthoud, A., *J. chim. phys.,* **10,** 624 (1912).
23. Bircumshaw, L. L., and Riddiford, A. C., *Quart. Rev.,* **6,** #2, 157 (1952).
24. Bliznakov, G., and Kevkova, E., *Z. physik. Chem.,* **206,** 271 (1957).
25. Bogan, E. G., and Moyer, H. V., *Anal. Chem.,* **28,** 473 (1956).
26. Booth, A. H., and Buckley, H. E., *Can. J. Chem.,* **33,** 1162 (1955); *Nature* **169,** 367 (1952).
27. Borelius, R., *Ann. Physik.,* **28,** 507 (1937).
28. Bose, A. N., and Chatterji, A. C., *J. Indian Chem. Soc.,* **26,** 94 (1949).

29. Bradley, R. S., *J. Phys. Chem.*, **60**, 1347 (1956); *J. Chem. Soc. (London)*, 4530 (1952).
30. Bradley, R. S., Evans, H., and Whytlaw-Gray, *Proc. Roy. Soc. (London)*, **186A**, 368 (1946).
31. Bradley, R. S., and Drury, T., *Trans. Faraday Soc.*, **55**, 1848 (1959).
32. Brandes, H., *Z. physik. Chem.*, **126**, 196 (1927).
33. Brandstatter, M., "Spiral Growth of Crystals," 7½ mm. film #C-681. Inst. Wiss. Film. Gottingen (1954).
34. Bresica, F., and Lichstein, B., *J. Am. Chem. Soc.*, **79**, 1591 (1957).
35. Buckley, H. E., *Z. Electrochem.*, **56**, 275 (1952); *Proc. Phys. Soc. (London)*, B65, 578 (1952); Gomer and Smith, "Structure of Solid Surfaces," Chap. VIII, U. Chicago Press (1953).
36. Bukovsky, F., *Acta. Phys. acad. Soc. Hung.*, **8**, 109 (1957); *C.A.*, **52**, 15996.
37. (a) Bunn, C. W., "Chemical Crystallography," Oxford Press, 1945.
(b) Bunn, C. W., and Emmett, H., Ref. A-37, p. 119, 132.
38. (a) Burton, W. K., Cabrera, N., and Frank, F. C., *Nature*, **163**, 398 (1949); *Phil. Trans.*, **A243**, 299 (1951).
(b) Burton, W. K., *Penguin Science News Letter*, **21**, 26 (1951).
39. Cabrera, N., *J. Chim. Phys.*, **53**, 675 (1956).
40. Cabrera, N., in Gomez and Smith's, "Structure and Properties of Solid Surfaces," p. 295, U. Chicago Press, 1953.
41. Cagle, F. W., and Eyring, H., *J. Phys. Chem.*, **57**, 942 (1953); **164**, 305 (1958).
42. Cahn, J. W. and Hilliard, J. E., *J. Chem. Phys.*, **28**, 258 (1958); **30**, 1121 (1959); **31**, 688 (1959).
43. Centnerszwer, *Z. physik. Chem.*, **141A**, 297 (1929).
44. Chirnov, Z., *Kristallografiya*, **1**, 117 (1956).
45. Christiansen, J. A., *Acta Chem. Scand.*, **5**, 674 (1951); **8**, 909, 1665 (1954).
46. Christiansen, J. A., and Nielsen, A. N., *Z. Electrochem.*, **56**, 465 (1952).
47. Clancy, V. J., *Nature*, **166**, 275 (1950).
48. Coalstad, S. E., *J. Soc. Chem. Ind.*, **65**, 206 (1946).
49. Collins, F. C., *Z. Electrochem.*, **59**, 404 (1955).
50. Collins, F. C., and Leineweber, J. P., *J. Phys. Chem.*, **60**, 389 (1956).
51. Courtney, W. G., *J. Chem. Phys.*, **27**, 1349 (1957).
52. Curie, P., *Bull. soc. franc. mineral.*, **8**, 145 (1885).
53. Danilov, V. I. and Malkin, V. I., *Zhur. Fiz. Khim.*, **28**, 1837 (1945); *C.A.*, **50**, 1401.
54. Dankov, P. D., and Gorunova, K. M., *J. Phys. Chem. URSS*, **23**, 5, 616 (1949).
55. Davies, C. W., and co-workers, A-37, p. 103; *Trans. Faraday Soc.*, **51**, 812, 1232 (1955).
56. Dehlinger, U., and Wertz, E., *Ann. Phys.*, **39**, 226 (1941).
57. Deicha, J., *Bull. soc. franc. mineral.*, **72**, 286 (1949).
58. Deyer, F., *Z. physik. Chem.*, **48**, 467 (1904).
59. Domokos, G., and Malicsko, L., *Acta Phys. Acad. Sci. Hung.*, **10**, 185 (1959); *C.A.*, **54**, 13798.
60. Donovan, J. W., Bogucki, R. F., M.S. theses, College of the Holy Cross, 1953, 1954.
61. Doremus, R. H., *J. Phys. Chem.*, **62**, 1069 (1958).
62. Duke, F. R., and Brown, L. M., *J. Am. Chem. Soc.*, **76**, 1443 (1954).
63. Dunning, W. J., in Garner's, "Chemistry of the Solid State," London, Butterworths, 1955.

64. Dunning, W. J., and Shipman, A. J., *Proc. Agric. Ind.*, X Int. Congr., Madrid, 1954.
65. Dunning, W. J. and Notley, N. T., *Z. Electrochem.*, **61,** 55 (1957).
66. Elbaum, C., and Chalmers, B., *Can. J. Phys.*, **33,** 196 (1955); *C.A.*, 49, 9346.
67. Farkas, L., *Z. physik. Chem.*, **125,** 236 (1927).
68. Faro, I., Small, T. R., and Hill, F. K., *J. Appl. Phys.*, **23,** 40 (1952).
69. Fawcett, W. J., *Trans. Roy. Soc. Can.*, **7,** 218 (1913).
70. Fischer, H., "Electrokristallization von Metallen," Berlin, Springer, 1954.
71. Fischer, J. C., Holloman, J. H., and Turnbull, D., *J. Appl. Phys.*, **19,** 775 (1948); *J. Chem. Phys.*, **17,** 71 (1949); *Science*, **109,** 168 (1949).
72. Fletcher, V. A., *J. Chem. Phys.*, **29,** 572 (1958); **30,** 1476 (1959).
73. Flood, H., *Z. physik. Chem.*, **170A,** 286 (1934).
74. France, W. G., in Alexander's "Colloid Chemistry," V, 443, New York, Reinhold, 1944.
75. Frank, F. C., *et al.*,
    (a) Ref. A-37.
    (b) *Proc. Roy. Soc. (London)*, **A198,** 205 (1949).
    (c) *Phil. Trans.*, **A243,** 299 (1951).
    (d) Solvay Conf. 1951.
    (e) *Phil. Mag.*, **42,** 670 (1951), **43,** 72 (1952).
    (f) *Z. Electrochem.*, **56,** 429 (1952).
76. Freundlich, H.,
    (a) *Z. physik. Chem.*, **75,** 245 (1910).
    (b) "Capillary Chemistry," 3rd. ed., transl., Dutton, N.Y., 1922.
77. Frisch, H. L., *J. Chem. Phys.*, **27,** 93 (1957).
78. Gapon, E. M., *J. Russ. Phys. Chem.*, **61,** 1729 (1929); *C.A.*, **25,** 5339; *Ukrain. Khim. Zhur.*, **4,** 161, 505 (1929).
79. Gay, R., *Bull. soc. franc. min. et crist.*, **72,** 251 (1949); *C.A.*, **43,** 6062.
80. Gey, W. A., *et al.*, *J. Am. Chem. Soc.*, **78,** 1803 (1956), *J. Phys. Chem.*, **61,** 507 (1957).
81. Giddings, J. C., and Eyring, H., *J. Phys. Chem.*, **62,** 305 (1958).
82. Gilpin, V., McCrone, W., Smedal, A., and Grant, H., *J. Am. Chem. Soc.*, **70,** 208 (1948).
83. Glasstone, S., Laidler, K., and Eyring, H., "The Theory of Rate Processes," New York, McGraw-Hill Book Co., 1941.
84. Goldztaub, G., and Kern, R., *Acta Cryst.*, **6,** 842 (1953).
85. Gopal, R., *J. Indian Chem. Soc.*, **20,** 183 (1943), **27,** 43 (1950); *Z. anorg. Chem.*, **278,** 46 (1955).
86. Gorbachev, S. V., and Shlykov, A. V., *Zhur. Fiz. Khim.*, **291,** 777 (1955); *C.A.*, **50,** 9082.
87. Gorbunova, K. M., Ref. A-41, p. 39; *Compt. rendu. acad. sci. URSS*, **48,** 15 (1945); *C.A.*, **40,** 4589.
88. Graf, L., *Z. Metallkunde*, **42,** 336, 401 (1951); **45,** 36 (1954).
89. Griffin, J., *Phil. Mag.*, **41,** 196 (1950); **42,** 775 (1951).
90. Grut, E., in "La Cristallisation du Sucre," Brussels, C.I.T.S. 1954.
91. Gyulai, F., *Z. Krist.*, **A91,** 142 (1935).
92. Haber, F., *Ber. deut. chem. Ges.*, **6,** 1721 (1922).
93. Hackerman, N. and Simpson, N. H., *Trans. Faraday Soc.*, **52,** 628 (1956).
94. Hahnert, H. and Kleber, W., *Kolloid Z.*, **162,** 36 (1959).
95. Harbury, L., *J. Phys. Chem.*, **50,** 190 (1946); **51,** 382 (1947).

96. Hartshorne, N. H., *et al.*, A-37, p. 149; *J. Chem. Soc.* (*London*), 3705 (1955), 224, 2122 (1957).
97. Hass, G., *Naturwiss.*, **25,** 232 (1937).
98. Haward, *Trans. Faraday Soc.*, **35,** 1401 (1939).
99. Heidenreich, *J. Appl. Phys.*, **14,** 23 (1943).
100. Herzfeld, K. F., and Reed, S. G., *Z. Electrochem.*, **56,** 308 (1952).
101. Higuchi, W. I., and O'Konski, C. T., *J. Coll. Sci.*, **15,** 14 (1960).
102. Hille, M., Rau, H., and Schlipf, *Z. Electrochem.*, **63,** 233 (1959).
103. Hirano, K., *Sci. Rept. Tohoku U.*, **38,** 971 (1954); *C.A.*, **49,** 10696, 14440.
104. Hirth, J. P., and Pound, G. M., *J. Chem. Phys.*, **64,** 619 (1960).
105. Hoffman, J. D., *J. Chem. Phys.*, **29,** 1192 (1958).
106. Holmes, E. L., Rutter, J. W., and Winegard, W. C., *Can. J. Phys.*, **35,** 1, 223 (1957); *C.A.*, **52,** 826.
107. Honigmann, B.,
    (a) *Z. Electrochem.*, **58,** 323 (1954).
    (b) *Z. Electrochem.*, **61,** 74 (1957).
    (c) *Z. Krist.*, **106,** 199 (1955).
    (d) Private communication.
108. Horn, F. H., Fullam, E. F., and Casper, J. S., *Nature*, **169,** 928 (1952).
109. Hulett, G. A. and Allen, L. E., *J. Am. Chem. Soc.*, **24,** 667 (1902).
110. Hume-Rothery, W., "Atomic Theory," London, Inst. of Metals, 1946.
111. Humphrey-Owen, S. P. F., A-37, p. 144; *Proc. Roy. Soc.* (*London*), **A197,** 218 (1949); *Acta Cryst.*, **8,** 112 (1955).
112. Indenbom, *Kristallogratiya*, **3,** 113 (1958); *C.A.*, **52,** 9702.
113. Ives, M. B., and Hirth, J. P., *J. Chim. Phys.*, **33,** 517 (1960).
114. Jackson, K. A., and Chalmers, B., *Can. J. Phys.*, **34,** 473 (1956).
115. Jacobs, P. W. M., and Tompkins, F. C.; in Garner's, "Chemistry of the Solid State," Chap. 7, London, Butterworths, 1955.
116. James, T. H., in "Advances in Catalysis," p. 122, New York, Academic Press, 1950.
117. Jantsch, L. D., *Z. Krist.*, **108,** 185 (1956).
118. Jenkins, J. D., *J. Am. Chem. Soc.*, **47,** 902 (1925).
119. Johnsen, A., *Zentral. Min. Geol.*, 87 (1917).
120. Jones, W. J., and Partington, J. R., 1913 et seq.; summarized by Partington, J. R., *J. Phys. Chem.*, 36, 1853 (1932); "Treatise on Physical Chemistry," IV, p. 539, London, Longmans-Green Co., 1952.
121. Kaischew, R., *Compt. rendu bulgare sci.*, *Sci. mat. nat.*, **1,** #2, 23 (1948); *C.A.*, **44,** 8192.
122. Kaischew, R., *Acta. Phys. acad. sci. Hung.*, **8,** 75 (1957); *C.A.*, **52,** 15996.
123. Kantrowitz, A., *J. Chem. Phys.*, **19,** 1097 (1951).
124. Karagounis, G., *Helv. Chim. Acta*, **36,** 1681 (1953).
125. Khlopin, V. G., and Tolstaya, M. A., *J. Phys. Chem. U.S.S.R.*, **14,** 941 (1940); *C.A.*, **35,** 3870.
126. Kirkaldy, J. S., *Canadian J. Phys.*, **37,** 739 (1959), **38,** 1343 (1960).
127. Kirkwood, J. G., and Buff, F. P., *J. Chem. Phys.*, **17,** 338 (1949), **18,** 991 (1950), **19,** 1591 (1951), **23,** 419 (1955).
128. Kleber, W., *Kolloid. Z.*, **94,** 39 (1941).
129. Kleber, W., *Neues Jahrb. Min.*, 106 (1943), 1 (1945–48), 251 (1955).
130. Knacke, O., and Stranski, I. N., *Ergeb. Exakt. Naturwiss.*, **26,** 383 (1952).

131. Koenig, F. O., *J. Chem. Phys.*, **18,** 449 (1950).
132. Kolthoff, I. M., "Aging of Precipitates," e.g., *Science*, **84,** 376 (1936); *J. Am. Chem. Soc.*, **76,** 1510 (1954).
133. Komarova, T. A., and Figurovski, N. A., *Zhur. Fiz. Khim.*, **28,** 1774 (1954); *C.A.*, **50,** 1429.
134. Kondo, S., *J. Chem. Phys.*, **25,** 662 (1956).
135. Koselev, V., *Hutnicke Listy*, **4,** 299 (1958).
136. Kossel, W., *Nachr. Ges. Wiss. Gottingen, Math. physik Klasse*, 135 (1927), *Ann. Physik.*, **21,** 455 (1934); **33,** 651 (1938).
137. Kowarski, L., *J. chim. physique*, **32,** 469 (1935); *Compt. Rend.*, **194,** 2126 (1932).
138. Kozlovski, M. I., *Kristallogratia*, **3,** 209, 236, 483 (1948); *C.A.*, **53,** 7708, 8756.
139. Kreuger, G. C., and Miller, C. W., *J. Chem. Phys.*, **21,** 2018 (1953).
140. Krishtal, Yu. A., *Doklady Akad. Nauk. SSSR.*, **98,** 395 (1954); *C.A.*, **49,** 15341.
141. Krishtal, Yu. A., *Nauch. Doklady Vysaki Shkoly. Met.*, **4,** 197 (1958); *C.A.*, **53,** 18579.
142. Krumhansl, J. A., *Ann. Rev. Phys. Chem.*, p. 77, Palo Alto, Calif., 1957.
143. LaMer, V. K. and Pound, G. M., *J. Chem. Phys.*, **17,** 1337 (1949).
144. LaMer, V. K., and Dinegar, R. H., *J. Am. Chem. Soc.*, **73,** 380 (1951).
145. Lang, A. R., *J. Appl. Phys.*, **28,** 497 (1957).
146. Laszlo, T., *Acad. Rep. Pop. Romane*, **4,** 79 (1953); *C.A.*, **50,** 14306.
147. LeBlanc, M., and Schmandt, *Z. physik. Chem.*, **77,** 614 (1911).
148. Lemmlein, G. G., and Dukova, E. D., *Kristallografiya*, **1,** 112 (1956); **2,** 428 (1957); *C.A.*, **51,** 33; **53,** 2726. *Doklady Akad. Nauk. SSSR*, **102,** 77 (1955); *C.A.*, **49,** 15342.
149. Linke, K., *Naturwiss.*, **31,** 230 (1943); *C.A.*, **38,** 9.
150. Lorenz, W., *Z. physik. Chem.*, **202,** 275 (1953).
151. Luyet, B. J. and Gehenio, P. M., "Life and Death at Low Temperatures," Normandy, Missouri, Biodynamica, 1940.
152. Marc, R., *Z. physik. Chem.*, **61,** 385 (1908); **67,** 470 (1909); **68,** 104 (1909); **73,** 685 (1910); 76, 584 (1911).
153. Marcelin, A., *Ann. phys.*, **10,** 185 (1918); with Boudin, S., *Compt. rendu*, **191,** 31 (1930).
154. Marshall, J. S., and Gunn, K. L. S., "Artificial Stimulation of Rain," Woods' Hole Conference, 1955, New York, Pergamon Press, 1957.
155. Martynov, V., *J. Phys. Chem. (USSR)*, **23,** 278 (1949).
156. Mason, B. J., *Endeavor*, **10,** 205 (1951).
157. Mason, B. J., and Ludlam, F. H., "Micro Physics of Clouds," *Rep. Phys. Soc. Progr. Phys.*, **14,** 147 (1951).
158. McIntosh, D., *Proc. Roy. Soc. Canada*, **III,** 13, 265 (1919).
159. McLachlan, D. Jr., Carlson, A., Christtensen, C. J., and King, A., *Bull. Univ. Utah*; **42,** No. 9 (1952).
160. Miers, H. A., *Phil Trans.*, 202, 459 (1904).
161. Miers, H. A., *Mineral. Mag.*, **15,** 39 (1908).
162. Moelwyn-Hughes, E. A., "Kinetics of Reaction in Solution," 2nd. ed., p. 320, Oxford Press, 1947.
163. Morris, J. B., and Strickland-Constable, R. F., *Trans. Faraday Soc.*, **84,** 1378 (1954).
164. Mott, N. F., *Nature*, **165,** 295 (1950).
165. Murphy,K. P., M.S. thesis, College of the Holy Cross, 1957.

166. Nacken, R., *Neues. Jahrb. Min. Geol. u Pal.* **2,** 133 (1915).
167. Nakaya, Ukicharo, "Snow Crystals," 510pp., Harvard, Mass., Harvard Press, 1954.
168. Nernst, W., *Z. physik. Chem.*, **47,** 52 (1904).
169. Neuhaus, A., and Meyer, H. J., *Z. Elektrochem.*, **61,** 37 (1957).
170. Neumann, K., and coworkers, *Z. physik. Chem.*, *(N.F.)*, **2,** 241 (1954); *Z. Elektrochem.*, **61,** 70 (1957), **64,** 297 (1960); *Ann. Phys.*, **41,** 319 (1942).
171. Newkirk, J. B., *Acta Met.*, **3,** 121 (1955).
172. Nielsen, A. E., *J. Coll. Sci.*, **10,** 576 (1955); *Acta Scand. Chem.*, **11,** 1512 (1957).
173. Niggli, P., *Z. anorg. Chem.*, **110,** 55 (1920).
174. Nitschmann, A., *Z. Krist.*, **102A,** 285 (1940).
175. Noyes, A. A., and Whitney, W. R., *Z. physik. Chem.*, **23,** 689 (1897).
176. O'Konski, C. T., and Higuchi, W. I., *J. Chem. Phys.*, **60,** 1598 (1956).
177. O'Rourke, J. D., and Johnson, R. A., *Anal. Chem.*, **27,** 1699 (1955).
178. Ostwald, W.,
    (a) *Z. physik. Chem.*, **34,** 496 (1900).
    (b) *Z. physik. Chem.*, **22,** 289 (1897); "Lehrbuch," 2, II, 383 (1911).
    (c) *Kolloid Z.*, **28,** 258 (1921).
179. Padoa, and Galeati, *Gazz. chim. ital.*, **35,** 181 (1904).
180. Pahl, M., *Z. phys. Chem.*, **184A,** 245 (1939).
181. Papapetrou, A., *Z, Krist. Min. Petrog.*, **A92,** 89 (1935).
182. Philip, J. C., *Trans. I. Chem. Eng. (London)*, **16,** 200 (1938).
183. Pines, B. Ya., *J. Exptl. Theoret. Phys. U.S.S.R.*, **18,** 29 (1948); *Zhur. Tekh. Fiz.*, **22,** 1985 (1952); *C.A.*, **50,** 1401.
184. Pound, G. M., *Ind. Eng. Chem.*, **44,** 1278 (1952).
185. Pound, G. M., and LaMer, V. K., *J. Am. Chem. Soc.*, **74,** 2323 (1952).
186. Pound, G. M., Simnad, M. T., and Yang, L., *J. Chem. Phys.*, **22,** 1215 (1954).
187. Powers, H. E. C., *Nature*, **178,** 139 (1956).
188. Probstein, R. F., *J. Chem. Phys.*, **19,** 619 (1951).
189. Read, W. T., "Dislocations in Crystals," p. 145, New York, McGraw-Hill Book Co., 1953.
190. Reinders, W., *Rec. trav. chim.*, **51,** 589 (1932).
191. Reischer, D. E., *Science*, **115,** 682 (1952).
192. Reiss, H., *J. Chem. Phys.*, **18,** 996, 1840 (1950).
193. Richards, W. T., *J. Am. Chem. Soc.*, **54,** 479 (1932); **58,** 2243 (1936).
194. Riddiford, A. C., *J. Phys. Chem.*, **56,** 745 (1952).
195. Ritzel, A., *Z. physik. Chem.*, **77,** 213, 677 (1911).
196. Royer, L., *Bull. soc. franc. mineral.*, **51,** 1 (1928).
197. Salli, I. V., *Doklady Akad. Nauk. SSSR.*, **89,** 61 (1953); *Zhur. Exptl. i Theoret. Fiz.*, **25,** 208 (1953); *C.A.*, **49,** 7912.
198. Saratovkin, D. D., "Dendritic Crystallization," trans. from Russian, New York, Consultants Bureau, 1958.
199. Schlipf, J., *Z. Krist.*, **107,** 35 (1956).
200. Schwarz, M., *Z. physik. Chem.*, **178A,** 241 (1934).
201. Sears, G. W.,
    (a) *Acta Met.*, **3,** 367 (1955), **4,** 268 (1956).
    (b) *J. Chem. Phys.*, **24,** 868 (1956), **25,** 154 (1956), **26,** 1549 (1957), **27,** 1308 (1957).
    (c) *J. Chem. Phys.*, **32,** 1317 (1960).
    (d) *J. Chem. Phys.*, **33,** 494 (1960).

202. Seith and Aten, *Z. physik. Chem.*, **10B,** 296 (1930).
203. Shekhter, A. B., Echeistova, A. I., and Tretyakov, I. T., *Zhur. Fiz. Khim.*, **24,** 206 (1950); *C.A.*, **44,** 6224.
204. Shockley, W., *Trans. Am. I. Min. and Met. Engs.*, **194,** 829 (1952).
205. Sill, R. C., and Skapiski, S., *J. Chem. Phys.*, **24,** 644 (1956).
206. Smythe, M.,
    (a) Private communication.
    (b) *Proc. X Congr. Int. Soc. Sugar Cane Tech.*, 1959, New York, D. Van Nostrand Co., Ind., 1960.
207. Smoluchowski, R., "Phase Transformations in Solids," New York, John Wiley & Sons, 1951.
208. Spangenberg, K., *Neues Jahr. Mineral. Geol.*, **A57,** 1197 (1928).
209. Spangenberg, K., *Handb. Naturwiss.*, X, 362, Jena (1934).
210. Stauff, *Z. physik. Chem.*, **187A,** 107 (1940).
211. Stavely, L. A., and Thomas, D. G., *J. Chem. Soc.*, (*London*), 2572 (1951), 1727 (1952).
212. Stern, J. H. and Gregory, N. W., *J. Phys. Chem.*, **61,** 1230 (1957).
213. Stranski, I. N., *et al.*,
    (a) *Z. physik. Chem.*, **136,** 259 (1928).
    (b) *Z. physik. Chem.*, **142,** 467 (1929), **130,** 135 (1930).
    (c) *Z. Electrochem.*, **36,** 25 (1930).
    (d) *Naturwiss.*, **20,** 905 (1932).
    (e) *Z. physik. Chem.*, **26B,** 317 (1934).
    Physik Z., **36,** 393 (1931).
    (f) *Z. physik. Chem.*, **163A,** 399 (1932).
    Z. Naturforsch., **49,** 121 (1949).
    Z. Electrochem **53,** 1 (1949).
    (*g*) *Naturwiss*, **37,** 289 (1950).
214. Straumanis, M., *Z. physik. Chem.*, **13B,** 316 (1931); **19B,** 63 (1932).
215. Strickland-Constable, R. F., *Proc. Roy. Soc.* (*London*), **A245,** 93 (1958).
216. Strunz, H., "Mineralogische Tabellen," Leipzig, 1941.
217. Suits, C. G., *Sci. Monthly*, **76,** 90 (1953).
218. Sultan, F., *Phil. Mag.*, **43,** 1099 (1952).
219. Suzuiko, K., *J. Chem. Soc. Japan, Ind. Chem. Sect.*, **55,** 652 (1952); *C.A.*, **48,** 7823.
220. Symposium on Mechanism of Phase Transitions in Metals, London, 1955, *Nature*, **177,** 419 (1956).
221. Tammann, G., *Z. physik. Chem.*, **81,** 171 (1913).
222. Taylor, M., *J. Chem. Soc.* (*London*), 1678 (1947).
223. Tezek, B., *et al.*, *J. Coll. Sci.*, Suppl. #1, 168 (1954).
224. Thomson, G. P., *Proc. Phys. Soc.* (*London*), **61,** 403 (1948).
225. Tilmans, Y. Y., *Doklady Nauk. SSSR.*, **78,** 83 (1951); *C.A.*, **45,** 8854.
226. Tilmans, Y. Y., *J. Gen. Chem. SSSR.*, **22,** 385 (1952); *C.A.*, **46,** 8923.
227. Tolansky, S., "Multiple Beam Interferometry," Oxford Press, 1948; "Surface Microtopographer," New York, Interscience Publishers, Inc., 1960.
228. Tolman, R. C., *J. Chem. Phys.*, **16,** 758 (1948), **17,** 118, 333 (1949).
229. Trimble, H. M., *J. Am. Chem. Soc.*, **58,** 1868 (1936).
230. Turnbull, D.,
    (a) *Acta Met.*, **1,** 8, 684 (1953).

(b) Symposium on Thermodynamics of Physical Metallurgy. Am. Soc. Metals, p. 282, Cleveland, 1950.
(c) *J. Appl. Phys.*, **20,** 817 (1949); **21,** 804 (1950). *J. Chem. Phys.*, **18,** 198, 768 (1950); **20,** 411 (1952).
(d) "Solid State Physics," III, p. 266, 275, 299, Academic Press, New York, 1956.
(e) "Proc. Conf. Phys. Cloud Precipitation Particles," I, p. 354, Woods Hole, 1955.
(f) with Vonnegut, B., *Ind. Eng. Chem.*, **44,** 1292 (1952).
(g) *Trans. Am. Inst. Min. Met. Engrs.* **175,** 774 (1948).

231. Twomey, S., *J. Chem. Phys.*, **30,** 941 (1959).
232. Ubbelohde, A. R., *Quart. Rev.*, **IV,** #4, 369 (1950).
233. Valeton, J. J. P., *Phys. Z.*, **21,** 606 (1920); *Z. Krist.*, **59,** 168, 335 (1923); **60,** 1 (1924).
234. Valeton, J. J. P., *K. Sachs. Ges. Wiss. math. physik. Klasse. Leipzig*, **67,** 1 (1915).
235. van der Heuvel, A. P., and Mason, B. J., *Nature*, **184,** 519 (1959).
236. VanHook, A.,
(a) *J. Phys. Chem.*, **44,** 751 (1940).
(b) "Proc. X Congr. Int. Soc. Sugar Cane Tech., 1959," New York, D. Van Nostrand Co., Inc., 1960.
(c) Unpublished observations.
237. Vermilyear, D. A., *J. Phys. Chem.*, **25,** 1254 (1956).
238. Vogel, R., *Z. anorg. Chem.*, **116,** 21 (1921).
239. Volmer, M.,
(a) *Physik. Z.*, **22,** 646 (1921).
(b) with Estermann, J., *Z. Physik*, **7,** 1 (1921).
(c) *Z. physik. Chem.*, **119,** 277 (1926).
(d) with Flood, H., *Z. physik. Chem.*, **170A,** 273 (1934).
(e) with Weber, A., *Z. physik. Chem.*, **119,** 225 (1926).
(f) with Schultze, W., *Ibid.*, **156A,** 1 (1931).
(g) *Z. Electrochem.*, **35,** 555 (1921).
(h) with Adhikari, G., *Z. Physik*, **35,** 170 (1928), *Z. physik. Chem.*, **119,** 40 (1926).
(i) with Moll, F., *Z. physik. Chem.*, **136,** 183 (1928).
(j) *Trans. Faraday Soc.*, **28,** 359 (1932), *Ver. deut. Ing.*, **74,** 163 (1936).
(k) with Marder, M., *Z. physik. Chem.*, **154A,** 97 (1931).
(l) *Z. physik. Chem.*, **102,** 267 (1922).
240. Vonnegut, B., *Chem. Rev.*, **44,** 277 (1949); *J. Appl. Phys.*, **18,** 593 (1947).
241. von Pickhardt, E., *Z. physik. Chem.*, **42,** 17 (1902).
242. Wagner, C., *Z. physik. Chem.*, **71,** 401 (1910).
243. Walton, J. H. and Brann, A., *J. Am. Chem. Soc.*, **38,** 317 (1916); **40,** 1168 (1918).
244. Webb, W. W., Dragsdorf, R. D., and Forging, W. D., *Phys. Rev.*, **108,** 498 (1957).
245. Weickmann, H. K., Ref. A-39, p. 207.
246. Wells, A. F., *Phil. Mag.*, **37,** 184, 217, 605 (1946); *Ann. Reports (London)*, **43,** 62 (1947).
247. Whetstone, J., *Trans. Faraday Soc.*, **51,** 973, 1142 (1955); *J. Chem. Soc. (London)*, 4841 (1956).
248. Wilde, K. A., *J. Appl. Phys.*, **30,** 577 (1959).
249. Willmarth, W. W. and Nagamatsu, H. T., *J. Appl. Phys.*, **23,** 1089 (1952).

250. Wulff, G., *Z. Krist.*, **34,** 449 (1901).
251. Wulff, L., cited by Buckely, Ref. A-1, p. 144.
252. Yamamoto, T., *Sci. Papers Inst. Phys. Chem. Res.* (*Tokyo*) **35,** 228 (1939).
253. Zeldovich, J. B.,
(a) *J. Exptl. Theoret. Phys.* (*U.S.S.R.*), **12,** 525 (1942).
(b) *Acta. Physicochem. URSS*, **18,** #1, 1 (1943).

Chapter 4

REPRESENTATIVE DATA ON NUCLEATION AND GROWTH

General

Numerical data on crystallization are many and varied[176] and deal with several of the aspects of this process. Some of the data deals separately with the nucleation or growth parts of the process concerned, but more frequently these two consecutive processes are not distinguished. The present chapter endeavors to tabulate representative kinetic data, indicate principal sources, and also suggest their theoretical and practical implications. The catalog does not pretend to be complete, but only suggestive of the sort and forms of values available in the literature. Many papers dealing with growth do not include all the specifications necessary for standardization of values and therefore are not included. To the writer's knowledge, the only previous listing is that in the *International Critical Tables*.[72] The present compilation is an extension of one that the author had prepared in manuscript form for the projected revision of the *Annual Tables of Physical Constants and International Critical Tables* in 1944 under the editorship of the late Dr. N. Thon.[4]

The data in the literature are not always convenient for purposes of collating. They have most frequently been determined and assembled in order to answer specific theoretical and practical questions and to ascertain the optimum conditions for production on a commercial scale. It is hoped that the present collection may be useful in these same ways but even more that the references cited may expedite literature work for other research workers in this field.

Methods for Determining Rates of Crystallization

One must immediately distinguish nucleation rates from the subsequent growth rate of individual nuclei. An intimate knowledge of the kinetics of these two contributing factors is necessary since the two steps occur simultaneously. Roginski,[140] and Roginski and Todes,[141] for instance, have demonstrated that net growth rates are in agreement with modern theories.

Todes,[166] as well as Van Hook,[170g] has also shown that the usual distribution of crystal sizes is in accord with acceptable laws of nucleation and growth.

Tammann's procedure is the one generally employed for the determination of nucleation rates on the macro scale. For this purpose the supercooled melt or solution is permitted to nucleate under specified conditions. The critical nuclei themselves are invisible and must be developed to visible size for counting. Fortunately, the nucleation curve is usually much steeper than the growth curve so that nucleation is effectively arrested by a change to less stringent conditions. With this technic Tammann[159] and others[59, 112a] delineated most of the outstanding features of the nucleation process in melts; namely, 1) Nucleation sets in suddenly as supercooling increases but soon diminishes as the crystallizing potential increases. Tammann accounts for the rather sharp fall in the nucleation frequency as due to the effects of the progressive accumulation of heat of crystallization in the case of one-component systems, and/or exhaustion of the solution in polycomponent cases, but these explanations have been disputed. 2) Results with particular materials are extremely variable and depend upon the history and size of the sample. 3) Both dissolved and suspended impurities may exert tremendous effects by either increasing or decreasing the nucleation numbers. 4) At high supercooling the viscous resistance to development of incipient nuclei is so great that amorphous bodies are formed. This "glass point" corresponds with the temperature of maximum nucleation* in many cases.

Microscopic methods are convenient in the study of nucleation and growth[A-39, 169d] and have been used by Pound, Madonna and Peake[135] to determine the onset of crystallization in supercooled water. Modern amplifying and counting technics have been adapted in many cases;[56, 150] especially in cloud-chamber investigations. Electrical conductivity[3, 169e] and turbidimetry[90] have been widely used for the determination of the time during which arbitrary but significant nucleation densities are established in crystallizing systems, and so have dilatometric[98, 134, 169e, 172] and electrometric[170b] methods.

In measuring growth rates one can focus attention upon either the growing body itself or upon the nutrient medium when this suffers a change in composition. In the former case, the increase in linear dimensions[17, 61, 67, 115, 170h] may be determined most conveniently when a solid body is formed, although the change in weight[A-3, 49, 86, 157] or the area[27] of individual faces may also be used. It is necessary to have the proper shape factor for correlating dimensions, area and weight, as well as the assurance of constancy

* The maximum nucleation number may be determined by ascertaining the point of maximum crystal formation in a tube along which a temperature gradient exists.

of habit during the growth.[170i] These and other important general conclusions regarding crystal growth and geometry are summarized by McCabe[104] as follows:

"1. A crystal that grows under constant external conditions remains very nearly geometrically similar to its original shape but relatively slight changes in conditions may alter the shape.

"2. The addition of small amounts of foreign substances may profoundly affect the shape of a growing crystal and its rate of growth.

"3. Different faces of the same crystal usually have different translation velocities.

"4. Although the exact mechanism and the order of reaction of the growing process are not definitely known, the rate of growth of any particular face in grams per square centimeter is a function of the supersaturation of the bulk of the solution in contact with that face.

"5. It is very doubtful that the differences in solubility of the various faces of a single crystal, or of different size particles of the same material, are large enough to influence crystal growth unless the crystals are less than about 0.002 mm in diameter.

"6. The screen analysis of the product of a crystallization process can be calculated from the screen analysis of the seeds and the total yield if the formation of new nuclei is neglected during the process and if all crystals are subjected to exactly the same conditions of growth."

In following the course of crystallization by changes in composition of the mother liquid any sufficiently sensitive method is satisfactory. Conductivity,[99] refractive index,[2, 170f] density,[71, 100] color, thermal effects,[29, 77] and polarimetry[122] have been used most widely, as well as adsorption and radioactive tracers.[138] The increasing area occasioned by growth must be reckoned with whether the member of growing centers remains fixed or not during the growing period. On account of the complexity of this area term solution methods are often used for only relative results. A common experimental expedient is to employ high seeding densities or short periods of observation in order to simulate conditions of constant growing area. These various cases are illustrated for the simplest case of a unimolecular growth rate as follows:

The velocity of growth is equivalent to the decrease in concentration, c, and is proportional to the supersaturation in these same concentration units as well as the number of nuclei, n, and the area of each: i.e.

$$-\frac{dc}{dt} = kna(c - c_O)$$

or

$$\ln \frac{c' - co}{c - c_o} = knat$$

provided both n and a remain constant from the beginning (c') until time t. c_o is the equilibrium or final concentration.

If n is small but constant the increase in a during the reaction may become significant.[170h, 173] This is proportional to $(c' - c)^{2/3}$, the weight increase during time t,

$$-\frac{dc}{dt} = kna'(1 + K(c' - c)^{2/3})(c - c_o)$$

where K is a shape factor. When n also increases during the determination it is sometimes suitable to treat the reaction as an autocatalytic[6] one, or

$$\frac{dx}{dt} = kx(1 - x)$$

where x is the faction converted. More explicit treatments of this common case of spontaneous adjustment of metastable systems are given in detail by Avrami,[7] Mehl,[75] etc.[28, 48]

The layer theory of growth suggests a convenient and rapid method for the determination of growth velocities in the form of the product of the rate of advance of the layer edge and the thickness. The latter may be determined by means of color tints or by specialized methods of interferometry.[116, 148, 167] The electron microscope is also very useful in the study of crystal growth.[33, 68, 108, 144] The use of spheres in both growth and dissolution processes is discussed in great detail by Buckley.[A-1]

The linear crystallization velocity of supercooled melts and rate of polymorphic change (L. C. V. or K G) is a growth parameter which was investigated in great detail by Tammann and his students. The procedure is essentially that first devised by Gernez[50] and consists essentially in inoculating the supercooled melt or supersaturated solution[25, 94, 128] contained within a tube or capillary held at definite temperatures. The progress of crystallization along the tube is easily discerned and the velocity is usually expressed in mm/min. This rate has no definite crystallographic meaning since it is composite of the different velocities of the several crystal faces, the habit of the crystal, multiple and induced grain formation, dissipation of the heat of crystallization, restriction of the container, etc.[36, 83, 101, 149] In spite of these many restraints the L.C.V. and its maximum, M.C.V., are fairly reproducible under closely specified conditions so that they are widely reported as characteristic crystallizing properties.

Methods of Expressing Growth Rates and Supersaturation

The usual forms of expressing the growth rate of single crystals are linear advance of specified faces per unit time and weight increment per unit surface of the entire crystal in the same unit time. The volume and area of any solid body may be expressed as $V = k_1 r_1^3$ and $A = k_1' r_1^2$, where k_1 and k_1' are particular shape factors for the principal dimension r_1. As the body grows

$$\frac{dV}{dr_1} = 3k_1 r_1^2 = 3\frac{k_1}{k_1'}A$$

or

$$\frac{dV}{Adt} = \frac{3k_1}{k_1'}\frac{dr_1}{dt}.$$

The weight increment per unit area is given by

$$\frac{1}{A}\frac{dW}{dt} = \frac{3}{\rho}\frac{k_1}{k_1'}\frac{dr_1}{dt}$$

where ρ is the density of the crystal. For finite changes in weight and dimension this expression integrates as,

$$3(w_2^{1/3} - w_1^{1/3}) = K(r_2 - r_1)$$

where the shape constants and density are assembled in an over-all constant K. This relationship is useful for converting linear to weight dimensions, and vice versa. If several dimensions are to be utilized, the total weight must be resolved into its several components; i.e.

$$dW = \left(\frac{\partial W}{\partial a}\right) da + \left(\frac{\partial W}{\partial b}\right) db + \left(\frac{\partial W}{dc}\right) dc$$

and if the habit is preserved

$$\frac{dW}{da} = \frac{\partial W}{\partial a} + \frac{b}{a}\frac{\partial W}{\partial b} + \frac{c}{a}\frac{\partial W}{\partial c}$$

The habit of the crystal will be preserved only if the rates of increase of each dimension are in proportion to the crystallographic dimensions. The conversion factor from linear to weight dimensions $\left(\frac{3}{\rho}\frac{k}{k'}\right)$ will then be inversely proportional to the axial intercepts. If the tangential velocity of enlargement of two faces of a crystal are t_a and t_b, while the velocities of advance normal of the faces are r_a and r_b, the relationship between the two is

$$t_a^2 - t_b^2 = r_b^2 - r_a^2$$

That supercooling and supersaturation are equivalent follows directly from the phase-rule understanding of the degree of freedom, or from the application of the Clausius-Clapeyron equation to the quasi-equilibrium condition which may be expected in the neighborhood of a transition point. In that case, the two slightly separated states may be represented by

$$\ln \frac{x_2}{x_1} = -\frac{\Delta H}{R}\left(\frac{1}{T_2} - \frac{1}{T_1}\right)$$

If the potentials x_2 and x_1 are not too different one from another, the first approximation is

$$\frac{x_2 - x_1}{x_1} = \frac{\Delta H}{RT_2} \frac{T_2 - T_1}{T_1}$$

The supersaturation, Δx, is thus a simple function of the supercooling (ΔT) provided the entropy of transition is constant.

A variety of units is employed to express supersaturation.[120] The equilibrium treatment of nucleation and growth immediately suggests the use of proper thermodynamic factors and these have been used in many cases.[41, 170, 171] However, in the case of solutions it is more usual to use ordinary concentration units such as molality, weight ratio, percentages, etc. The excess concentration over the equilibrium value is frequently designated the supersaturation, S, while the ratio is the degree of supersaturation, O; the symbol O stemming from the synonym oversaturation.

$$S = C - C_o \qquad O \text{ (or, } \alpha) = \frac{C}{C_o} \qquad O - 1 = S/C_o$$

Adjustment of Supersaturated Vapors

McDonald[107] points out that no antonym for sublimation is in popular use as a counterpart of freezing-melting and condensation-evaporation for the solid-liquid and liquid-vapor transitions, respectively. He proposes deposition (growth by deposition, depositional growth) for this purpose.

Excellent agreement on the critical supersaturation point is realized in the Wilson cloud-chamber experiment. This is illustrated in the following summary[133, 143] (Table 4-1) of Volmer and Flood's data. The computed P/P_∞ values have been calculated by straightforward application of the Becker-Döring and Frenkel theories, but this has been questioned by Barnard.[9] The meteorological importance of data on the spontaneous nucleation of water vapor is obvious (Chapter VI-9). A critical theoretical survey of this particular case is given by Rodebush,[139] and the data are reviewed

TABLE 4-1. OBSERVED AND CALCULATED CRITICAL SUPERSATURATIONS

Vapor	T_i	T_f	P/P_∞ Obs.	P/P_∞ Calc.	Critical Nucleus No. Molecules	Critical Nucleus Radius Å	Ref.
Water	350	320	2.87	—	—	—	42, 132
Water	323	292	3.74	—	—	—	42, 132
Water	308	276	5.07	—	—	—	42, 132
Water	302	275.2	4.2 ± 0.1	4.2	80	8.9	133
Water	—	266	6.9	4.7	(100)	—	139
Water	291	257	7.8	—	—	—	132
Water	288	261	5.0	5.0	72	8.0	133
Water	280	247	8.95	—	—	—	132
Methanol	295	270	3.0	1.8	32	7.9	A-18, 133
Ethanol	290	273	2.3	2.3	128	14.2	A-18, 133
n-Propanol	289	270	3.0	3.2	115	15.0	A-18, 133
i-Propanol	283	265	2.8	2.9	119	15.2	A-18, 133
n-Butanol	291	270	4.6	4.5	72	13.6	A-18, 133
Nitromethane	292	252	6.0	6.2	66	11.0	A-18, 133
Ethyl acetate	290	242	8.6 to 12.3	10.4	40	11.4	A-18, 133
Aniline (etc.)	—	—	—	—	(8)	8.44	22

by Ruedy[143] and by Pound.[133] It appears likely that similar considerations will pertain in the formation and settling of the debris of atomic explosions. This matter of concern for the new atomic age is discussed by Stewart.[155]

The temperature at which supercooled water droplets change into ice crystals spontaneously is −38.9°C.[146] Numerous foreign bodies catalyze this transformation and are known as freezing nuclei. The threshold temperature for ice formation on AgI, for instance, is −2.6°C, while on PbI_2 it is −6.0°C, on quartz, −8.2°C, topaz −23°C, etc.[47, 102, 169f] Those substances which catalyze the deposition of ice directly from the vapor state are designated sublimation nuclei. Ions and polar materials reduce the expansion ratio for fog formation in water vapor and their influence is considered by Volmer, Stranski, Barus,[11] etc.[131, 147] The condensation of water vapor in supersonic wind tunnels and the liquefaction of the components of air itself have been considered by Probstein, Kantrowitz, Lundquist, and others.

The growth of iodine crystals from the vapor state has been studied intensively by Volmer and Schultze in connection with the theory of two-dimensional nucleation. The experiment has been repeated a number of times in the writer's laboratory. Rates of the same order of magnitude were realized but the nonlinear portion of the curve at the lowest supercooling was not validated within the experimental accuracy. The growth rate was also observed to vary considerably with traces of air. The growth rates of naphthalene, phosphorus, As_4O_6, and Cd from the vapor are also considered by Knacke and Stranski,[78, 156] and Honigmann[67] outlines the rather sparse data available on Se, Cd, Sn, hexamethylene-tetramine, etc. The progress of the (011) faces of hexamethylene-tetramine remained steady for considerable periods of time but changed radically and indefinitely as the growth continued. The change, when faults were apparent, was an increase, often by a factor of 2 or 3. The maxima of these variations appeared to be linear in terms of supersaturation while the velocities during smooth growth showed a quadratic dependence.

The release of a superheated liquid involves nucleation and the abundant observations[19, 62] on ordinary superheating of liquids and gaseous solutions are shown by Takagi[158] to be agreeable to Volmer's theory. This phenomenon is of the greatest significance in the recent development of liquid scintillation counters.[37]

MELTS

General

Nucleation in melts generally sets in rapidly and subsides rather promptly as supercooling increases. The growth curve exhibits the same general form but does not rise as rapidly. It sustains its maximum value over a longer supercooling range.

Tammann regarded this general form as due to the exothermal heat of crystallization; the evolved heat raising the temperature of the interface and thus causing lower velocities of change than would be realized if the temperature were uniform throughout. With increased supercooling and in the region of constant velocity the interface is exactly at the melting rather than the bulk temperature.* At still lower temperatures the interface is actually lower than the freezing point.

Nacken,[18, 65] however, questioned this explanation chiefly on account of his observations on the growth of individual crystal faces. The fact that the crystals which develop from a melt are polyhedra shows that the rate of growth is anisotropic in direction. Nacken observed that the melting point was maintained at the interface as long as the heat of crystallization was greater than the heat loss. Hemispherical or similar solids were formed according to the crystal system. When the heat loss was greater than that evolved definite surfaces were formed on rounded solids. Additional faster-growing faces developed as the relative rate of heat loss became still greater. If Tammann's interpretation was correct these forms would be observed

* Pollatschek[130] did not find this to be the case.

only at the temperature of maximum-growth velocity. Nacken suggested that increasing viscosity compels the velocity to decrease at excessive supercoolings.

Impurities most frequently lower the velocity of growth of most crystals and Freundlich[45] attributed this effect in part to adsorption at the interface. His empirical adsorption equation represented the relative lowering of the crystallization velocity very well in many instances. However, adsorption is not the only factor involved. Dreyer[39] and others[73, 177] showed that materials which lower the viscosity of a melt also facilitated the crystallization, and Walton and Brann[174] pointed out a parallelism between lowering of the growth velocity and solvation.

Nucleation Data (Tables 4-2 and 4-3)

The nuclei number of melts is greatly influenced by the size and history of the sample and the condition of the container. Melts can also usually be subcooled more when in capillaries, or as small droplets, than in bulk. This is probably the result of more certain elimination of heterogeneous nuclei in small volumes.[38, 109, 112b, 134, 137, 169] The following selected nucleation data must therefore be interpreted as specific for each sample and only suggestive of the usual behavior of the substance. The nucleation rate and subsequent growth are usually augmented by orienting forces such as electric, magnetic, and sonic fields.[14, 32d, 81, 89, 170g]

Turnbull[169] summarizes the result of his studies as follows:

1. $\Delta T_{\text{max.}}$ for most liquids is more than 0.15 times the absolute melting point T_m.
2. $\Delta T_{\text{max.}}/T_m \sim 0.18$ for metal liquids which crystallize to the face-centered or body-centered cubic structures.
3. The ratio of the molar interfacial tension, σ_g, to the molar heat of fusion seems to be roughly 0.5 in the case of metals and $\sim$0.3 for semimetals and organic compounds.
4. The smaller subcooling achieved in large samples is unquestionably due to heterogeneous nucleation.

Danilov[32] classifies melts into three groups respecting their behavior upon supercooling:

1. Those which remain liquid at all degrees of supercooling. This may require deactivation of natural nuclei by preheating or removal by filtration.
2. Liquids which exhibit a definite limit of supercooling. Orthochloronitrobenzene and glycerol are examples of this class. The Volmer-Marder theory is applicable in such instances.
3. Glass formers. This tendency frequently disappears when liquids are

TABLE 4-2. MINIMUM TEMPERATURE OF SPONTANEOUS CRYSTALLIZATION

Substance	T_m (°K)	Maximum Subcooling ΔT		Reference	Remarks
		Large Samples	Small Samples*		
Hg	234.1	14	79, 46	169	Hg laurate and acetate films, resp.
Sn	505	31	110–120	169	Oxide coating
H_2O	273	36.8	39	169, 163	
Ga	302.8	55	76	169	
Bi	544	30	90	169	
Sb	903	—	135	169	
Pb	600.7	—	80	169	
Ag	1234	—	227	169	
Ge	1232	5–10	227	169	
Au	1336	—	230	169	
Cu	1356	—	236	169	
Mn	1493	—	308	169	
Ni	1725	—	319	169	
Co	1763	—	330	169	
Pd	1828	—	332	169	
Pt	2046	—	370	169	
Fe	1803	—	295	169	
Al	932	—	130	169	
P	317	115, 6	—	63, 80	1 mm diameter
Se	493	—	25	169, 64	
S	393	70	165	134	2 μ droplets
CH_3Cl	175.6	—	55.6	163	Clouds
NH_3	195.5	—	40.3	163	
CCl_4	250.2	—	50.4	163	
CBr_4	363.3	—	82	163	
C_6H_6	278.4	—	70.2	163	
$BrCH_2 \cdot CH_2Br$	282.7	—	66.5	163	
Diphenyl	344	—	86	163	
Naphthalene	353.1	—	94.4	163	
C_6H_5COOH	395.0	—	120	163	
Salol	314.6		—	32	
o-$ClC_6H_4 \cdot NO_2$	305.5	15, 5	—	32	
Na		3.5	—	32	
BF_3	144.5	—	17.8	32	
Cyclopropane	145.8	—	17.8	32	
CH_3Br	179.4	—	24.4	32	
CH_3NH_2	179.7	—	35.7	32	
SO_2	197.6	—	33	32	
$CHCl_3$	209.7	—	52.5	32	
Thiophene	234.9	—	50.7	32	

* Usually 50 μ diameter in Turnbull's experiments.

TABLE 4-3. TEMPERATURE AT WHICH NUCLEI CONCENTRATION IS A MAXIMUM
(The exact significance of these values is uncertain.)

Substance	Temp (°C)	Supercooling (°C)	Ref.
Glycerol	−61	79	160
Betol	20	71	159, 112
Piperine	40	89	159, 32
m-Dinitrobenzene	43.6	46	46
Naphthalene	72.2	8	46
Resorcinol	−10	120	159
Mannite	40	66	46

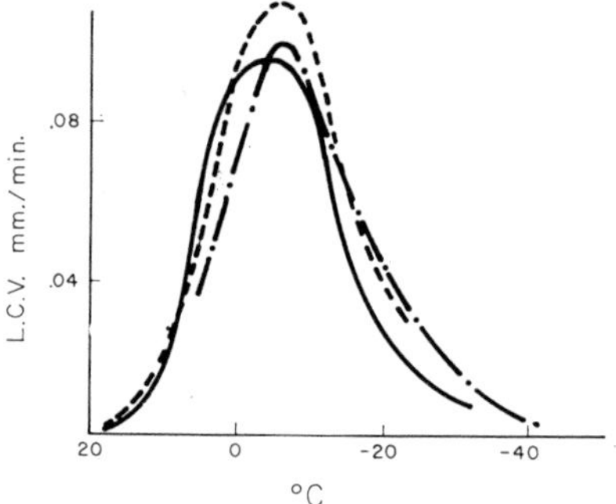

Figure 4-1. L.C.V. of glycerol.
— 100, 161
--- 171
-·- 171, capillaries

very pure and/or cooling rates are very slow. Tipson (Chap. 5) discusses the crystallizability of melts in the light of molecular structure and gives many references.

Linear and Maximum Crystallization Velocities

Relatively few determinations of the absolute growth rate of single crystals from supercooled melts are available.[A-45, 32, 115] Most investigations until recently have been concerned with the determination of the linear crystallization velocity (L.C.V.) (Table 4-5 and Figs. 4-1, 4-2 and 4-3), and its maximum value (M.C.V.) (Table 4-4), according to the general methods described by Tammann. The M.C.V. is a characteristic property of a compound under specified conditions[110, 164] and the theoretical implications of such data are discussed by Volmer,[171] Hillig and Turnbull,[64] and others.

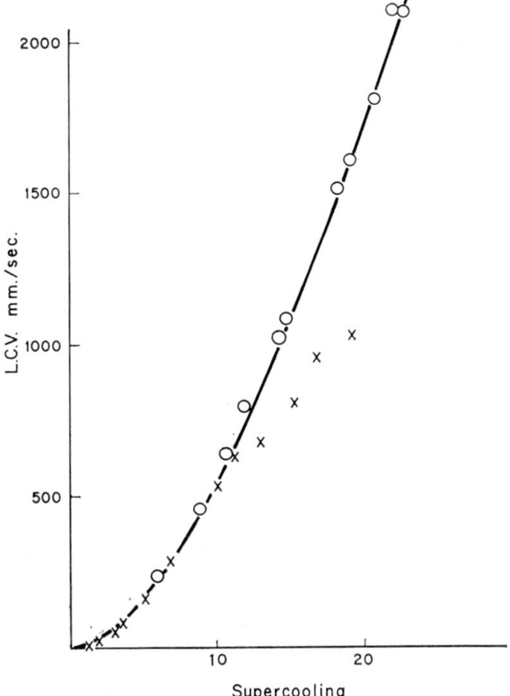

Figure 4-2. L.C.V. of phosphorus.
○—Powell, Gilman, and Hildebrand (1951)[132]
×—Gernez (1892)[50]

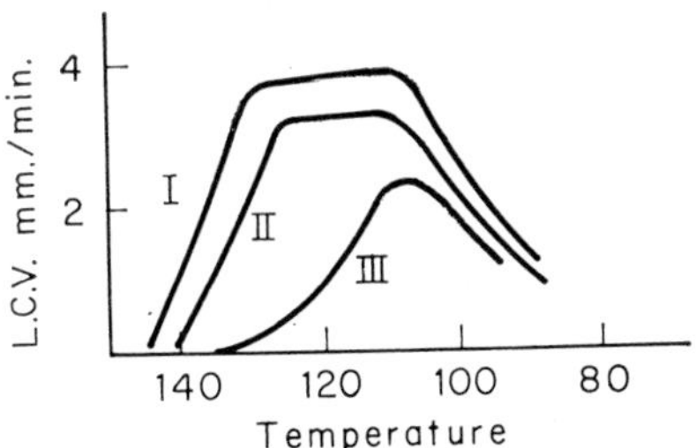

Figure 4-3. L.C.V.—Purity.[45]
I Triphenyl guanidine, Pure; M.P. 144.2°C.
II Triphenyl guanidine, +5% phthalide; M.P. 141.2°C.
III Triphenyl guanidine, +17.5% phthalide; M.P. 133.7°C.

TABLE 4-4. MAXIMUM LINEAR RATE OF CRYSTALLIZATION (M.C.V.) OF SUPERCOOLED MELTS

Crystallization rates other than maxima values are designated L.C.V. These are not significantly dependent on the inside diameter of the tube. Spontaneously crystallizing melts are designated with a value of ∞. The following values, as well as those of Table 4-5, are compiled from Refs. 4, 72, 159 and the references cited by Partington.[128]

Substance	Supercooling °C (Bath T − M P)	M. C. V. (mm/min)
Phosphorus	19	L.C.V. > 60,000
Butylphenol	28.1	1,117
Azobenzol	30	600
Benzil	34.8	433
Benzil + 8% Benzophenone	35	250
m-Di-nitro benzoic acid	20	31
Salol I M P = 41.68°	21.7, 22.0, 19.4	4.24, 3.46, 3.75
II M P = 38.8°	18.8, 18.8	3.98, 1.0
III M P = (28.3°)	13.8	4.41
Betol (I) M P = 94.4°	19.6	1.41
Methyl carbonate of cholesterol, M P = 112–3°	27	1.37
Chalcone M P 54.7	24.7	5.21
p-Methyl chalcone M P 75°	45	17.0
p-Ethyl chalcone M P 61°	36	1.15
p-Propyl chalcone M P 45.7°	20.7	3.62
o-Cresol, M P 30.35°	30.3	236
m-Cresol M P 11.9°	22	L.C.V. 10.4
p-Cresol M P 34.6°	24.6	L.C.V. 234
Racemic lactamide M P 76.4°	41.4	7.01
d-Lactamide I M P 42.8°	25.8	0.40
α-Bromocamphor	—	∞
Dotricontane	—	∞
$(CH_2Cl)_2$ M P −35.5°	14	2400
$(CH_2Br)_2$ M P 9.95°	7	2300
$(CH_2CN)_2$	—	∞
Cetyl alcohol	—	∞
Palmitic acid	—	∞
Stearic acid	—	∞
$C_{15}H_{31}COOC_2H_5$	—	∞
$C_{17}H_{35}COOC_2H_5$	—	∞
Cyclo C_6H_{12}	—	∞
Cyclo $C_6H_{11}OH$	—	∞
$C_{10}H_8$	—	∞
p-$C_6H_4Cl_2$	—	∞
Amphenylone	—	at 674
CCl_4	2–7	∞
CS_2	8–18	∞
Acetone	9–24	∞
C_4-C_8 Hydrocarbons and alcohols	—	0.3
o-Dichlorobenzene	19	2200
m-Dichlorobenzene	21	700
p-Dichlorobenzene	20	25,000
p-Dibromobenzene	27	7500
1,2,4-Trichlorobenzene	25	25
1,3,5-Trichlorobenzene	25	7000
1,3,5-Tribromobenzene	28	2400

TABLE 4-4. *Continued*

Substance	Supercooling °C (Bath T − M P)	M. C. V. (mm/min)
1,2-Triphenylethane	50	<1
1,1,1-Triphenylethane	39	80
1,2-Diphenylethane	30	700
1,1-Diphenylethane	27	<1
Diphenylmethane	23	530
Triphenylmethane	25	27
o-Dihydroxybenzene	29	1700
m-Dihydroxybenzene	37	400
p-Dihydroxybenzene	35	630
o-Diaminobenzene	41	7000
p-Diaminobenzene	37	10,000
m-Dinitrobenzene	49	6000
p-Dinitrobenzene	41	15,000
o-Brombenzoic acid	32	800
m-Brombenzoic acid	14	255
m-Bromaniline	22	48
p-Bromaniline	43	1600
Diphenyl	16	7500
1,2-Diphenyl ethylene	25	2000
1,1-Diphenyl ethylene	21	16
1,2,6-Xylenol	—	3000
1,2,3-Xylenol	—	810
1,2,5-Xylenol	—	300
1,3,4-Xylenol	—	132
1,3,5-Xylenol	—	280
o-Nitro phenol	25	L.C.V. 43.2
	45	L.C.V. 20.7
Racemic dimethyl tartrate		
I M P 48	21	0.66
II 50	23	3.20
III 61	34	L.C.V. 0.275
Glycerol	0.26	0.11
	−3.5	0.1
Piperidine I M P 36.5	20.5	6.5
Piperidine II M P 12.9	50–60	0.1
Picric acid	37	858
Piperonal	20	6.5
Benzophenone		
Rhombic M P 47.7	27.7	60, 55
Monoclinic M P 25	20	2.4
Aluminum	0	160
Sodium	43.5	360
Gold	—	(24)
Bismuth	—	20, 36
Lead	—	L.C.V. 170 at 329
		45 at 359
Lead and 5% Mercury	—	L.C.V. 100 at 309
Tin	—	2000
Tin, gray-white	—	6–8 at 25.8
$Na_2O \cdot 2SiO_2$	at 762°	0.106
$K_2O \cdot 2SiO_2$	98	0.208
$Li_2O \cdot 2SiO_2$	270	1.10

TABLE 4-5. SOME ISOLATED VALUES OF L.C.V.

Substance	Supercooling	L.C.V. (mm/min)
Benzene	5.5	2307
Toluene	20–29	295
p-Xylene	5.5	1620
Nitrobenzene	12.5	3333
o-Nitro toluene	36.1	1509
m-Nitro toluene	19.1	517.2
p-Nitro toluene	10.15	1250
Aniline	36.1	873
p-Toluidine	7.5	2142
Chloroacetic acid I M.P. 62.8°	28	0.636
II M.P. 56.3°	18	62.8
III M.P. 50.65°	12.6	1090
Racemic α-Br propionic acid M P 26.3°	39°	6.52
Formamide	6.9	254
β Dodecyl acetate M.P. 1.1°	16.6	38.78
β_1 Tridecyl acetate M.P. 8°	5	0.04
β_2 Tridecyl acetate M.P. 2.5°	7	12.5
$CHCl_3$	11.5	2100–2140
Ethyl ether	15.7	80.6
Ethyl acetate	31.4	16.1
Methyl alcohol	−123°C	56.6
Methyl alcohol 0.05–1.0% H_2O	−123°C	54.7–12

Figures 4-1 and 4-3, for instance, illustrate that the L.C.V. and corresponding maxima are fairly reliable characteristics which, however, require carefully standardized conditions for exact duplication. Tammann and others have examined the role of tube diameter, wall thickness, etc., in great detail. The crystallization velocity of a melt changes with the purity, as indicated in Figure 4-3, and the effect has been proposed as a method[5, 87, 106] of analysis of technical DDT, TNT,[51] pharmaceuticals, dye intermediates,[118] and other organic materials. Figure 4-4 displays the results with known mixtures of *p-p′* DDT(mp 108.5–109) with O-*p′* DDT(mp 74.0–74.5°C) as the second ingredient. It is possible by this method to analyze samples of technical DDT on a routine basis of one sample every 10 to 15 minutes with an accuracy of better than ±0.5%. Crystallization-velocity data of glasses (and other vitreous substances)[95, 97, 145] are very useful to the glass technologist. This was demonstrated by Tammann and emphasized by Leon'tjewa (Chap. 6), Grauer and Hamilton[54] and others[98]. Figure 4-5 and Table 4-6 are suggestive of the results obtained in this field. Bailey[8] describes the importance of crystallization-velocity data for the oil and fat chemist, their metallurgical significance is obvious, and numerous other applications will be alluded to in the following sections of this book.

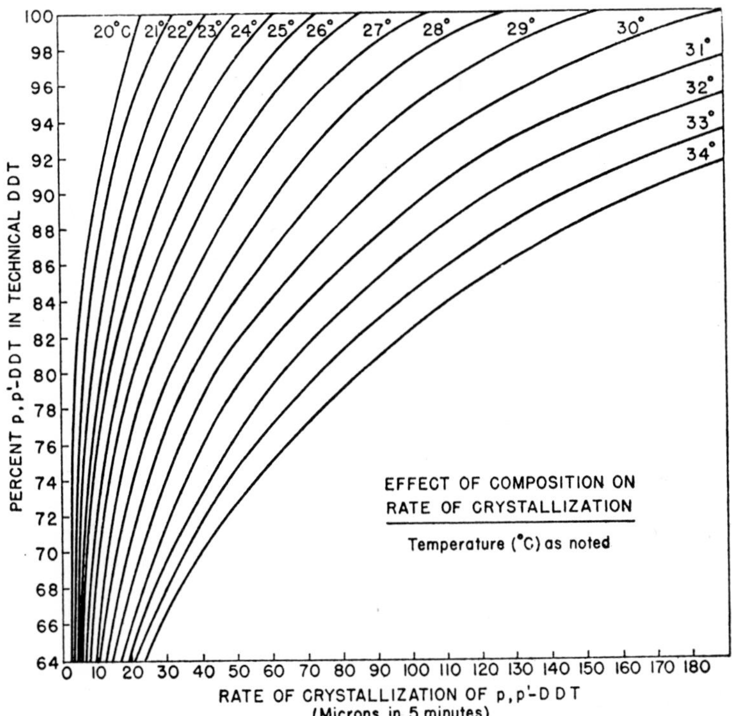

Figure 4-4. Rate of growth of crystal front of p,p'-DDT as a function of purity of mixture.[106]

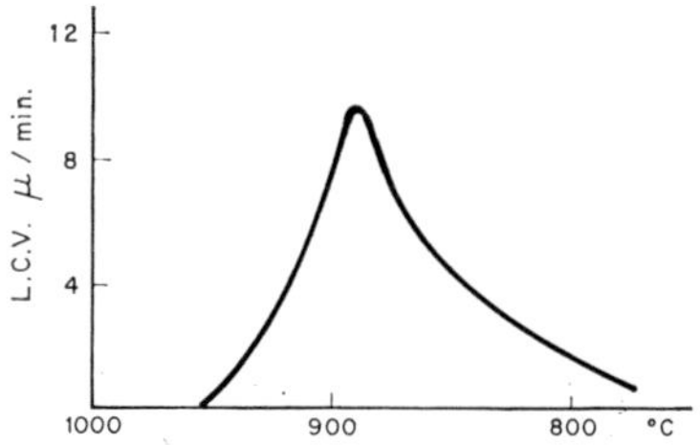

Figure 4-5. Rate of crystal growth of a glass.[54]

L.C.V.'s have been determined most completely in the case of water, glycerol, salol, tin, phosphorus, and benzene. Most recent values are summarized in Table 4-7. The empirical representations apply to relatively small supercoolings (ΔT), and the common form L.C.V. $\approx (\Delta T)^{1.7}$ is consistent with growth by means of screw dislocations.[70]

The speed at which water crystallizes (aside from the nucleation rate)

TABLE 4-6. RATES OF CRYSTAL GROWTH FOR GLASS-FORMING AND NONGLASS-FORMING MATERIALS[54]

Material	M.C.V. (μ/min)	Temp (°C)
Glass E 1105	9.8	895
Glass E 1222	63.3	890
Picric acid	800,000	85
Phosphorus	L.C.V. = 6×10^7	25

TABLE 4-7. CRYSTALLIZATION VELOCITY[A-45]

Substance	Velocity (cm/sec)	Comment
Water	$1.6 \times 10^{-1} \Delta T^{1.7}$	Grown in small bore glass tube
	$1.30 \times 10^{-2} \Delta T^{2.9}$	−2° to −3.1°C } Free growth
	$7.55 \times 10^{-2} \Delta T^{2.32}$	−3.1° to −6.5°C } Free growth
Glycerol	$1 \times 10^{-6} \Delta T^{1.65}$	0.3 mm ID glass tube
Salol	$8 \times 10^{-6} \Delta T^{2.6}$	7.5 mm tube 1 mm wall thickness
	$1.56 \times 10^{-5} \Delta T^{2.3}$	0.4 mm capillary 0.06 mm wall thickness
Tin	$7 \times 10^{-1} \Delta T^{1.8}$, about one-third above velocity	Reason for difference is unresolved
Phosphorus	$1.15 \Delta T^{1.67}$	
Benzene	$1.1 \times 10^{-1} \Delta T^{1.64 \pm 0.06}$	Glass capillaries
	$1.9 \times 10^{-1} \Delta T^{1.64}$	Silver capillaries

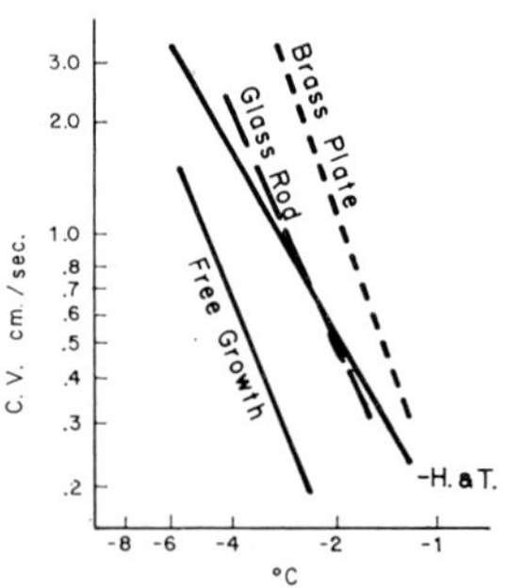

Figure 4-6. C.V. of ice.[92] H. & T.—Hillig and Turnbull,[64] in capillaries.

has been determined by dozens of investigators. The values given are some of the latest and are compared graphically in Figure 4-6. Early values and interpretations are discussed exhaustively by Dorsey[38] while the references cited review the later literature.

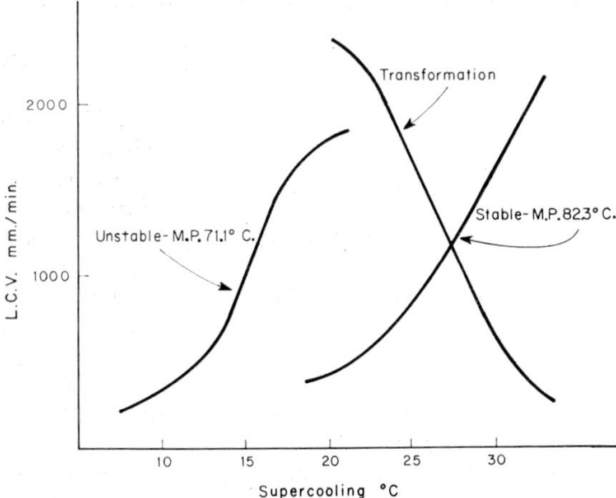

Figure 4-7. Linear crystallization velocity of acetamide.[53]

Polymorphic Change

Many polymorphic states exhibit transformations similar to the solidification of a melt and even sometimes proceed at comparable rates. This is illustrated in Figure 4-7 for the two polymorphs of acetamide.[53, 117]

Tammann has studied many such transformations with the usual technics. More recently, Hartshorne[61] and co-workers, as well as Danilov[32] and others,[10, 24, 96] have critically reinvestigated such systems as S, *p*-dichlorobenzene, HgI_2, CBr_4, etc. in the light of modern theories of solid-solid reactions and growth kinetics.

Crystallization from Solution

Matz[A-11] has compared the crystallization behaviors of solutions and melts (Table 4-8). Much information is available regarding the rates of crystallization of solutions, especially aqueous ones,[35] but little is amenable to systematic presentation or analysis in the light of modern theory.

Nucleation effects in relatively strong solutions have been most frequently presented in terms of the temperature of spontaneous crystallization (Table 4-9). Such data block out the typical supersolubility curves of Figures 4-8 to 4-11 and 1-5. The onset of crystallization of slightly soluble materials can be specified by an induction period, during which time a density of nuclei sufficient to give prolific, visible growth, is generated (Figure 4-12). The critical supersaturation at which the precipitation of slightly soluble materials is practically instantaneous is rather readily determined and is an important and significant variable. Actual counts of the

TABLE 4-8. COMPARISON OF CRYSTALLIZATION FROM SOLUTIONS AND MELTS[A-11]

Property	Solution	Melt
Temperature range	Usually 20 to 80°C	From M P to relatively low T
Nature of environment	Solvation	Independent molecules
Viscosity	Not very high	Sometimes high, as in glass formers
Diffusion	Solute-solvent diffusion	Self-diffusion coefficient about same as in solution
Supercooling	Maximum up to 30°C	Organic substances frequently high; glass formations; metals less, except Fe and Ni (100°)
Nucleation	Nucleation increases to a maximum with undercooling and then diminishes	
Crystal growth rate	Of the rate of microns μ/min to mm/min for dendrites	Larger than in solution, up to 10^3 mm/min
Impurities	Influence growth rate	
Uniformity of crystals	Variable, often poor	Often good
Dendrite formation	Occasionally, under labile conditions	Often, at the beginning of crystallization of metals
Dislocations	Few	Many
Diagram	Temperature-solubility	p-t near the triple point
Heat of solution or fusion	±, but 5–15 kcal/mole for many inorganics and 1–5 for many organics	Generally 1 to 5 kcal/mole
Miscellaneous	—	Recrystallize and orient in the crystal state

number of growth centers produced during the supersaturated condition may be uncertain on account of the difficulty of completely eliminating heterogeneous effects.

Growth rates in supercooled solutions are evaluated in terms of linear crystallization velocity (L.C.V.) of seeded solutions or more significantly as the rate of addition to single crystals.

Supersolubility Curves

The supersolubility behavior of a wide variety of aqueous and other solutions has been represented by three general patterns:[25, 52, 136, 153] (1) The supercooling under ordinary conditions, $T_s - T$, is approximately constant; (2) $T_s - T$ increases with repeated heatings; (3) spontaneous crystallization does not occur even on strong cooling. Most solutions belong to Class 2, and in the limit $\lambda(T_s - T)$* is approximately constant.[168] Table

* λ is the heat of crystallization.

TABLE 4-9. TEMPERATURE OF SPONTANEOUS CRYSTALLIZATION OF AQUEOUS SOLUTIONS (SUPERSOLUBILITY TEMPERATURE)

A cooling schedule of about 1° per minute is usually employed (Tammann) and the appearance of crystals within 5 seconds at any particular temperature may be taken as the criterion of crystallization. The absence of foreign nuclei cannot be guaranteed:

Substance	Saturation Temp.	Supercooling	Reference
KCl	28°C	20°C	171
	50	14.9	65
KBr	50	8	65
KI	40	8	65
	50	7.5	159
KNO_3	83.5	3	170a
	85	3	121
K_2SO_4	37	37	44
	45	20	44
$K_2Cr_2O_7$	81	46.3	171
	30	12	159
	10	10	44
$KHC_4H_4O_6$	30	12	159
$NaNO_3$	80	60	171
	50	8	170a
NH_4NO_3	85	4.5	121
	83.5	5.5	170a
$(NH_4)_2C_2O_4 \cdot H_2O$	37	12	44
	17	17	44
$H_2C_2O_4$	55	3	170a
	40	3	159
	30	3	159
	6	6	44
$NiSO_4$	50	20	159
$CaSO_4$	—	Extensive	159
Hydroquinone	40	3	159
Pyrocatechol	40	7	159
Trinitrocresol	50	20	159
Urea	34	3	170a
Sucrose	Metastable Zone, 0 = 1 to 1.2 "False Grain" Zone, 0 = 1.2 to 1.3 Labile Zone, 0 > 1.3		170d
$(NH_4)_2SO_4$	18.5–42.9°C	0 ~ 1.038–1.054	178
Alkali and alkaline earth formates, nitrates and halates.	—	—	77

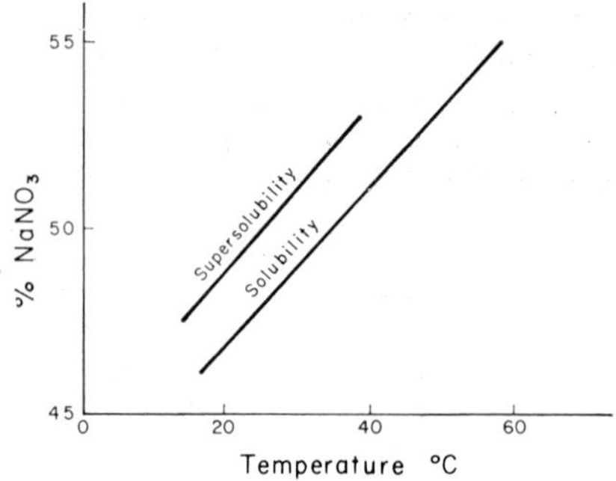

Figure 4-8. Supersolubility of $NaNO_3$ in water.[111, 161]

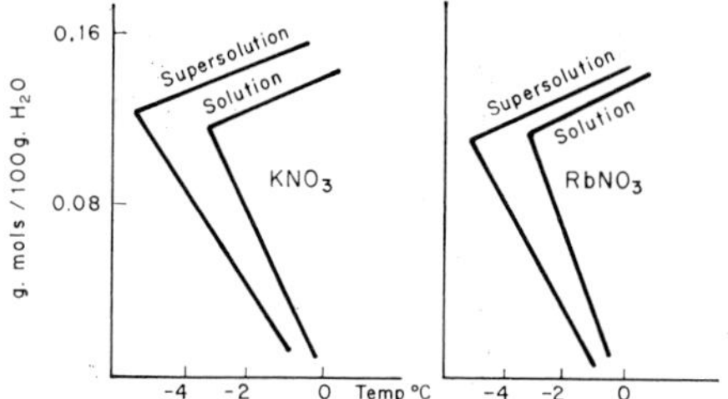

Figure 4-9. Supersolubility of K and Rb nitrates in water.[76]

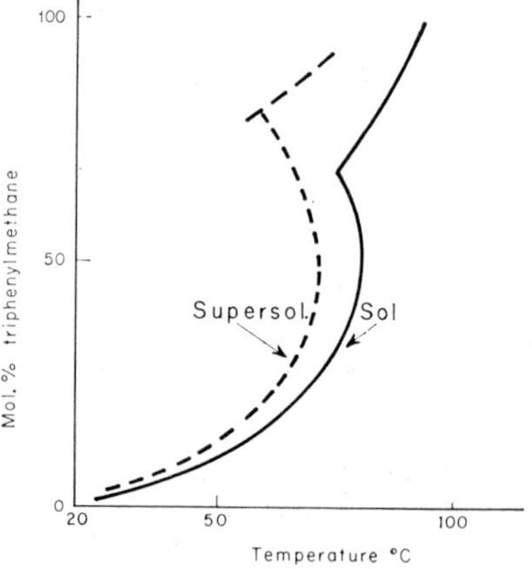

Figure 4-10. Supersolubility of triphenylmethane in benzene.[60]

4-10 illustrates that this limiting value is about 80 kcal deg mole^{-1} for many electrolytes in water. Hamburger[58] has proposed empirically that the maximum supersaturation which can be sustained by aqueous solutions such as KNO_3, $K_2Cr_2O_7$, etc. is approximately proportional to the 2/3 power of the molar volume.

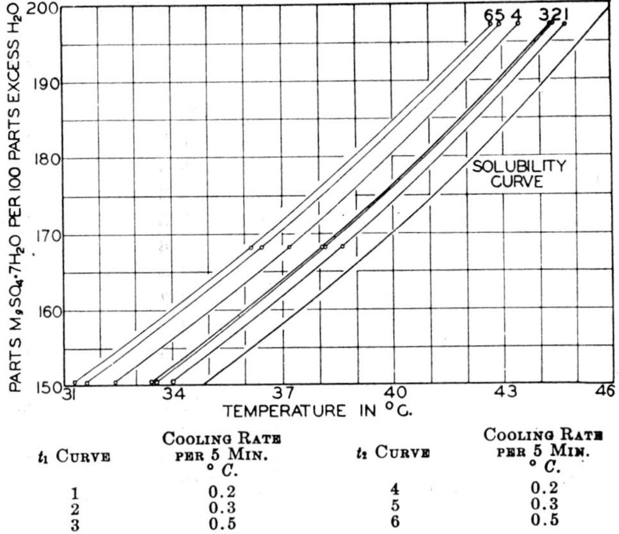

t_1 Curve	Cooling Rate per 5 Min. °C.	t_2 Curve	Cooling Rate per 5 Min. °C.
1	0.2	4	0.2
2	0.3	5	0.3
3	0.5	6	0.5

Figure 4-11. Effect of rate of cooling plotted as solubility and supersolubility curves.[165]

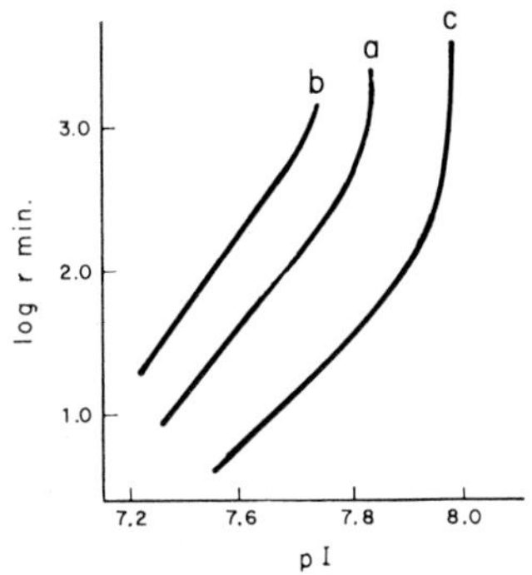

Figure 4-12. Induction period, calcium fluoride solutions.[74, 170c]
I = ion product
Equivalents/l. $Ca^{++}I$ $F^- < 5 > 0.1$

a) 18°C
b) 18°C, 0.1*M* NaCl
(c) 23°C

Ting and McCabe[165] found two reproducible supersolubility curves for $MgSO_4 \cdot 7H_2O$ in continuously cooled, stirred, and seeded solutions. The first one corresponded to the formation of new nuclei. The second, lying further in the field of supersaturation, corresponded with a sudden increase in the rate of formation of new crystals ("false grain" in the terminology

TABLE 4-10. SUPERSOLUBILITY OF AQUEOUS SOLUTIONS[25]

Substance	λ	$T_s - T$	$\lambda(T_s - T)$
KCl	4046	19.6	78897
KBr	5080	16.3	80804
KI	5110	15.5	79205
$KBrO_3$	9760	8.8	84788
KIO_3	6780	13.5	91490
$KClO_3$	9950	6.6	65670
KNO_3	8800	13.0	114400 (?)
$KClO_4$	12100	6.3	76230
KCNS	6100	13.0	79300
$NaNO_3$	5030	13.0	65399
$NaClO_3$	5600	12.0	67200
NaCl	1220	51.0	62220
NH_4Cl	3880	20.0	77600
$(NH_4)_2SO_4$	2370	24.0	56880
NH_4NO_3	6320	10.3	65016
$HgCl_2$	3300	25.0	82500
$CuSO_4$	2750	36.7	80925
$NaClO_4$	3600	20.0	72000
NH_4ClO_4	6360	12.0	76320
$Ba(ClO_4)_2$	9400	9.0	84600

of the sugar pansman). These two curves are the groups 1-2-3 and 4-5-6, respectively, in Figure 4-11.

It must be noted that these curves are for seeded and progressively cooled solutions. The first group of curves (t_1) differs from the usual Ostwald supersolubility in being quite close to the solubility curve. It is not the same as Mier's shower of crystals. The position depends on the amount and size of seeds, rate of cooling, speed of stirring, and concentration of solution. The position of the second group of curves (t_2) also depends upon the same variables.

McCabe and Ting feel that the mechanical stimulus of the stirrer was instrumental in causing much of these unusual effects. Grechnyi[55] also points out the variableness of the Ostwald metastable limit in the case of binary melts and quasi-eutectic structures.

Induction Periods

The induction period, τ, is that time required for the appearance of precipitation. Turbidity, conductivity, and other methods have been used to detect this onset of rapid adjustment.

1. Sodium oxalate at 25°C[44]

(0–1)	0.29	0.62	0.74	0.77	0.98	1.15
τ (secs)	12,600	6,300	ca. 720	600	300	0

2. Sodium picrate monohydrate at 25°C[44]

(0–1)	0.153	0.179	0.325	0.288	0.55
τ (secs)	420	360	195	90	90

3. Sodium bicarbonate at 30°C[13]

So (gl^{-1})	18	25	35	40
τ (min)	180	92	—	40
CV (gl^{-1} min^{-1})	0.06	0.22	0.73	—
τ max (min)	350	140	50	—

4. Lead sulfate at 25°C[16, 44]

(0–1)	0.5	0.7	1.01	1.5
τ (secs)	54	38	13	8

5. Lead iodide at 25°C[44] (1.2% agar solutions)

(0–1)	0.26	0.5	0.75	0.84	1
τ (secs)	ca. 72 hr	30	9	0	6

6. Barium sulfate* at 25°C[44]

(0–1)	9	14	19	29	39	49	59.6
τ (secs)	128	108	90	63.5	39	21	9

7. Strontium sulfate at 25°C[23, 44]

(0–1)	1.1	3	9	14	19	24
τ (secs)	62	30	21	15	11	5

8. Calcium sulfate dihydrate at 25°C

(0–1)	2	4	5	6	9	12
τ (secs)	224	148	55	29	15	5

9. Calcium oxalate at 25°C[44]

(0–1)	9	14	19
τ (secs)	580	75	25

10. Barium succinate at 25°C[23]

(0–1)	0.80	1.00	2.00	3.00	4.00
τ (hrs)	24	21.1	2.34	1.85	0.30

11. Silver chromate at 25°C[16, 44, 69, 79, 170a] (aqueous solutions and gelatin sols and gels)

$$(0\text{–}1)\ \tau = 6.3 \times 10^{-8}; \qquad O = \frac{a^2_{Ag^+} \cdot a_{CrO_4^{=}}}{\text{Solubility Product}}$$

12. Silver chloride at 25°C[34]

$$Sc \times 10^{10} = 3.74 - 0.60\,n$$

Sc is the critical concentration product when nuclei develop spontaneously and *n* is the ionic ratio of the ions as a faction less than 1.

13. CaF_2—Figure 4-12
14. $K_2Cr_2O_7$—Figure 4-13

* A great deal of experimental and theoretical work has been done on this system as well as other difficultly, moderately and even fairly soluble substances. See Chap. 3, p. 111 and Refs: 1, 15, 26, 30, 31, 30, 43, 90, 91, 125, 126, 129, 169.

Absolute Grain Densities

A few typical results depicting the actual number of crystal centers appearing in particular instances are depicted in Figures 4-14 and 3-6. The second set compares the observations in two different laboratories. Both groups of workers conclude that these data for sucrose solutions are compatible with the Volmer-Becker theory of nucleation. Dunning and his co-workers also reach the same conclusion in their studies of the kinetics of the crystallization of cyclonite (1,3,5-trinitro-1,3,5-triazo cyclohexane) from aqueous nitric acid and aqueous acetone. The following Table 4-11 illustrates the direct microscopic count of nuclei generated at 25°C when the solvent contained 52.4% acetone.

Amsler and Scherrer[3] have studied the rate of nucleus formation in supersaturated solutions of KCl, KBr, and KI and find essential agreement with the Volmer theory of this process. Preckshot and Brown,[A-38] and

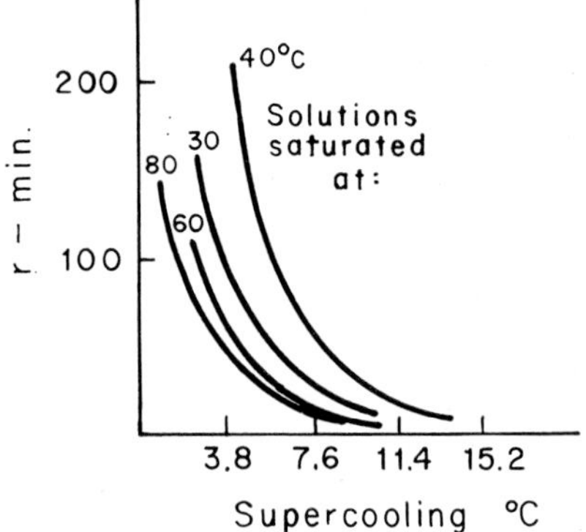

Figure 4-13. Induction periods, $K_2Cr_2O_7$ solutions.[161]

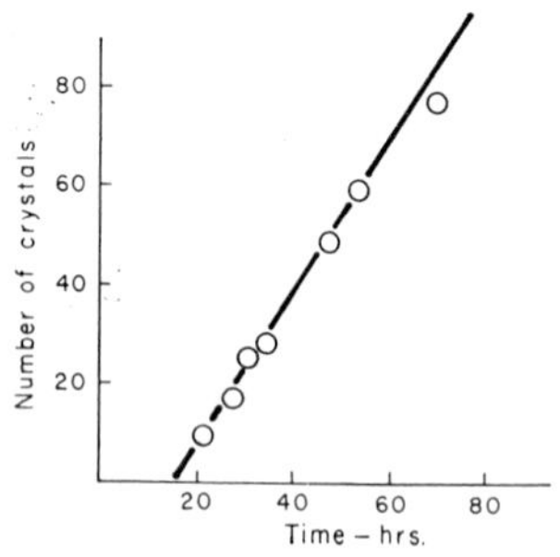

Figure 4-14. Nuclei density in sugar syrups.[3-64] 25°C, 90 ml, C/C_∞ = 1.206 (See Fig. 3-6).

TABLE 4-11. NUCLEATION OF CYCLONITE SOLUTIONS A-40

Supersaturation $\frac{c}{c_\infty}$	Nucleation Stage (sec)	Nuclei cm^{-3} sec^{-1}
5.75	20	75,000
5.14	16.5	24,100
4.66	22	19,500
3.80	18.5	4,680
3.37	22	4,370
2.85	23	1,160
2.90	21.5	970
2.87	27	380

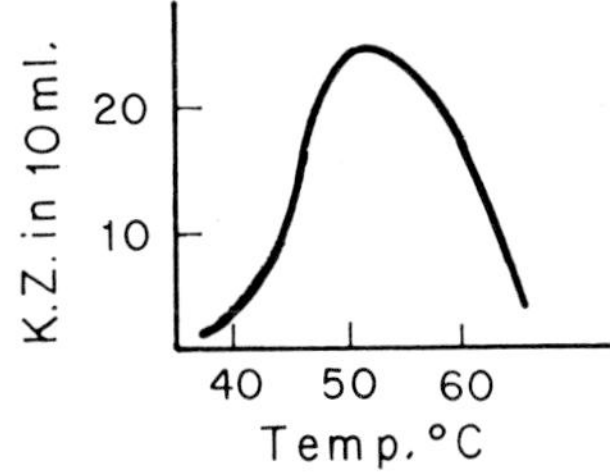

Figure 4-15. Nucleation in KCl solutions.[82] Saturated at 64°C, undercooled 1 min, unstirred solution.

Hirano, Suzuiki, and Otsuki[65] have more recently also investigated the nucleation behavior of KCl and $CuSO_4$ solutions and likewise find agreement with the more refined forms of this same theory. KNO_3 solutions[175] have been investigated similarly. Stauff[154] and Thiessen[162] report on the beginnings of crystallization of solutions of $KClO_3$ and several soaps, respectively. Figure 4-15 is a straightforward Tammann representation of nucleation in KCl solution, and Figure 4-16 indicates the influence of added NaCl.

Nucleation in solid systems, which is so important for metallurgical considerations, follows the pattern suggested by theory when strain is taken into account.

L.C.V. and M.C.V. from Solutions

Much of the work in this field is of little absolute significance because values of nuclei numbers and/or size are not specified. Rates are also very sensitive to minute amounts of contaminants, temperature coefficients are frequently large, and in some cases viscosity is a determining factor. The literature on this subject is reviewed very carefully by Partington.[128]

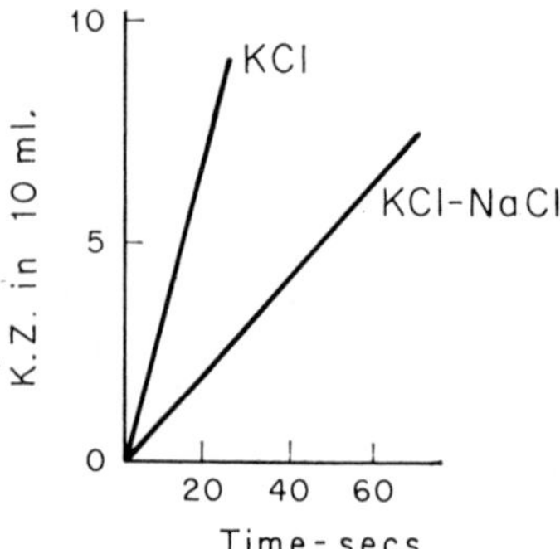

Figure 4-16. Nucleation in KCl and KCl-NaCl solutions.[82] Both saturated at 64°C, cooled to 20°C, unstirred solutions.

TABLE 4-12. LINEAR VELOCITY OF CRYSTALLIZATION OF AQUEOUS SOLUTIONS

Solution	Temperature (°C)	L.C.V. (mm/sec)
Water	−9.1	61
0.1*M* KI	−9.1	38
0.1*M* HCl	−9.1	42
0.1*M* NaCl	−9.1	41
0.1*M* $CaCl_2$	−9.1	26
0.1*M* $FeCl_3$	−9.1	11.8
0.5*M* KNO_3	−9.1	23.0
0.1*M* C_2H_5OH	−9.1	29.0
0.1*M* $K_2Cr_2O_7$	−9.1	33.0
0.1*M* Glycerol	−9.1	29.0
0.1*M* Sucrose	−9.1	6.6
0.1*M* Raffinose	−9.1	4.6
0.1*M* Lactose	−9.1	5.6
0.02*M* Lactose	−9.1	38
0.02*M* Brucine sulfate	−9.1	20.0
Gelatin—3.75 g/L	−7.1	23
Gelatin—15.0 g/L	−7.1	10.6
Oxygen-saturated	−9.1	54

Table 4-12 from Walton's extensive investigations[174] illustrates that the L.C.V. is generally lowered by the addition of a solute.[36, 84] Figures 4-17 and 4-18 illustrate the behavior when crystallization occurs on the other side of the phase diagram.

Growth Rate of Single Crystals

The following list is a representative selection from current literature sources but is far from complete.

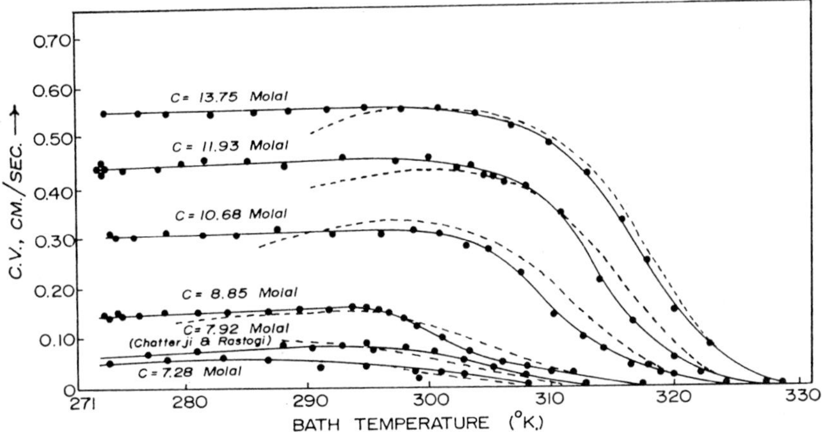

Figure 4-17. C.V. as a function of the bath temperature for several concentrations of sodium acetate (expressed as molality of the anhydrous salt). Points and solid curves are experimental. Broken curves are those given by the equation:

$$V = A'e^{-(E'-E)RT_{sat}} \cdot e^{-E/RT} \cdot e^{-BT_{sat}}/RT(T_{sat} - T)$$

with $A' = e^{33.37}$, $(E' - E)/R = 7809$, $E/R = 2820$, and $B/R = 23.5$. E and E' are the activation energies of the crystallization and dissolution processes, respectively.[36]

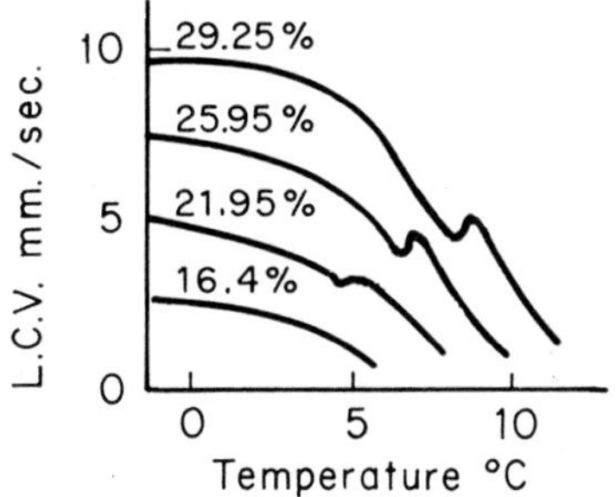

Figure 4-18. L.C.V. of $Na_2SO_4 . 10H_2O$.[84] Composition as % Na_2SO_4 .

Sucrose. Surely, sucrose is one of the most important materials for which crystallization data is necessary from the practical point of view. Kucharenko[86, 112] studied the rate of growth of this substance from aqueous solution some years ago and his original data are summarized in Table 4-13. These data have been critically analyzed and extended by the present writer.[170d, h]

TABLE 4-13. RATE OF GROWTH (MG/M² MIN.) OF SUCROSE AT DIFFERENT SUPERSATURATIONS (S) AND TEMPERATURES. SMOOTHED DATA OF KUCHARENKO.[86]

(S = % sucrose in syrup/% sucrose in saturated syrup at same temperature)

S/°C	0	20	30	40	50	60	70
1.005	—	40	75	145	240	340	850
1.010	5	80	150	285	490	720	1700
1.015	—	120	225	490	800	1340	2560
1.020	9	150	380	675	1200	2210	4000
1.025	—	190	495	855	1800	3100	—
1.030	14	230	625	1060	2300	—	—
1.035	—	275	755	1300	2870	—	—
1.040	19	320	910	1540	3510	—	—
1.045	—	360	1115	1800	4060	—	—
1.050	25	420	1320	2085	—	—	—
1.055	—	480	—	2580	—	—	—
1.060	32	525	—	—	—	—	—
1.065	—	575	—	—	—	—	—
1.070	38	620	—	—	—	—	—
1.08	45	—	—	—	—	—	—
1.09	52	—	—	—	—	—	—
1.10	62	—	—	—	—	—	—
1.11	76	—	—	—	—	—	—

Common Salt.[43-123]

	V^{hkl} in μday^{-1} at 30°					
Degree Supersaturation	(110)	(210)	(111)	(100)	(111)	(100)
1	98	50.7	35.7	0	46.7	0
3	243	162	81.3	0	101.1	12.5

$CuSO_4 \cdot 5H_2O$. Figurovskii and Komarova[43] find the rate of growth of these crystals, $\Delta P/Sdt$ in g(cm²)$^{-1}$ min^{-1}, to be given by $\Delta P/S\Delta t = kx^2$, where x is the relative supersaturation. $k = 0.019$ (and 0.005 for $KAl(SO_4)_2 \cdot 12H_2O$). McCabe and Stevens[105] have studied the crystallization of batches of this same material while cooling in order to maintain constant supersaturation. The rate, r_g, at which such crystals grow in agitated solutions is given by $1/r_g = (1/[r_o + Bu]) + (1/r_i)$, where r_o is the rate without agitation, r_i the interfacial growth rate, u the relative velocity of movement between crystals and solution, and B a constant. The appropriateness of this equation is illustrated in Figure 4-19. Chatterji,[25] Hixson and Knox,[66] and Matusevich[103] have also studied this same system as well as $MgSO_4 \cdot 7H_2O$, KNO_3, $K_4Fe(CN)_6$, KCl, and $BaCl_2$; while Mosebach[116] has examined the layer-wise growth of crystals of $CuSO_4 \cdot 5H_2O$, $K_2Cr_2O_7$ and $K_3Fe(CN)_6$ in aqueous solutions.

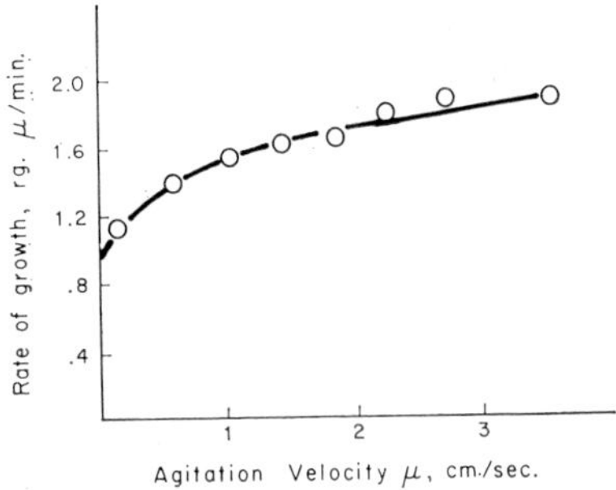

Figure 4-19. Effect of agitation velocity on rate of growth of copper sulfate.[105]

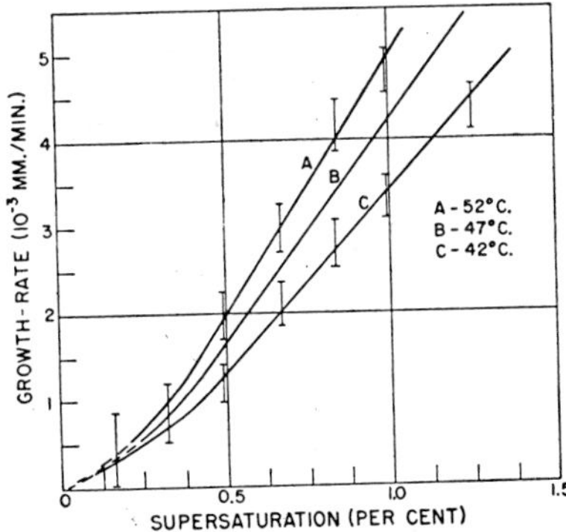

Figure 4-20. Growth rates at various temperatures.[17]

$K_2Cr_2O_7$. Todes and Litunovskii[93, 166] compare the rates of growth and dissolution of crystals of $K_2Cr_2O_7$ in aqueous solution, and conclude that the same transport phenomenon controls in each case. Results are represented by the theoretically acceptable equations:

$$\lambda \text{ crys.} = 2.59 \times 10^{-5} \exp \left[\frac{0.0842}{\ln \dfrac{co + x}{C_o}} \right]$$

$$\lambda \text{ solution} = 31.65 \times 10^{-5} \exp \left[\frac{-0.025}{\ln \dfrac{(co - x)}{C_o}} \right]$$

where x is the excess or deficiency in concentration with respect to saturation, C_o; and λ is the rate of change of linear dimensions.

E.D.T. Booth and Buckley[17] grew single crystals of ethylene diamine tartrate under controlled conditions and measured the growth rates directly in the solution by means of a traveling microscope. For the ($\bar{1}$ $\bar{1}$ 0) and (1 $\bar{1}$ 0) pair of faces, the fastest growing form, steady growth at constant supersaturation was interrupted by occasional short periods of more rapid growth. Rejecting these erratic "spurts," reasonable reproducible values could be obtained and Figure 4-20 illustrates the dependence of these steady states upon supersaturation.

Table 4-14 summarizes the results of Kunisaki[88] for this same material and Table 4-15 those for A.D.P. These results are approximately linear in terms of supersaturation over the entire range studied but become almost quadratic in the neighborhood of the origin.

$Na_2SO_4 \cdot 10\ H_2O$.[113, 114]

$\Delta W/\Delta S = 10^3\ Ke^{0.0178t}$; $\Delta W/\Delta S$ in g(cm^2)$^{-1}$, t in minutes
K = 12.57 at 27.1°C with average supersaturation of 0.17°C
K = 13.90 at 29.26°C with average supersaturation of 0.21°C
K = 16.26 at 30.9°C with average supersaturation of 0.16°C

$MgSO_4 \cdot 7\ H_2O$.[114]

$\Delta W/\Delta S = 10^3\ Ke^{0.0175t}$; K = 22.13 at 31.62°C with average supersaturation of 0.50°C
K = 18.5 at 29.25°C with average supersaturation of 0.30°C

TABLE 4-14. GROWTH RATES OF E.D.T.[88]

Temperature of Growth (°C)	Supersaturation Degree %	Growth Rates (mm/day)	
		(1$\bar{1}$0)	(100)
27.5	0.54	0.33	0.034
	0.65	0.46	0.057
	0.08	0.64	0.09
	1.02	0.89	0.12
36	0.54	0.82	0.07
	0.85	1.38	0.16
	1.17	2.05	0.28
38	0.62	—	0.16
	0.73	—	0.21
42	0.56	1.43	0.23
	0.66	1.70	0.31
	0.75	1.94	0.36

TABLE 4-15. GROWTH RATES OF A.D.P.[88]

Temperature of Growth (°C)	Supersaturation Degree (%)	Growth Rates (mm/day)	
		Pyramidal	Prismatic
31	0.85	0.76	0.25
	1.25	—	0.54
	1.36	2.06	0.61
	1.98	3.82	1.04
38.5	0.73	1.40	0.42
	0.86	210	—
	1.20	311	—
	1.33	—	1.24
	1.59	5.04	—
	1.92	6.35	2.11
42.5	0.63	—	0.51
	1.13	—	1.32
	1.76	—	2.62
43	0.62	1.97	—
	1.13	4.55	—
	1.75	7.31	—

TABLE 4-16. RELATIVE CRYSTALLIZATION VELOCITIES OF ALUMS[57]

Type of Alum	(111)	(110)	(100)	(122)	(112)	(012)
K-Al	1	4.8	5.3	9.5	11	27
K-Cr	1	4.3	0.2	—	17.9	34.7
NH_4-Al	1	1.9	1.8	—	3.2	5

TABLE 4-17. EFFECT OF TEMPERATURE ON CRYSTALLIZATION VELOCITY OF ALUM[152]

Temperature	(111)	(100)	(110)	(221)
29°	0.21	1.12	1.0	1.99
19°	0.17	0.61	1.0	1.46

Alums. Buckley[20] finds the relative rates of growth of the (111), (110) and (100) faces of K alum to be 1, 1.15, and 1.2, respectively. Paine and France[127] report a much higher ratio (1.75) for the ratio of the (100) to the (111) face in pure solutions, but the value drops rapidly in the presence of impurities; 0.004/g of diamine sky blue per 100 cc actually reversing the trend to a ratio of 0.75. Stirring during growth also has an effect on these ratios of growth.

Gunther[57] finds the values given in Table 4-16, and Spangenberg[152] finds the relative velocity of growth of the faces of K alums quite sensitive to temperature (Table 4-17).

Skryabin[151] discusses the kinetics of K alum crystallization from solution under a variety of conditions, and so does Campbell.[24]

REFERENCES

1. Adamovich, L. P., and Parfimova, K. G., *Zhur. Anal. Khim.*, **5**, 339 (1950); *C.A.*, **45**, 934.
2. Amagasa, M., *J. Chem. Soc.* (*Japan*) **39**(Suppl), 263 (1936).
3. Amsler, J., and Scherer, P., *Helv. Phys. Acta.*, **14**, 318 (1941); **15**, 699 (1942).
4. Anon., *Chem. and Eng. News*, April 25 (1942).
5. Ascher, K. R. S., and Bergmann, E. D., *Bull. Res. Council Israel*, **3**, 255 (1953); *C.A.*, **48**, 11165.
6. Austin, J. B., and Rickett, R. L., Tech. Publ. #964, Am. Inst. Mining Met. Engrs., 1938.
7. Avrami, M., *J. Chem. Phys.*, **9**, 177 (1941).
8. Bailey, J. E., "Melting and Solidification of Fats," New York, Interscience Publishers, Ind., 1950.
9. Barnard, A. J., *Proc. Roy. Soc.* (*London*), **A220**, 132 (1953).
10. Barum, D. A., *Ukrain, Khim. Zhur.*, **22**, 137 (1956); *C.A.*, **50**, 14331.
11. Barus, C., "Nucleation and Conductivity in the Atmosphere," Washington, D. C., Carnegie Inst., 1906–10.
12. Bates, F. J., and Associates, "Polarimetry and the Sugars," U.S. National Bureau of Standards, C440, Washington, D.C. 1942.
13. Belopolski, A. P., and Margolis, F. G., *J. Appl. Chem.* (*U.S.S.R.*), **20**, 331 (1947); **24**, 931 (1951); *C.A.*, **42**, 2061; **48**, 14133.
14. Berlaga, R. Ya., *J. Exptl. Theret. Phys. U.S.S.R.*, **9**, 889, 1397 (1939).
15. Bogan, E. J., and Moyer, H. V., *Anal. Chem.*, **28**, 473 (1956).
16. Bolam, T. R., *J. Chem. Soc.* (*London*), **117**, 844 (1920);
    Trans. Faraday Soc., **22**, 151, 162 (1926)
    29, 864 (1933)
    37, 549 (1941).
17. Booth, A. H., and Buckley, H. E., *Can. J. Chem.*, **33**, 1155, 1162 (1955); *Nature*, **169**, 367 (1952).
18. Bradley, R. S., *Quart. Rev.*, **5**, 329 (1951).
19. Briggs, L. J., *J. Chem. Phys.*, **26**, 784 (1957); *J. Appl. Phys.*, **26**, 100 (1955).
20. Buckley, H. E., *Z. Krist.*, **23**, 443 (1930).
21. Burgus, W. G., and Groen, L. J., *Faraday Disc.*, #**23**, 183 (1957).
22. Bykov, A. G., and Tevlrovskii, E. N., *Zhur. Eksp. i Teoret. Fiz.*, **19**, 328 (1949); *C.A.*, **45**, 9998.
23. Campbell, A. N., and co-workers, *J. Am. Chem. Soc.*, **57**, 387 (1935); *Trans. Faraday Soc.*, **33**, 300 (1937).
24. Campbell, N. P., *J. Chem. Soc.*, **107**, 475 (1915).
25. Chatterji, A. C., *et al.*, *J. Indian Chem. Soc.*, **26**, 94 (1948); **28**, 337, 602 (1951); *J. Am. Chem. Soc.*, **59**, 1 (1955).
26. Chepelovetski, M. L., *J. Phys. Chem.* (*USSR*), **13**, 561 (1939); *C.A.*, **32**, 2008, **34**, 1540.

27. Chernou, A. A., *Acta Krist.*, **9**, 977 (1956).
28. Chien, J., *J. Am. Chem. Soc.*, **70**, 2256 (1948).
29. Chretien, A., Heubel, J., and Trimole, P., *Compt rend.*, **239**, 814 (1954).
30. Christiansen, J. A., and Nielson, A. E., *Acta Chem. Scand.*, **5**, 673 (1951); **8**, 1665 (1954); *Z. Electrochem.*, **56**, 465 (1952); *J. Coll. Sci.*, **10**, 577 (1955).
31. Collins, F. C., and Leineweber, J. P. L., *J. Phys. Chem.*, **60**, 389 (1956).
32. Danilov, V. I., *et al.*,
    (a) *J. Exptl. Theret. Phys. USSR*, **9**, 66 (1939); **10**, 1305 (1940).
    (b) *Zhur. Eksp. i Teoret. Fiz.*, **18**, 886 (1948); **19**, 313 (1949); *C.A.*, **45**, 9965.
    (c) *Doklady Akad. Nauk S.S.S.R.*, **73**, 1169 (1950); *C.A.*, **45**, 1402.
    (d) *Ibid*, **68**, 843 (1949); *C.A.*, **45**, 6450.
    (e) *Zhur. Fiz. Khim.*, **28**, 1037 (1954); *C.A.*, **50**, 1401.
33. Dausin, I. M., *Brit. J. Appl. Phys.*, **4**, 177 (1953).
34. Davies, C. W., and Jones, A. L., A-37, p. 109; *Trans. Faraday Soc.*, **51**, 812, 1232 (1955).
35. Dawson, I. M., and Watson, D. H., *Proc. Roy. Soc. (London)*, **A239**, 349 (1957).
36. Dietz, Jr., P. L., Brukner, J. S., and Hollingsworth, C. A., *J. Phys. Chem.*, **61**, 944 (1957).
37. Dodd, C., *Endeavor*, **15**, 206 (1956).
38. Dorsey, N. E.
    (a) "Properties of Ordinary Water Substance," New York, Reinhold Publishing Co., 1940;
    (b) *Trans. Am. Phil. Soc.*, **38**, 284 (1948).
39. Dreyer, F., *Z. Phys. Chem.*, **48**, 480 (1954).
40. Duke, F. R., and Brown, L. M., *J. Am. Chem. Soc.*, **76**, 1443 (1934).
41. Dunning, W. J., *et al.*
    (a) Xth Cong. Int. Agricoles, Madrid, 1–25 (1954);
    (b) Ref A-45, p. 446;
    (c) *Acta Met.*, **12**, 219 (1959); **13**, 495 (1960).
42. Farley, F. J. M., *Proc. Roy. Soc.*, **A212**, 530 (1952).
43. Figurovskii, N. A., and Komarova, T. A., *Zhur. Fiz. Khim.*, **28**, 1479 (1954); *C.A.*, **49**, 11373; *Zhur. Inorg. Khim.*, **2**, 938 (1957).
44. Fisher, W., *Z. Anorg. Chem.*, **145**, 343 (1925); **153**, 67 (1926).
45. Freundlich, H., *Z. Phys. Chem.*, **76**, 245 (1910).
46. Fuchtbauer, G., *Z. Phys. Chem.*, **48**, 549 (1904).
47. Fukuta, N., *J. Meteorol.*, **15**, 17 (1958).
48. Garner, W. F., "Chemistry of the Solid State," New York, Academic Press, 1955.
49. Gerasimenko, A. A., and Golovin, P. V., *Ukrain. Khim. Zhur.*, **21**, 527, 797 (1955); *C.A.*, **50**, 14248.
50. Gernez, D., *Compt. rendu*, **95**, 1278 (1882).
51. Gey, W. A., Dalbey, E. R., and Van Dolah, R. W., *J. Am. Chem. Soc.*, **78**, 1803 (1956); *J. Phys. Chem.*, **61**, 507 (1957).
52. Gopal, R., *Z. Anorg. Chem.*, **278**, 46 (1955); *J. Indian Chem. Soc.*, **25**, 443 (1948).
53. Granahan, L., M. S. thesis, College of the Holy Cross (1949).
54. Grauer, O. H., and Hamilton, E. H., *J. Research Natl. Bur. Standards*, **44**, 495 (1950).
55. Grechnyi, Ya. V., *Doklady Akad. Nauk. S.S.S.R.*, **84**, 89, 335 (1952); *C.A.*, **48**, 1128, 9778.
56. Gunn, R., *Rev. Sci. Instr.*, **20**, 291 (1949).

57. Gunther, O., Dissertation, 1929, cited by LeClerc, E., *Rev. Universelle des Mines*, Liège (1947).
58. Hamburger, J., *Chem. Weekblad*, **35**, 886 (1938).
59. Hammer, C., *Ann. Phys.*, **33**, 445 (1938).
60. Hartley et al., *J. Chem. Soc. (London)*, **89**, 1012 (1906); **93**, 825 (1908).
61. Hartshorne, N. H., *et al.*, *J. Chem. Soc. (London)*, 1860 (1935), 1636 (1938), 1097 (1951), 2122 (1952), 370 (1935), 2122 (1957); A-37, p. 149, *Disc. Faraday Soc.*, #25, 196, 224 (1957).
62. Harvey, E. N., *J. Am. Chem. Soc.*, **67**, 156 (1945).
63. Hildebrand, J. H., and Rotaree, G. J., *J. Am. Chem. Soc.*, **73**, 2524 (1951).
64. Hillig, W. B., and Turnbull, D., *J. Chem. Phys.*, **24**, 914 (1956); *J. Phys. Chem.*, **60**, 56 (1956).
65. Hirano, K., *Sci. Repts. Tohoku U.*, First Ser. **38**, 97 (1954); *C.A.*, **49**, 14440.
66. Hixson, A. W., and Knox, K. L., *Ind. Eng. Chem.*, **43**, 2144 (1951).
67. Honigmann, B., *Z. Electrochem.*, **58**, 322 (1954); **61**, 74 (1957). *Z. Krist.*, **106**, 3 (1955).
68. Horne, R. W., and Attlwell, R. H., *Nature*, **180**, 910 (1957).
69. Howard, J. R., and Nancollas, C. H., *Trans. Faraday Soc.*, **53**, 1449 (1957); *Nature*, **176**, 833 (1955).
70. Hudson, J. B., Hillig, W. B., and Strong, R. M., *J. Phys. Chem.*, **63**, 1012 (1959).
71. Ingelman, B., *Socker Handl.*, **3**, 5 (1947).
72. International Critical Tables (I.T.C.), Vol. 1, p. 335, Vol. 5, p. 60, New York, McGraw-Hill Book Co., 1929.
73. Jenkins, J. D., *J. Am. Chem. Soc.*, **47**, 902 (1915).
74. Jensen, A., *Z. Phys. Chem.*, **180A**, 93 (1937).
75. Johnson, W. A., and Mehl, R. F., Tech. Publ. #1089, *Am. Inst. Mining Met. Engrs.*, (1939).
76. Jones, B. M., *J. Chem. Soc. (London)*, **93**, 1644 (1908).
77. Kiriyama, R., *J. Chem. Soc. Japan*, **70**, 260 (1949), **71**, 114, 507, 558 (1950); *C.A.*, **45**, 2740, 5001.
78. Knacke, O., and Stranski, I. N., *Ergeb. Exact. Naturw.*, **26**, 383 (1952).
79. Kobayuski, K., and Shibuya, K., *J. Chem. Soc. Japan*, **71**, 128 (1950); *C.A.*, **45**, 4529; *Sci. Reports, Tohoku Imp. Univ.*, **37**, 125 (1953); *C.A.*, **48**, 9145.
80. Kolnik, S. S., *et al.*, *J. Am. Chem. Soc.*, **68**, 2305 (1946).
81. Kondoguri, V. V., *Phys. Z. Soviet. U.*, **9**, 603 (1936); *Z. Phys.*, **47**, 589 (1928).
82. Koppen, R., *Z. anorg. Chem.*, **228**, 169 (1936).
83. Kozlovskii, M. I., *Kristallografiya*, **2**, 760 (1957); *C.A.*, **52**, 5073.
84. Krichevskaya, E. L., *J. Phys. Chem. (USSR)*, **19**, 382 (1945).
85. Krueger, C. C., and Miller, C. W., *J. Chem. Phys.*, **21**, 2018 (1953).
86. Kucharenko, J. A., *Planter and Sugar Mfg.*, **53**, #19 to **54**, #4 (1928).
87. Kulkarni, S. B., Kuber, M. V., and Biswasi, A. B., *J. Sci. Ind. Res. (India)*, **17B**, 212 (1958); *C.A.*, **53**, 7737.
88. Kunisaki, Y., *J. Inst. Elect. Comm. Engrs. Japan*, **36**, 672 (1953); *J. Chem. Soc. Japan, Ind. Chem. Soc.*, **60**, 987 (1957).
89. Kutznetzov, V., *J. Phys. U.S.S.R.*, **5**, 229 (1941).
90. La Mer, V. K., and co-workers, *J. Am. Chem. Soc.*, **72**, 4847 (1950), **73**, 380 (1951).
91. Larkam, W., B. S. Thesis, U. of Idaho, 1936.
92. Lindenmeyer, C. S., Orrok, G. T., Jackson, K. A., and Chalmers, B., *J. Chem. Phys.*, **27**, 822 (1957).

93. Litunovskii, N. I., and Todes, O. M., *Zhur. Tekh. Fiz.*, **23**, 1125–43 (1953); *C.A.*, 49, 4385.
94. Livingston, R., "Physico-Chemical Experiments," 3rd Ed., p. 75, New York, Macmillan Co., 1957.
95. Luyet, B. J., *J. Phys. Chem.*, **43**, 881 (1939).
96. Lyubov, B. Ya., *Ukrain. Khim. Zhur.*, **84**, 277 (1952); *C.A.*, **47**, 9126.
97. Malkin, V. I., *Zhur. Fiz. Khim.*, **28**, 1966 (1954); *C.A.*, **50**, 4606.
98. Mandelkern, L., A-45, p. 467.
99. Marc, R., *Z. Phys. Chem.*, **73**, 685 (1910).
100. Martinez, C., *Bull. soc. franc. min.*, **75**, 63 (1952); *C.A.*, **46**, 64969.
101. Masing, G., *Wiss. Ver. Siemens Konzern*, **8**, 144 (1929); *C.A.*, **24**, 2366.
102. Mason, B. J., and Hallett, J., *Nature*, **179**, 357 (1957).
103. Matusevich, L. N., *Zhur. Priklad. Khim.*, **25**, 1157 (1952), **27**, 148 (1954); *C.A.*, 48, 7937, 9778, 49, 9995; *J. Appl. Chem. (USSR)*, **27**, 139 (1954).
104. McCabe, W. L., in Perry's "Chemical Engineers Handbook," p. 1777, New York, McGraw-Hill Book Co., 1941, *Ind. Eng. Chem.*, **21**, 30, 112 (1929).
105. McCabe, W. L., and Stevens, R. P., *Chem. Eng. Progress*, **47**, 168 (1951).
106. McCrone, W., Smedal, A., and Gilpin, V., *Anal. Chem.*, **18**, 578 (1946); *J. Am. Chem. Soc.*, **70**, 208 (1948).
107. McDonald, J. E., *J. Chem. Ed.*, **35**, 205 (1958); *J. Chem. Phys.*, **28**, 170 (1958).
108. Menius, A. C., and Turner, T. J., *Phys. Rev.*, **74**, 125 (1948).
109. Meyer, J., and Pfaff, W., *Z. anorg. Chem.*, **224**, 305 (1935).
110. Michel, J., *Bull. soc. chem. Belge.*, **48**, 105 (1939).
111. Miers, H. A., and Issac, F., *J. Chem. Soc. (London)*, **89**, 413 (1906).
112. Mikhnevich, G. L., and coworkers,
    (a) *Phys. Z. Sovetunion*, **13**, 103 (1938); *C.A.*, **32**, 4849, **34**, 7690, **52**, 852.
    (b) *Spornik Fiz. Mat. Faki Nauch. Issledovate, Inst. Fiz. Odessk Xniv.* 5, 109, 115 (1954); *C.A.*, 52, 852.
113. Mokievskii, V. A., *Kristallografiya*, 4, 3 (1955); *C.A.*, **52**, 32.
114. Montillon, G. H., and Badger, W. L., *Ind. Eng. Chem.*, 19, 809 (1927).
115. Morris, J. B., and Strickland-Constable, R. F., *Trans. Faraday Soc.*, **50**, 1378 (1954).
116. Mosebach, R., *Z. Naturforsch.*, **5a**, 504 (1950).
117. Muller, H. C., *Z. Phys. Chem.*, **86**, 177 (1914).
118. Murphy, J. E., M. S. Thesis, College of the Holy Cross, 1948.
119. Nacken, R., *Zentr. Mineral. Geol.*, 191 (1917); *Neues Jahr. Min. Geol.*, **2**, 133 (1915).
120. Naveau, G., in "La Cristallisation du Sucre," p. 40, Bruxelles, Commission Internationale technique de Sucrerie de Betteruve, 1953.
121. Nayar, M. R., *Bull. Acad. Sci. Agra. Oudh. Allahabad, India*, **1**, 100 (1931).
122. Nees, A. R., and Hungerford, E. H., *Ind. Eng. Chem.*, **28**, 893 (1936).
123. Neuhaus, A., *Z. Krist.*, **18**, 15 (1928).
124. Neumann, K., and Micus, G., *Z. Physik. Chem. (Frankfurt)*, **2**, 25 (1954).
125. Oden, S., and Werner, *Arkiv. Kemi. Min. Geol.*, **9**, #23 (1925), **9**, #32 (1926).
126. O'Rourke, J. D., and Johnson, R., *Anal. Chem.*, **27**, 1699 (1955).
127. Paine, P. A., and France, W. J., *J. Phys. Chem.*, **39**, 425 (1935).
128. Partington, J. R., "Advanced Treatise on Physical Chemistry," New York, Longmans-Green Co., 1952.
129. Peisach, J., and Brescia, F., *J. Am. Chem. Soc.*, **7**, 65946 (1954).

130. Pollatschek, H., *Z. Phys. Chem.*, **142A**, 289 (1929).
131. Pollerman, M., *Z. Electrochem.*, **56**, 313 (1950).
132. Powell, C., *Proc. Roy. Soc.*, **A119**, 553 (1928).
133. Pound, G. M., *Ind. Eng. Chem.*, **44**, 1278 (1952); *A-39*, Vol. 3, p. 97.
134. Pound, G. M., and LaMer, V. K., *J. Am. Chem. Soc.*, **74**, 2323 (1952).
135. Pound, G. M., Madonna, L. A., and Peake, S. L., *J. Coll. Sci.*, **8**, 187 (1953).
136. Rastogi, R. P., and Chatterji, A. C., *Z. Phys. Chem.*, **205**, 261 (1956); *J. Phys. Chem.*, **59**, 1 (1955).
137. Richards, W. T., *J. Am. Chem. Soc.*, **54**, 479 (1932); **58**, 2243 (1936).
138. Robinson, R. H., *J. Chem. Ed.*, **32**, 317 (1955).
139. Rodebush, W. H., *Chem. Rev.*, **44**, 269 (1949); A-38 p. 1289.
140. Roginski, S. E., *Acta Physicochem., U.S.S.R.*, **10**, 825 (1939); *C.A.*, **33**, 8072.
141. Roginski, S. E., and Todes, O. M., *Acta Physicochem. U.S.S.R.*, **12**, 531 (1943); *C.A.*, **35**, 7263.
142. Rosenberg, A., and Winegard, W. C., *Acta Met.*, **2**, 242 (1954).
143. Ruedy, R., *Can. J. Res.*, **A22**, 77 (1944).
144. Ruska, E., and Wolff, D. W., *Z. Wiss. Mikroskop.*, **62**, 465 (1956).
145. Sato, T., and Kaneko, H., *Tech. Rept. Tohoku U.*, **14**, 45 (1955); *C.A.*, **45**, 7941.
146. Schaefer, V. J., *Science*, **104**, 457 (1946).
147. Scharrer, L., *Ann. Physik.*, **35**, 619 (1939).
148. Sears, G. W., *J. Chem. Phys.*, **24**, 868 (1956); **25**, 637 (1956).
149. Serota, *Compt. Red. Acad. Sci. U.S.S.R.*, **36**, 175 (1942); *C.A.*, **37**, 2644.
150. Sinclair, D., and LaMer, V. K., *Chem. Rev.*, **44**, 245 (1949).
151. Skryabin, A. K., *Zhur. Fiz. Khim.*, **31**, 780 (1957); *C.A.*, **52**, 58.
152. Spangenberg, K., *Z. Krist.*, **61**, 189 (1925).
153. Srikantan, B. S., *et al.*, *J. Ind. Chem. Soc.*, **27**, 627 (1950); **28**, 585 (1951); **30**, 149, 467 (1953).
154. Stauff, J., *Z. Phys. Chem.*, **187A**, 107 (1940).
155. Stewart, K., *Trans. Faraday Soc.*, **52**, 161 (1956).
156. Stranski, I. N., *Naturw.*, **37**, 292 (1950).
157. Stuckenbruck, L. C., M. S. thesis, U. of Iowa, 1947.
158. Takogi, S., *J. Chem. Phys.*, **26**, 784 (1957); *J. Appl. Phys.*, **26**, 100 (1955).
159. Tammann, G., "States of Aggregation," New York, D. Van Nostrand Co., 1925.
160. Tammann, G., *Z. anorg. Chem.*, **193**, 76 (1930).
161. Tammann, G., and Gronow, *Z. anorg. Chem.*, **200**, 57 (1931).
162. Thiessen, *Z. anorg. Chem.*, **174**, 267 (1929); (London) **180**, 57 (1927).
163. Thomas, D. G., and Stavely, A. K., *J. Chem. Soc. (London)*, 4569 (1952); 224 (1954).
164. Timmermans, J., "Physico-chemical Constants of Pure Organic Compounds," New York, Elsevier Publishing Co., 1950.
165. Ting, H. H., and McCabe, W. L., *Ind. Eng. Chem.*, **26**, 1201 (1934).
166. Todes, O. M., *Acta Physicochem. U.S.S.R.*, **13**, 617 (1940). *J. Phys. Chem., U.S.S.R.*, **15**, 708 (1941); *C.A.*, 47, 821.
167. Tolansky, S., "Multiple Beam Interferometry," Oxford U. Press, 1948; "Surface Microtopography," New York, Interscience Publishing Co., 1960; *Endeavor*, **9**, #36, 196 (1950).
168. Tovbin, M., *Ukrain. Khim. Zhur.*, **21**, 32 (1955); *C.A.*, **45**, 5493.
169. Turnbull, D.
    (a) "Solidification," p. 282, Am. Soc. Metals, Cleveland, Ohio, 1950.

(b) "Solid State Physics," Vol. 3, p. 283, New York, Academic Press, 1956.
(c) *J. Chem. Phys.*, **18,** 769 (1950);
(d) *J. Appl. Phys.*, **21,** 808 (1950);
(e) *Acta. Met.*, **1,** 684 (1953).
(f) with Vonnegut, B., A-38, p. 1292.

170. Van Hook, A., and co-workers
(a) *J. Phys. Chem.*, **41,** 593 (1937).
(b) *J. Phys. Chem.*, **44,** 751 (1940); **45,** 1194 (1941); **46,** 395 (1942).
(c) *Northwest Science*, **13,** 45 (1939).
(d) Honig's, "Sugar Technology," Vol. 2, p. 113, Amsterdam, Elsevier, 1959.
(e) Ref. A-37.
(f) *Ind. Eng. Chem.*, **36,** 1042 (1944).
(g) *Proc. Am. Soc. Sugar Beet Tech.*, **6,** 570 (1950); **9,** 590 (1957);
(h) *Int. Sugar J.*, **55,** 332 (1953); **61,** 167 (1959).
(i) *Ind. Sacc. Ital.*, **61,** 227 (1958).

171. Volmer, M., and Marder, A., *Z. Phys. Chem.*, **154A,** 97 (1931).
Volmer, M., and Weber, A., *Z. Phys. Chem.*, **119,** 277 (1926).
172. Vonnegut, B., *J. Coll. Sci.*, **3,** 563 (1948).
173. Wagner, C., *Z. Physik. Chem.*, **71,** 401 (1910).
174. Walton, A., *J. Am. Chem. Soc.*, **38,** 317 (1916); **40,** 168, 1148 (1918).
175. White, M. L., *Univ. Mich. Microfilm*, #7070, 77 pp. (1954).
176. Wilke, K. Th., *Fortschr. Min.*, **34,** 85–150 (1956); *C.A.*, **51,** 5492.
177. Wilson, H. A., *Phil. Mag.*, **50,** 238 (1900).
178. Yamamoto, T., *J. Chem. Soc. Japan*, **71,** 114 (1950); *C.A.*, **45,** 5001.

Chapter 5

CRYSTALLIZATION IN THE LABORATORY AND IN THE PLANT

LABORATORY CRYSTALLIZATIONS

Crystallization is a very common operation in ordinary laboratory practice; usually being carried out for the purpose of separating solid materials in purified forms, or for the preparation of well-defined and pure single crystals for study or display. Hundreds of schemes and apparatus have been perfected for these purposes. Buckley[A-1] and Matz[A-11] both contain excellent descriptions of methods and devices for the production of good samples of crystals, and Tipson[127] is most complete in his catalogue of the techniques and apparatus used in the production of crystalline compounds. Palmer,[95] amongst others,[29] has a short but instructive chapter on ordinary laboratory crystallization and the basic properties of crystals.

Preparative Crystallization

In the most usual case of preparative crystallization as practiced in the chemical laboratory, it is generally best to purify the melt or solution to the maximum extent possible before proceeding to the crystallization step itself. This purification may often be accomplished by repeated crystallization itself or by treatment with clarifying agents. Activated carbon and similar materials are frequently used in the case of organic solutions and chemical treatments are very common. A case in illustration of this last is the alkalization of brine solutions in order to remove heavy metals. Ion exchange and related treatments are also very beneficial in many instances.

The purified melt or solution is then filtered or centrifuged in order to remove suspended material and brought to the point of crystallizing by evaporative concentration, reduction of solubility by addition of an unfavorable solvent, or cooling. Ordinary laboratory ware is used in most instances, but a wide variety of modifications has been improvised according to special circumstances. Figure 5-1 illustrates only one simple arrangement of the wide variety described by Tipson. Filtration before and after crystallization as well as concentration and washing can be performed in

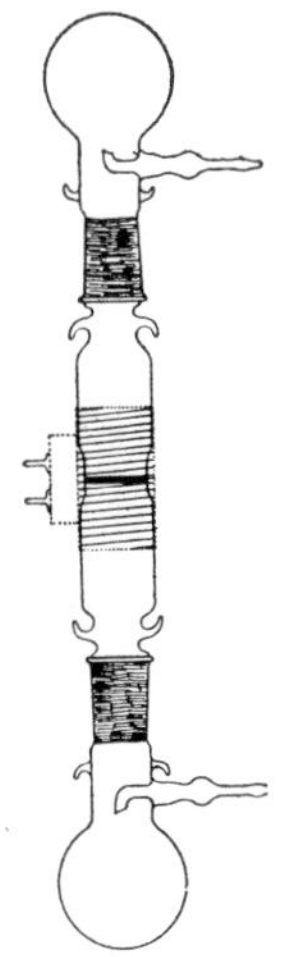

Figure 5-1. Filtration apparatus. After Tipson.[127]

equipment such as this and, if necessary, the separation steps can be quickened by pressure or centrifugation.

When using solvent pairs one really resorts to methods of trial and error although a few basic principles as laid down by Hildebrand[50] are helpful in selecting proper conditions.[127] These rules, which follow immediately from the solubility equation:

$$\log N = \frac{-L}{R}\left(\frac{1}{T} - \frac{1}{Tm}\right)$$

are:

1. The solubility of a given solid is greater the higher the temperature.
2. A solid having a higher melting point is less soluble at a given temperature than one having a lower melting point.
3. If two solutes have equal melting points the one with the greater heat of fusion will be less soluble.

The common solvents in ordinary laboratory work are water, methyl alcohol, ethyl alcohol, acetic acid, acetone, ether, petroleum ether, chloroform, carbon tetrachloride, etc. The first five are recognized as powerful hydrolytic solvents and dissolve polar substances according to the alchemists' rule that "like dissolves like." Within any class the solvent power increases with the boiling point; thus ethyl alcohol (boiling point 78.1°C) dissolves twice as much naphthalene as methyl alcohol (boiling point 64.7°C). The addition of water to such solutions reduces the solubility for napthalene drastically, thus illustrating the use of solvent pairs in preparative work. Some commonly used pairs are:

methyl alcohol-H_2O	Ether-methyl alcohol
ethyl alcohol-H_2O	Ether-acetone
acetic acid-H_2O	Benzene-petroleum ether
acetone-H_2O	etc., etc.

Most ordinary systems crystallize more or less promptly once the proper supercooling or supersaturation is established. However, many cases are encountered (probably more frequently with large, unsymmetrical, organic molecules than with smaller, more symmetrical polar ones)[12,63,131,145] in which the crystallization may be reluctant to start and even continue at a very slow pace once initiated. In the first instance the immediate recourse is to induce crystal formation by means of scratching, agitating, or addition of seed material. This last may be a fragment of even impure material or isomorphous substance, if available. Spontaneous evaporation of a thin film of the mother liquor often provides the small amount of starting material required. Shock in a variety of forms, as discussed in a later section, may also prove effective in particular refractory cases. Stretching while being cooled has proven successful in the case of rubber and other plastic syrups. Patience is all that is required in other cases. "A turanose syrup, for example, was kept many years before it crystallized; when once crystalline it was readily recrystallized. Similarly, methyl-D-riboside crystallized after standing for nine months."[127]

Before resorting to these extreme measures the technician should investigate the prospect of favoring more prompt crystallization by means of lessened viscosity and/or further purification. The use of solvent pairs is especially useful in the former regard, particularly "poor" solvents which reduce solvation interactions. Impurities generally impede crystallization although there are cases[A-37,146] in which even traces are reputed to be beneficial.

Display Crystals

Interest in the preparation of good specimens of large single crystals is long lasting but until recently the art of producing them was practiced chiefly by the mineralogist and amateur scientist.[A-5,35,66,123] Many of the requirements for good growth from solutions had been perfected by the early years of the present century, as well as high temperature methods for more refractory materials and metals (viz. Verneuil, 1902). Large, single crystals of Rochelle salts were produced during the time of World War I[91]

Figure 5-3. 2× photographs of "Kandi" crystals produced by Pfeiffer and Langen.[99]

"Natural crystals often exceed in size those grown synthetically"; and, Barrer (Ref. A-37, p. 330) continues, "One reason why the largest natural crystals may exceed synthetic silicate crystals in size is undoubtedly the time factor, although in part this factor has been overcome by the use of mineralizers." The examples mentioned by Barrer are included in the following short list (Table 5-1) which has been assembled from various references to large natural and laboratory crystals.

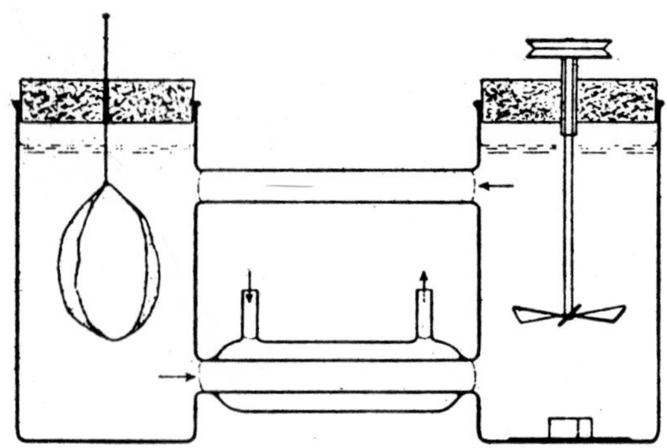

Figure 5-4. Crystallization apparatus. After Nacken.[87,127]

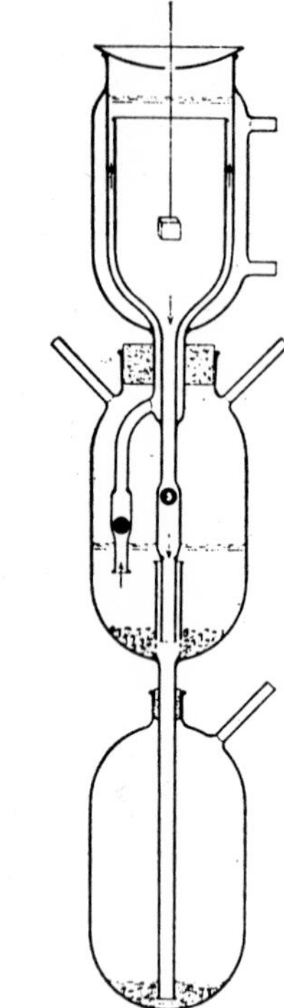

Figure 5-5. Crystallization apparatus. After Nacken.[87,127]

Fractional Crystallization

One of the oldest and still best methods of purification is a series of fractional crystallizations. The simplest, idealized system is a binary mixture which does not form solid solutions (i.e., Figure 5-9). This may be separated

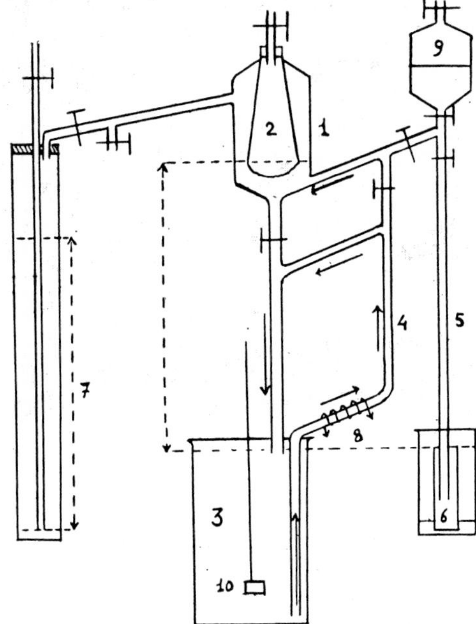

Figure 5-6. Thermal syphon.[22]

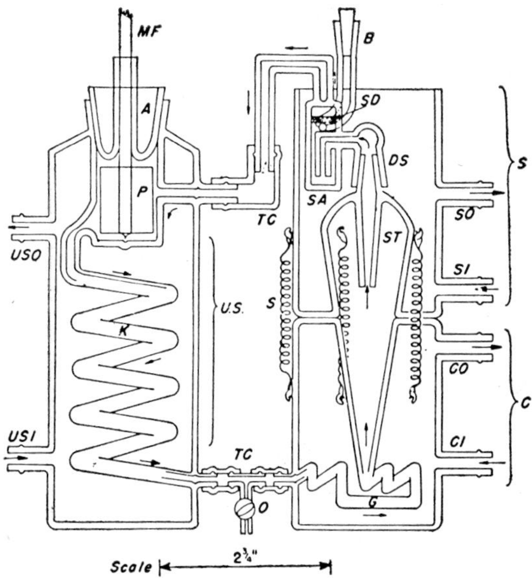

Figure 5-7. Miniature crystallization.[67]

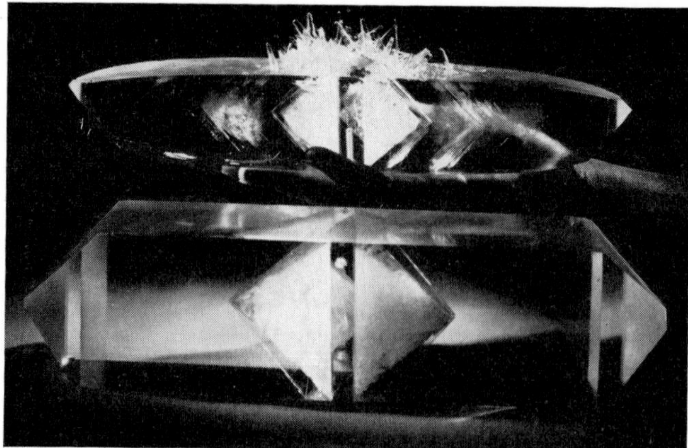

Figure 5-8. Large ADP crystal. (*Courtesy Bell Telephone Laboratories.*)

into pure A or B (according to which is in excess of the eutectical composition*) and eutectic by mere melting and subsequent cooling to a temperature just above the eutectic point. Repetition of this process eliminates the slight amount of undesired component which may have adhered mechanically to the solid which separates. The discarded fractions may be combined and reworked in a systematic way in order to increase the yield of the pure component. The simplest sequence of operations for this purpose is indicated in Figure 5-10; of which one of the fractions is the purified material and the other contains the impurity. When, as is customary, a solvent is utilized, the separation is in no wise different excepting the possibility of formation of the various binary and ternary eutectics. Otherwise, the solvent acts beneficially as an inert medium which facilitates the operations and collects the undesired portion.

If solid-solid solutions form it is still possible to obtain a highly purified material but in greatly reduced amount. The operations are represented schematically in the phase diagram of Figure 5-11. Melt or solution of composition X is cooled to temperature T at which solid of composition S separates and liquid L remains. Repeated melting of S and cooling to a lower temperature T_2 increases the purity of these crystals but sacrifices some yield. Further recrystallizations at progressively higher temperatures eventually lead to small quantities of B in very high purity. The mother liquors must be recycled in order to improve the recovery of B and some

* Even the eutectic composition may at times be upset due to the difference in rates of nucleation and growth of the separate components. Similarly, a solution simultaneously supersaturated with both borax and KCl will form only KCl crystals on rapid cooling. The borax crystallizes later at a much slower rate.

TABLE 5-1. LARGE CRYSTALS

Natural

Crystal	Size	Reference
Spodumene	40 ft long, >40 tons	A-37, p. 330
	47 ft long, >90 tons	109
Beryl	18′ × 4′ diameter, 19 tons	A-37
Mica leaves	12′ dia	A-37
Feldspars	4–5′	A-37
Asbestos fibers	15–25 cm	A-37
Quartz-Brazil	11½″ dia × 7½′ long, >5 tons	109, 68
Quartz	1000 lbs	75
Quartz	2.7 × 1.5 m	93
Topaz	154 lbs	68
Diamond-Cullinan	3,616 cts	—
"Blue" ice	Entire surface of large lakes	130

Synthetic

Crystal	Size	Reference
Fluorite—from melt	6″ diam	A-37
NaCl, KBr, etc—from melt (Stöber)	12″ diam × 6½″	A-37
W and Mo (Pintsch wires)	10–20 cm	90
Emerald (Chatham)	~1000 ct	5
Ruby (thermal)	700 ct	7
Quartz (hydrothermal)	2 lb	Chap. 6 Sect. 5
	1 lb	139b
Cd Selenide (melt)	17 g	49
Napthalene (melt)	2½′ long	71
$NH_4H_2PO_4$—from aqueous solution	10″ long × 1 side, 3–4 Kg 55 cm × 15 cm, 21 Kg	A-37, p. 316, 90
Rochelle salt	2 Kg	62
	4–5 Kg	102, 117
K alum*	240 lbs	36
$Li_2SO_4.H_2O$	12 × 5 × 4 cm	90
EDT	½ Kg (regular production)	90
Guanadine aluminum sulphate·$6H_2O$	234 g	102, 117

* A 90# alum crystal was exhibited at the 1940 World's Fair in New York City while a 9-lb. sugar crystal was on display at the San Francisco Fair at the same time.

very elaborate methods and combinations have been perfected to this end. These are discussed in detail and in quantitative aspect by Tipson[127,128] and others.[13,38,59,81] The reverse process of purification by fractional melting is also highly efficient[8] and has most recently been developed to a very high degree of perfection in the modification known as "zone melting."[97]

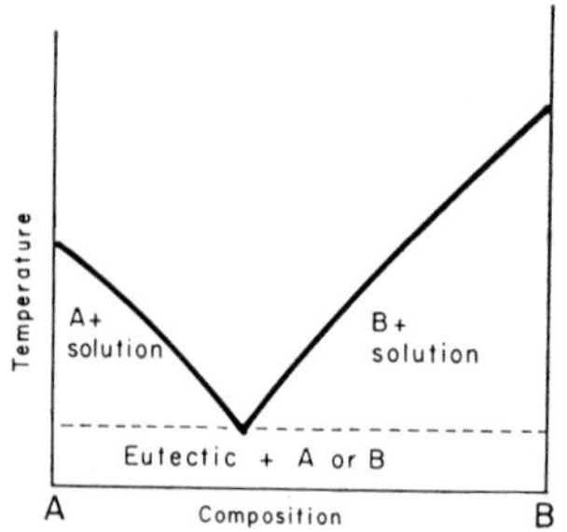

Figure 5-9. Simple eutectic diagram.

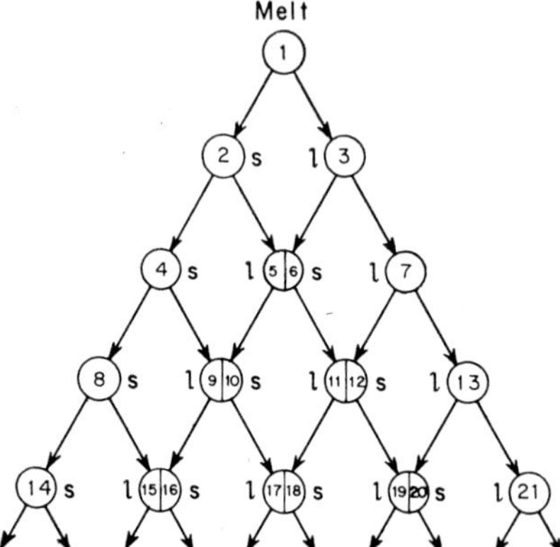

Figure 5-10. Fractional crystallization.

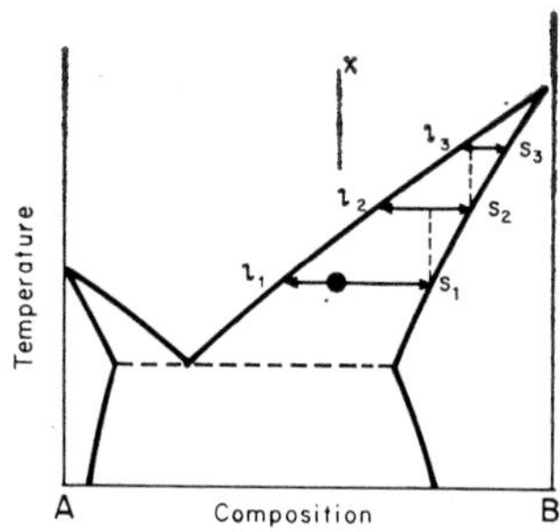

Figure 5-11. Phase diagram, s-s solution formation.

Extremely pure metals, of which boron is only a single example,[54] and other substances have been prepared in this way. Older applications of fractional crystallization and melting are the classical purification of radioactive material by the Curies, the isolation of the rare earths by C. James and, on the commercial scale, the sweating of paraffin waxes,[34,37,44,47,80] and winterizing of vegetable oils.[31,51,100]

Purity and Size

The impression still persists in some quarters that large crystals are purer than small crystals. This probably stems from the fact "that this was true to a large extent when tank crystallizers were used. In this case, the fine crystals were frequently mixed with the sludge at the bottom of the tank and were, therefore, not very pure, while the larger crystals were deposited on the suspension rods or on the sides of the tanks out of contact with the insoluble materials."[126] In old sugar cones there was a definite gradation of color, purity, and size along the length of the cone. However, with modern equipment and in ordinary laboratory practice no such generalization can be made, granted that separation of mother liquor and washing are adequate.

Impurities are influential on the development of crystals, most prominently on the habit of the separating solid. Such effects are most revealing about the mechanism of crystal growth and are discussed in great detail by Buckley, Wells,[143] and many others.[144] Insofar as the present question of the purity of a batch of crystals is concerned, impurities may be either entrapped in the growing crystals or may actually be incorporated into the lattice or adsorbed on the surface. In the first respect, mother liquor or suspended material may be included in the crystal, especially if the growth rate is high and as the crystals become larger. Under these circumstances the usual secondary features of growth, such as flaws, fissures, stratification lines, vicinal faces, bits, etc., increase and augment the opportunity for inclusions (such inclusions may serve to distinguish synthetic from natural gemstones).[4,45] On the other hand, if small crystals are produced the amount of adsorbed impurity may be large on account of the great surface. If the crystals are produced rapidly the concentration of impurity at the growing surface may be inordinately high as exhaustion of the mother liquor continues, resulting in occlusion of impurities on crystals. The distribution of sizes and the crystal density are also probably very important under these non-equilibrium conditions. Most likely, the only safe generalization based on experience that can be made is that the purest crystals will usually be obtained by slow growth from a gently stirred melt or solution.[111,114]

Some general conclusions regarding the production of refined sugar will serve to indicate the general fate of impurities[60] during the production of a product which is usually better than 99.9% pure. No special complications of double-compound formation, solid-solid solutions, etc. exist in this system.

1. The higher the purity of the mother liquor, the freer the crystals of impurities.
2. Separation of crystals and mother liquor must be as complete as possible, and washing must be thorough.
3. Small-grained sugars and those of crystals of uneven size are more difficult to free of mother liquor.
4. Washing in a centrifuge is neither complete nor uniform. Crystals and wash must be mingled and repurged. Partial dissolution of the outer shell of the crystal vastly improves this operation.

These workers demonstrated that over 50% of the ash and nitrogen components of the residual impurity was located in the outer 5% of the crystal, whereas less soluble components, color, and colloids were distributed more uniformly. This distribution probably differs in other compounds.[110] Tagged atoms should be most helpful in such studies; as, for instance, used by Booth[18] in the co-crystallization of foreign ions with NaCl (Figure 5-12).

Influence of Surface Active Agents, Promotors, etc.

The effects of surfactants on the crystallization process warrant special consideration since the interfacial tension occurs in the fundamental nucleation and growth equations as a power term and promises a very powerful effect on the course of crystallization. Limited reports on the drastic alteration of the crystallizing behaviors of metastable systems by addition of surface active materials emphasize the significance of the interfacial tension factor. Most investigations involve aqueous solutions and indicate

Figure 5-12. Auto-radiograph of a section through an octahedral crystal of NaCl containing co-crystallized ThB. Octahedral form produced by the presence of $BiCl_3$ in the solution. The section was cut parallel to the (001) face. The highest concentrations of lead are on the edges of the faces. Enlarged ×6.[18]

improvements when the surface tension of the liquid is lowered; although Packter[94] found that chelating organic acids, polyelectrolytes, and surface active agents markedly reduced the formation and growth of nuclei of soluble salts of Ag, Cu, Pb, and Al.

The Gibbs' adsorption equation

$$\Gamma = -\frac{1}{RT}\frac{d\sigma}{d\ln c} = -\frac{c}{RT}\frac{d\sigma}{dc}$$

where Γ is the surface excess, and $d\sigma/dc$ the interfacial tension-concentration coefficient, means that the surface concentration of a solution with a positive coefficient is less than the equivalent bulk concentration and, vice versa, greater when the coefficient is negative. The stability of a supersaturated solution in the first case may be considered as due to the dissolution of the embryos formed within the bulk solution in the adjacent undersaturated surface layer. This metastable condition will prevail until the concentration is increased to the point where this interface is just saturated. The bulk concentration at this point would correspond to the supersolubility limit. By the same token, a surfeit of embryos would exist in the surface layer of a concentrated surface active solution so that little or no supersaturation would be possible. Now, the interfacial tension of solid separating from solution, σ_{sl}, is not directly measurable, but is defined by the Young triangle of component forces as

$$\sigma_{gl} = \sigma_{sg} + \sigma_{sl}\cos\theta$$

Here the σ's are the interfacial tensions of the appropriate boundaries, solid-liquid-vapor, and θ the angle of wetting. Separating solid is usually completely wetted by the mother liquor, so $\theta = 0$. If the surface tension of the solid, σ_{sl}, remains fixed a definite correlation then exists between the interfacial tension, σ_{sl}, and surface tension of the liquid, σ_{lg}. Hence, surfactants should favor crystallization provided they are not adsorbed in the surface of the crystal, whereas surface inactive systems should resist prompt crystallization.

Only sparse experimental evidence bears directly upon this distinction. von Weimarn[138] reports that lowering the surface tension increases the number of crystallization centers, and Chatterji and Rastogi[23] find that surface active agents reduce the limit of supersaturation of KCl in aqueous solution to a marked extent. Gopal and Rastogi[42] point out that high interfacial tensions are necessary for supersaturation of liquids in liquid. These several Indian groups of workers have classified both aqueous and nonaqueous solutions according to the different degrees of supersaturation which they can sustain and it would be interesting to correlate these with the surface tension—concentration properties of the systems involved. Unfortunately, adequate information is not available for this purpose. The author[136c] has indicated that the nucleating behavior of sucrose syrups is in accord with this qualitative picture, and Tovbin[129] suggests a similar connection between surface activity and stability of supersaturated mixed salt solutions.

Milone and Cetini[83] find contrawise that surface active agents (i.e. Leonil-S, a sulfated ether alcohol) retard the growth and alter the habit of potassium alum as a result of being strongly adsorbed on certain faces.[28] This occurs only for those crystals formed in the surface of the solution, those appearing in the body of the solution being perfectly normal. They also report that such agents inhibit the precipitation of $CaCO_3$[A-37,48] as well as promoting deformed crystals. Semenchenko,[116] studying the crystallizing behavior of molten salts, found that smaller particles were obtained when the surface tension was diminished by the addition of second components. Sugihara and Newnam[122] find that detergents benefit the purification of organic compounds by crystallization from water, and traces of sodium oleate seem to improve the growth of quartz crystals.[140] Avakyan and Lashko[10] also note that surface active agents increase the rate of crystallization of the KCl-$K_2Cr_2O_7$ eutectic from solution but Michaels and Colville[82] observe just the opposite in the growth of adipic acid from solution. Horbe, Knacke, and Prescher[53] discuss the marked influence of capillary active substance on nucleation in industrial processes.

Thus, these rather few references from the literature suggest that alterations in surface activity by the addition of minute amounts of appropriate agents may effect great changes in the crystallizing behaviors of melts and solutions. The action of promoters, mineralizers, poisons,[112] retarders,[48] etc.[144] may be related phenomena, and the entire subject is of sufficient practical importance to warrant further intensive study.

Ultrasonic Irradiation, etc.

The sensitiveness of supersaturated systems to mechanical shock and disturbances of various kinds has been known for a long time. Buckley describes some early experiments on pressure, percussion, agitation, etc., and Matz devotes a section to a discussion of the influence of ultrasound, X-rays, radioactive rays, and electrical and magnetic fields. These and other forces generally have a beneficial effect upon crystallization in the sense of accelerating the nucleation and growth process. Some work on the influence of sonic and ultrasonic irradiation on the crystallization of sugar syrups has been carried out in the author's laboratory over the past several years and the following discussion summarizes these investigations.[136b]

The magnetostrictive devise employed is represented in Figure 5-13. The immediate effect of even momentary irradiation of supersaturated sucrose solutions is the formation of prolific grain. The number of crystals per unit volume grown upon this base is larger the higher the supersaturation of the treated syrup and also increases with the duration of irradiation in an autocatalytic way. Table 5-2 illustrates this first factor and Figure 5-14 the second. For the first case, supersaturated solutions of the designated concentrations were irradiated at 8KC and fixed power level for 30 seconds. The syrups stronger than 0 = 1.2 were then diluted to that concentration for the development of the seeds whose numbers, with respect to those produced in the corresponding controls, were determined by microscopic count. The results obtained are extremely variable but those represented are typical of solutions prepared in the usual way without any undue precautions to exclude fortuitous contamination with foreign nuclei. When such precautions are taken the number of seeds produced by irradiation is

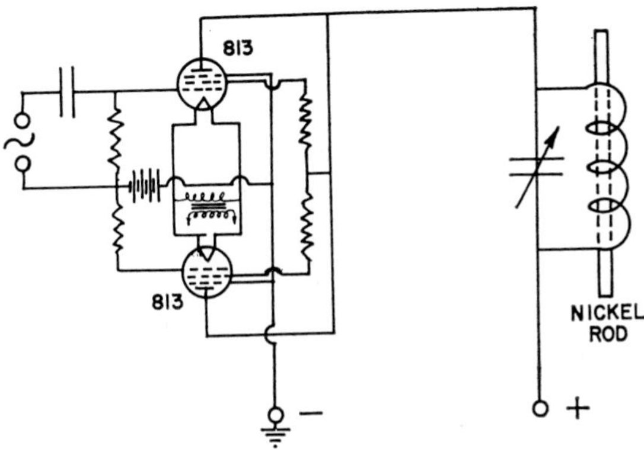

Figure 5-13. The electronic circuit consisted essentially of a standard oscillator with sufficient grid driving power for one or two stages of power amplification. The above circuit, for example, is typical of the final stage used to drive magnetostrictive transducers.

For barium titanate transducers less power was usually required, a single stage being ample for the smaller transducers. These were inductively coupled to the final tank circuit.

TABLE 5-2. EFFECT OF SUPERSATURATION ON SEED DENSITY. (IRRADIATION AT 8 KC FOR 30 SECS.)

0............	1.1	1.2	1.4	1.5	1.75	2.0	2.2
Relative seed density.....	1.0	2.0	3.5	3.0	5.5	7.0	12

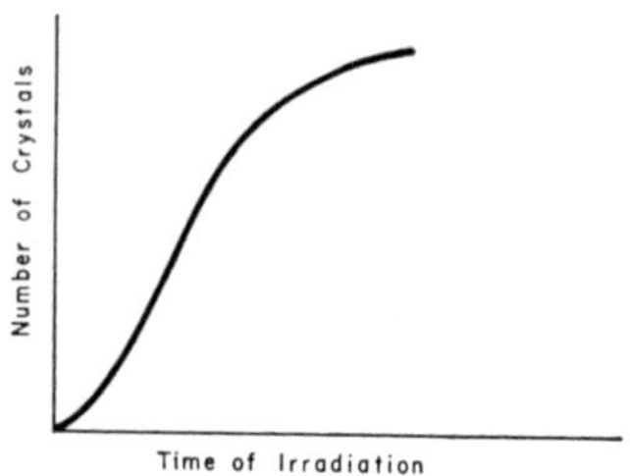

Figure 5-14. Autocatalytic nature of irradiation.

generally less than before, and in a few instances no different than the controls. This suggests the involvement of a heterogeneous mechanism rather than the spontaneous generation of additional nuclei by the high energy sound field itself.

Figure 5-14 is schematic only, since these results are extremely variable while yet following the trend indicated. The limiting effect of prolonged irradiation suggests that the strong attriting power of the disturbance is chiefly effective on the newly deposited growth and this diminishes as the syrup becomes exhausted. The size distribution of the crystals suffers greatly as irradiation proceeds since nucleation and growth occur simultaneously all the while.

The foregoing results were realized at 8 KC, which is approximately midway in the effective decimal range of 1–100 KC. Within these limits extremely high power levels of at least approximately 2 sonic watts/cm^2 are necessary (Figure 5-15). The threshold level of about 2 watts/cm^2 concurs with the onset of cavitation although this is not always evident. Viscosity appears to have a significant influence here.

The variations of these observations, the strong influence of size, shape, and arrangement of container, and transducer, the influence of age, treatment, and condition of the solution treated, and the further multiplication of grain in the presence of added foreign bodies during irradiation all suggest a dispersive or heterogeneous, rather than an agglomerating or homogeneous mode of action of the sound waves. Since an appropriate base is almost always present in sugar syrups as ordinarily prepared (A-37, p. 112), sonic irradiation provides a convenient method for rapidly multiplying growth centers from this source. And, since this marked increase is almost instantaneous, it provides a means of establishing a high density of embryos upon which it is possible to build a crystal crop of uniform size. This, then, is the advantage which graining by sound offers for industrial exploitation. In laboratory runs, uniformity grades of 20%* have been realized as an improvement over the 25–30% usual in plant operation.

* Dispersion coefficient of the normal Gaussian distribution curve.

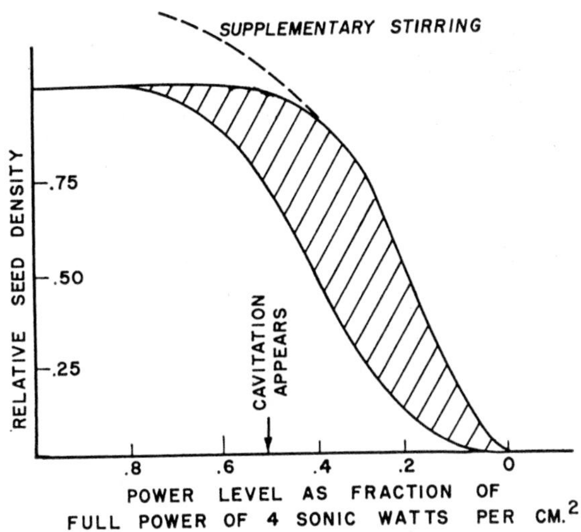

Figure 5-15. Critical power level.[136b]

The question remains, does sonic and ultrasonic irradiation influence the rate of growth of an established crystal? There are many positive answers in the literature but it is difficult to separate the real effect from the apparent. In the case of sugar solutions this was attempted by fastening the crystal directly on the transducer. In a typical experiment, such as illustrated in Figure 5-16, regular growth of a well-formed crystal was established before oscillating at the frequency of the magnetostrictive bar to which it was cemented. After a period of measurable growth the normal rate was again assured before resuming stimulated growth. In the particular case illustrated this was resumed at a level above the critical. Fortunately, the crystal was not loosened but false grain appeared. This is reflected in the diminished growth rate. The small increase observed in this particular run, and others under a wide variety of conditions and different frequencies well into the ultrasonic range, are no more than equivalent to rotating the crystal in the solution at about 200 rpm. The principal effect of irradiation is thus on the nucleation process rather than on the growth.

CRYSTALLIZATION AS A UNIT OPERATION

The practice of crystallization has developed very largely as an art; guided, until recently,[2,11,21,41,61,69,77,86,104,106] by the application of only elementary crystallization theory. Many of the empirical regulations exercised in industrial crystallizations have their bases in the Ostwald-Miers supersolubility concept. For practical purposes this sometimes poorly defined metastable limit dictates the concentration above which crystals

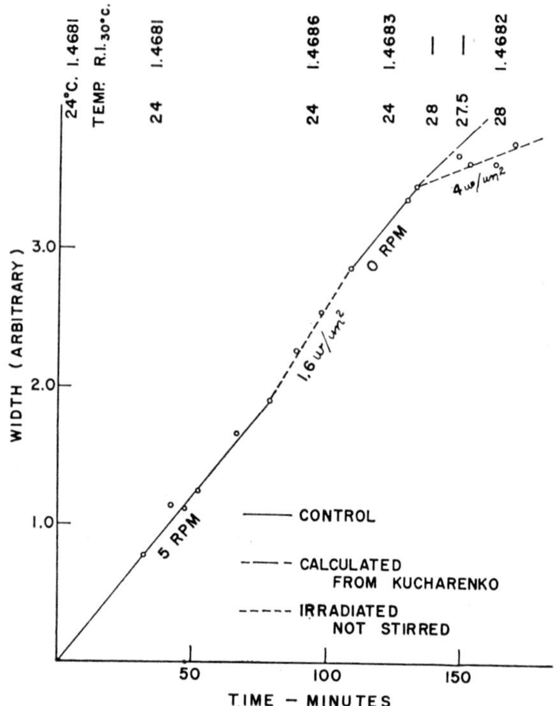

Figure 5-16. Growth rate under irradiation at 8 kc.[136b]

form, as distinct from a lower concentration range within which they merely grow. The metastable limit should not be exceeded if inordinate crystal densities are to be avoided. In some cases there exists an intermediate zone of concentration within which crystals already present appear to catalyze the formation of additional centers of growth, but in whose absence no nuclei at all appear. It is not always clear whether the observed effects in this region are truly catalytic, the result of attrition of new growth, or a manifestation of only a slowly accruing nucleation mechanism.

The sugar boiler exploits all three regions of the supersaturated field in the practice of his art. In the oldest and still occasionally used technic of "boiling to grain" he concentrates the syrup rapidly until the labile zone is attained. Here, a prolific number of nuclei form spontaneously, after which the concentration is immediately dropped by dilution with fresh undersaturated syrup so that the crystals grow to the desired size. If the initial concentration is somewhat less and within the intermediate zone of supersaturation, the crystallizing base may be established by "shocking." For this purpose a very small amount of seed is introduced. This multiplies rapidly to give the necessary footings for further growth at a lower concentration. Both these methods of graining entail a degree of uncertainty since both function at extremely high concentrations where nucleation is very sensitive to extraneous inoculation, condition of the solution, size, shape, and arrangement of the crystallizing vessel, etc. The surest and most widely used procedure in most of the sugar industry is that of full pan seeding. In this case the concentration of the syrup never exceeds that of the metastable zone. The nuclei required for growth are added in the form of seed crystals whose form, amount, etc. have been determined by trial.

The same principles apply in other industries although the separate regions of crystallization are not always so pronounced, nor is the growth rate in most cases so slow.[124]

In addition to the supersolubility principle governing good crystallization practice, McCabe prescribes a number of rules which have much evidence in their favor. Jeremiassen and Svanoe[56] enumerate four factors for controlled crystallization, as follows:

1. Supersaturation must not exceed certain limits to avoid crystallization on wall and new nucleation.
2. Large crystal area must be provided, and its efficient utilization secured by constant exposure to fresh solution. This is necessary to prevent excessive supersaturation and allow high rate of production.
3. Constant motion is necessary to prevent agglomeration, but not too violent to avoid new crystals by attrition.
4. Rate of formation of new nuclei should equal rate of removal.

Both growth rate and nucleation rate generally increase with decreasing temperature but the former not as rapidly as the latter. Tammann exposed the same relative order by directing attention to the fact that his nucleation frequencies curves were generally steeper and more abrupt than the growth curves of the same material. This suggests that the initial formation of nuclei is a more difficult process than the subsequent growth to monocrystals. In modern terms, the entropy of activation for this first stage is much greater than the following extension since it involves the production of order in three dimensions in place of deposition in an already ordered crystal surface. Ubbelohde,[132] Turnbull,[115] Dunning,[33] and others have already applied some of these modern crystallization theories in some cases but there still remains much to be done in unifying theory and practice in this regard.[A-37,11b,76,126]

Equipment

The classification, description, and discussion of crystallization equipment have been considered by a number of writers. Badger and McCabe,[11b] for instance, classify crystallization equipment in the following simple way:

1. Batch or discontinuous apparatus
   (a) Atmospheric cooling, no stirring
   (b) Artificial cooling, with stirring
2. Continuous apparatus
   (a) Swenson-Walker
   (b) Wulff-Bock
3. Vacuum Crystallizers

These various crystallizers may also be grouped as either classifying or non-classifying, the former operating so that crystals are retained in the unit until they reach a minimum size before discharge. The supersaturation necessary for growth is produced by:

1. Cooling without evaporation
   (a) Natural cooling
   (b) Forced cooling by water or brine
2. Evaporation without cooling
3. Adiabatic evaporation and cooling

This scheme of classification has been extended, elaborated and modified by other writers.[A-4,A-20,A-21,74,118,126] Schoen[118] points out that many of the recent developments are recorded exclusively in patent issues.

Batch Process—Atmospheric Cooling. This was formerly a very common method of producing crystals and which persists in only a few instances such as grainer salt, salt by solar evaporation, and the purification of laboratory chemicals by recrystallization. The general procedure in tank crystallization consists in the preparation of a hot, almost saturated, solution which is then placed in appropriate vessels and allowed to cool naturally. A mass of interlocking crystals of a wide variety of sizes forms slowly. The crop of crystals is apt to be impure due to occluded mother liquor and sludge. When the crystallization is complete the mother liquor is drained off and the crystals harvested. No special control is practiced in this method and excessive labor and floor space are required for quantity production.

Batch Process—Artifical Cooling. Considerable improvement and increased capacity are accomplished by means of controlled cooling and constant agitation. Water or air are used almost universally for the first purpose. Rapid cooling usually causes a greater crystal density and corresponding smaller size. Aggregation is also lessened and the size distribution is more uniform. Both nucleation and growth tend to be aggravated at the cooling surface and if the crystals adhere thereto the rate of heat transfer may suffer accordingly. Proper agitation and controlled cooling schedules tend to minimize these effects.

Figures 5-17 and 5-18 illustrate a Lafeuille rotary crystallizer such as

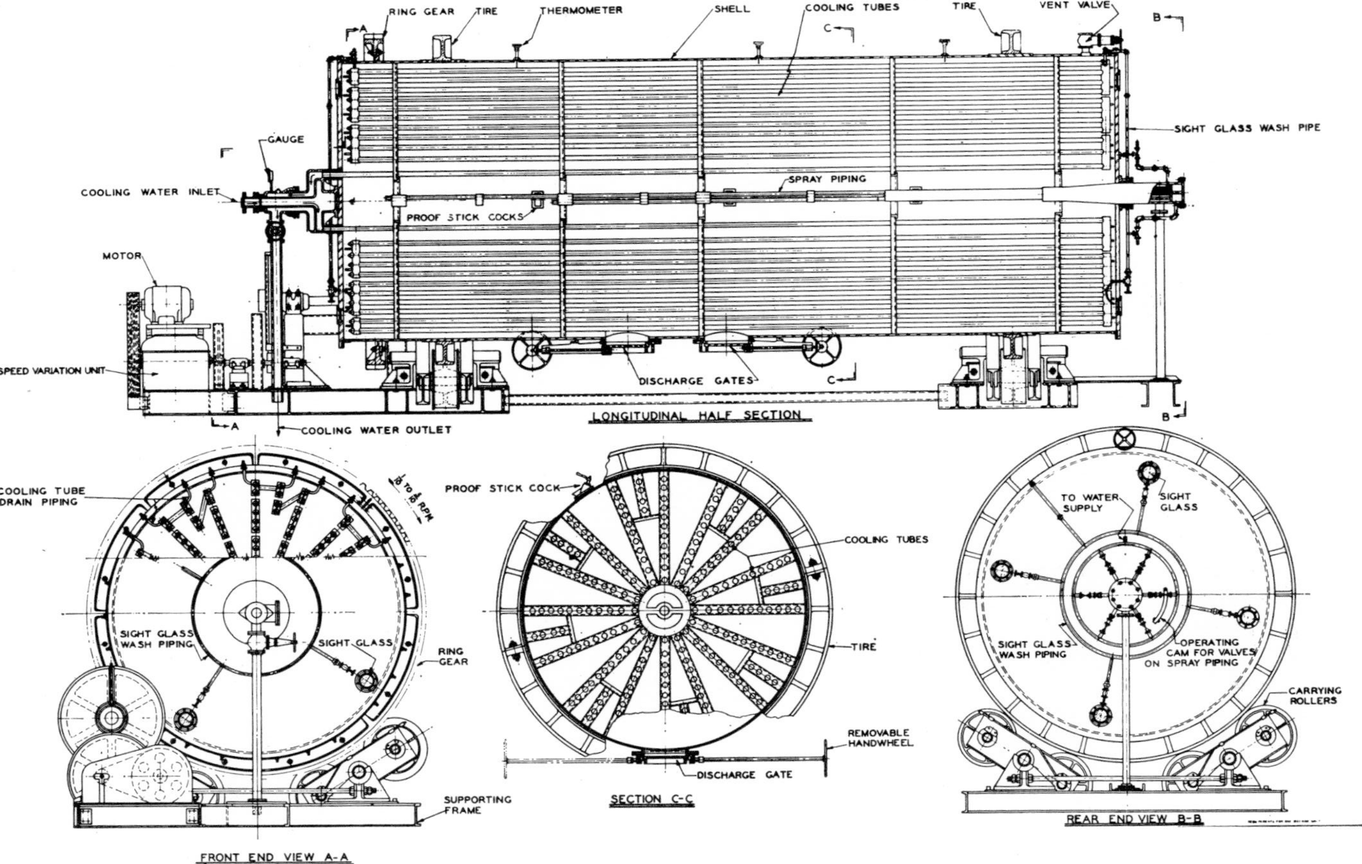

Figure 5-17. Lafeuille crystallizer. (*Courtesy of the Dorr Co.*)

Figure 5-18. Lafeuille crystallizer. (*Courtesy of the Dorr Co.*)

widely used in finishing the crystallization of low-grade cane and beet sugars. Agitation is realized by rotating the entire machine thereby forcing the solution to cascade through the radial banks of cooling coils. Cooling water circulates through these coils in order to promote uniform cooling and optimum crystallization. The relatively large ratio of area to volume, about 2 sq ft per cu ft, is a decided improvement over jacketed vessels and permits rapid crystallization. The similar double-pipe,[113] Werkspoor,[129] and other units may be operated in a continuous batch manner.[17]

The obvious advantage of continuous crystallization found early expression in the Wulff-Bock, Swenson-Walker, and similar designs. The Wulff-Bock crystallizer[43] consists of a slightly inclined trough which rocks from side to side, while baffles direct the flow of slurry in an irregular path along the length of the unit. Cooling is accomplished by means of natural air convection which can be accelerated by forced draft. This apparatus is useful for growing large, uniform crystals.

The Swenson-Walker crystallizer consists essentially of a long, half-round trough cooled by water or brine in an outer jacket and fitted with a low-speed, spiral agitator. The purpose of this agitation is not only to improve the heat transfer and assist the motion of the slurry along the trough but also to prevent accumulation of crystals on the bottom and to cause them to shower through the solution. This leads to better shape, size, and distribution of sizes. Units, 10 feet long by 2 feet wide, are a common standard section and these may be coupled end to end to furnish required capacity. Figure 5-19 depicts such a unit. The Swenson-Walker crystallizer can be used either as a batch or continuous machine but is generally operated in a countercurrent continuous manner.

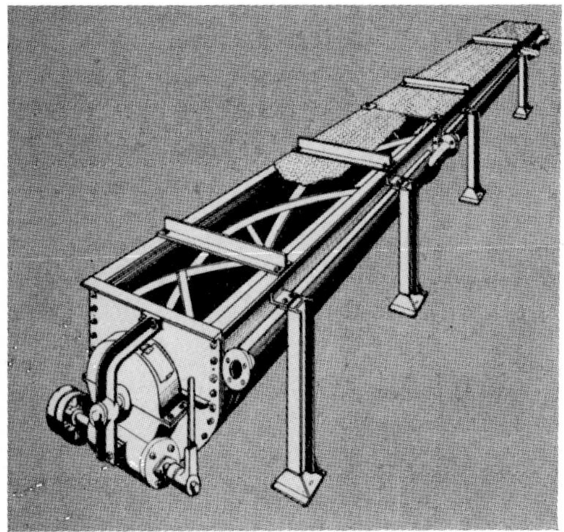

Figure 5-19. Swenson-Walker crystallizer.

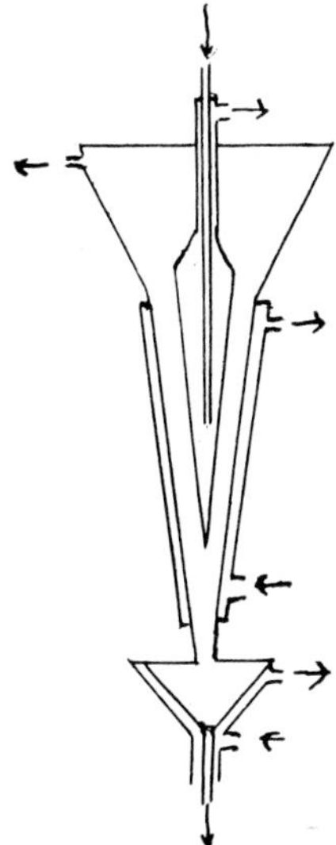

Figure 5-20. Howard crystallizer.

The Howard crystallizer (Figure 5-20) is a conical vessel through which solution is circulated upwards from the narrow end. Both external and internal cooling promote crystallization. This proceeds until the large crystals sink, against the upward convection, into a collecting section. The

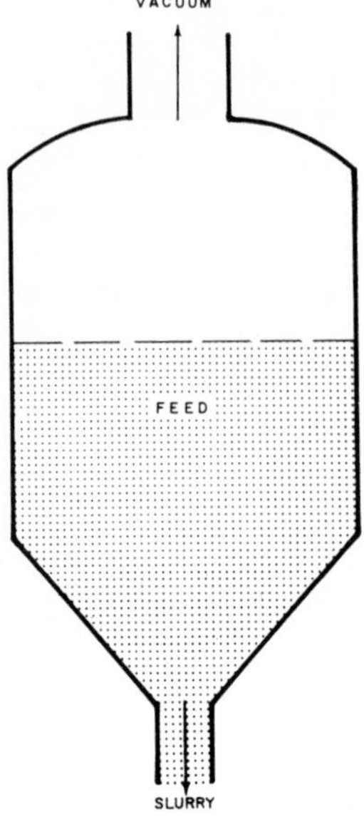

Figure 5-21. Vacuum crystallizer.

flow rate is low so that smaller crystals are not carried over in the overflow. The effluent is repurified if necessary, concentrated and re-cycled.

Vacuum Crystallizers

Crystallizing under vacuum immediately provides two valuable features: 1) The attendant evaporation produces necessary supersaturation; and 2) This supersaturation is augmented when the process is conducted adiabatically so that the temperature of the solution falls.* Both aspects are incorporated in the wide variety of designs of vacuum evaporators that are in operation in many industries.

In principle, vacuum is maintained in the cone-shaped main body (Figures 5-21 and 5-22) by means of a steam ejector or vacuum pump. Feed, usually as preconcentrated solution, enters and flashes into vapor, thus agitating the solution and keeping the crystals in suspension. This natural agitation may be supplemented by mechanical stirring. The crystals grow until they settle and are removed by means of a vapor lock pump or by a barometric leg (Figure 5-23). In batch-wise operation the entire slurry ("massecuite" or "fillmass" in sugar parlance) is discharged to centrifugals or other separating machines. In another extreme mode of operating the unit may be operated as a spray crystallizer,[A-11] in which case provision

* Lower temperatures are also desirable in processing heat-sensitive materials.

Figure 5-22. Vacuum crystallizer. (*Courtesy Honolulu Iron Works Co.*)

must be made for removing an extremely thick or "tight" mass of crystals and mother liquor.

The evaporator-crystallizer incorporates a heater in the circulating system, as illustrated in Figures 5-24 and 5-25, so as to assist the concentration by means of removal of solvent. The cooling crystallizer[128] (Figure 5-26) produces the necessary supersaturation by cooling the circulating liquor. These crystallizers all operate within the metastable zone and new nuclei to replace those withdrawn in the product are supplied by inoculation and/or impact and attrition. Evaporation and crystal building occur simultaneously within one body in the conventional vacuum crystallizer but are carried out in separate parts in the "Krystal," Jeremiassen" or "Oslo" designs. These arrangements each have their special advantages and disadvantages and are discussed in detail by Seavoy and Caldwell,[113] and Svanoe.[128] McCabe[76] visualizes the condition within a continuous vacuum crystallizer as follows:

> "Assume that the agitation and circulation in such a crystallizer are adequate to ensure homogenous conditions throughout the crystallizing liquid. Assume also that the crystallizer is fed constantly with solution of a given concentration and temperature and that the pressure in the crystallizer is constant.
>
> "Under steady-state conditions there must be a definite and constant

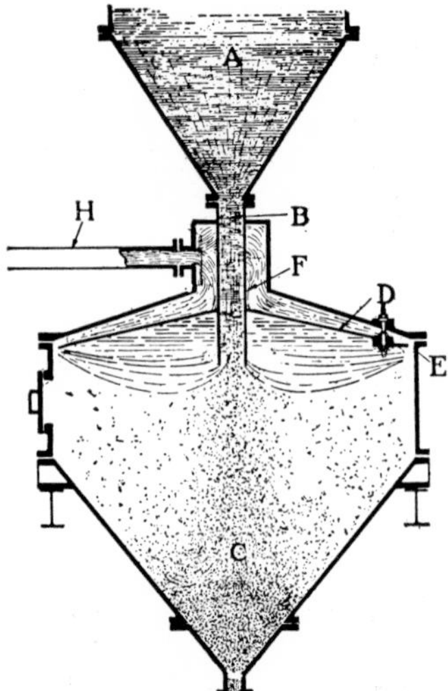

Figure 5-23. Continuous salt filter. The salt crystals are formed in the bottom of the evaporator body "A." The cone bottom of the evaporator is connected to the discharge pipe "B" through which the mixture of salt and brine is drawn into the jacketed separator "C." The crystals settle to the bottom. The mother liquor rises slowly and flows through the annular space "E," controlled by the distributing plate "D." The clear liquid is withdrawn through "H" by a centrifugal pump, thus producing a positive circulation in the separator and withdrawal from the evaporator. (*Courtesy Buflovak Equipment Co.*)

number of crystals in the crystallizer at all times. These crystals will have a definite size distribution and a steady state is reached if the rate of formation and growth does not change with time. Assume also that the operation of the crystallizer is such that a crystal will not be able to leave the crystallizer until it has reached a definite size. Under steady-state conditions the entering solution immediately flashes to equilibrium temperature. The flash results in a certain amount of evaporation and considerable cooling which develops a definite supersolubility in the solution. The solution is mixed quickly with the bulk of the solution in the crystallizer and a definite supersaturation can be assumed to exist in the bulk of the liquid. It is the relatively high supersaturation contributed by the flashed solution that maintains the supersaturation at a definite average value in competition with the efforts of the crystals to destroy the supersaturation. If the flashed solution is blended rapidly enough with the liquor in the crystallizer it will not form new nuclei previous to its incorporation with the bulk of the liquid. Since at all times there is a definite number of crystals of a definite size range, and also a definite supersaturation in the solution, there will be a definite rate of

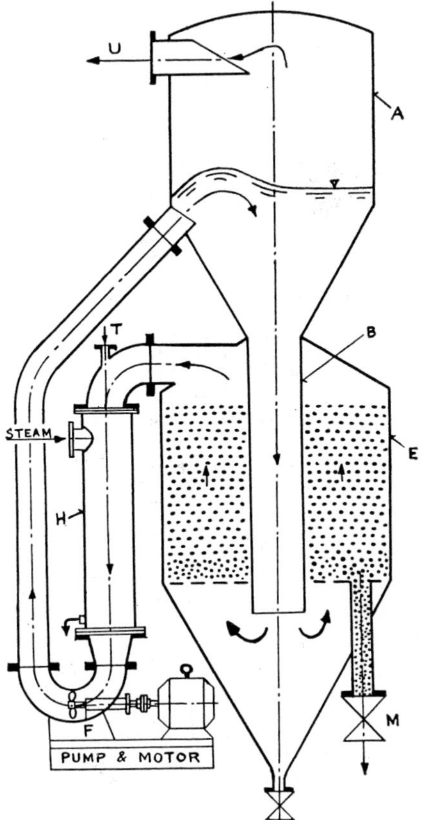

Figure 5-24. Evaporator-crystallizer.[121]

formation. Since there will be formed a constant number of crystals per unit time, the rate of formation of crystals must be equal to the rate at which crystals are withdrawn from the crystallizer. The rate of nucleation must adjust itself in such a manner that it equals the number of crystals withdrawn per unit time. Also, the rate of growth must adjust itself in such a manner that the crystals formed will grow to the desired size in the time available for their growth. If the rate curves are regular, there is only one supersaturation that will give both a correct rate of formation and a correct rate of growth. For larger crystals growth rate rather than nucleation rate must be emphasized, and a low supersaturation will exist in the crystallizer. For smaller crystals nucleation will increase relative to growth, and larger supersaturation will be necessary. Rate of withdrawal (assuming that adequate flashing and vapor libera-

Figure 5-25. Crystal crystallizer. (*Courtesy Struthers Wells Corporation.*)

tion can be maintained) controls all these factors automatically. If the rate of withdrawal from the crystallizer is slow the crystals withdrawn will be large. The capacity of the crystallizer will decrease, of course, as the size of the crystals is increased."

The type of equipment to be used in a crystallization process depends primarily upon the solubility characteristic of the system to be processed. Table 5-3 may serve as a preliminary guide in the selection of equipment.

Figure 5-27 is, incidentally, a sketch from the same publication from which this table is taken. Other companies[24] offer similar pilot-plant units.[66] The following list, after Thompson[126] and the Chemical Engineering Catalog, partially indicates a few suppliers of commercial crystallizing equipment.

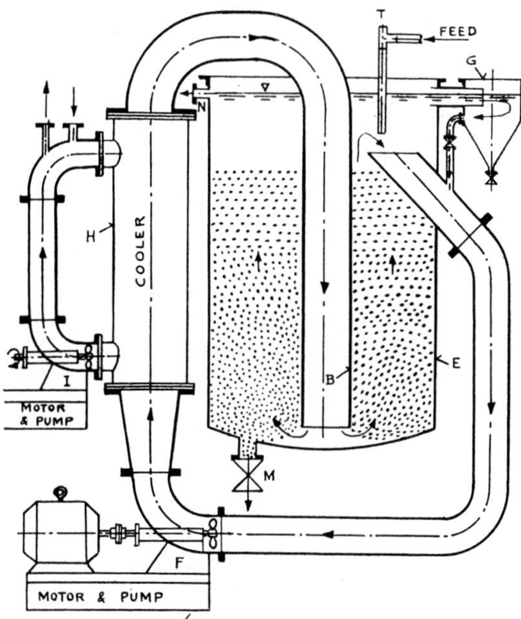

Figure 5-26. Cooling crystallizer.[121]

Size Distribution

The compatability of the distribution of sizes of crystals observed in a spontaneously generated crop with modern theories of nucleation and growth has already been indicated (Chap. 4, Ref. 140, 141, 166). The significance of this variation in the sizes of crystals for the design and operation of crystallizing units and for packaging and storing requirements will be considered in the present section. McCabe's ΔL law[77] is of inestimable value in this regard. It states that all geometrically similar crystals of the same material suspended in the same solution grow at the same rate if the growth is measured as the increase in length of geometrically corresponding distances on all the crystals. When no new crystals are produced it is then possible to calculate the screen analysis of the product from that of the seed material since, ideally, the size distribution does not change during growth in the metastable zone.[72] The computation is performed most conveniently in a graphical way.

If D is the size opening of a particle screen and W the weight of the material retained by this screen,

$$W = f(D)$$

where f is some function expressed by the plot in Figure 5-28. If α is the

TABLE 5-3. SELECTION OF CRYSTALLIZERS

Effect of Temperature Rise on Solubility in Water	Equipment to be Used	Example
I. Small increase in solubility	Evaporator-crystallizer (Salting-out evaporator)	Sodium chloride
II. Decrease in solubility (Inverted solubility)	Modified evaporator-crystallizer	Anhydrous Sodium sulfate Gypsum Iron sulfate Monohydrate
III. Substantial increase in solubility	A. Vacuum crystallizer B. Water or brine cooling crystallizer	Potassium alum Glauber salt Copperas Potassium nitrate
IV. Moderate increase in solubility	Modified vacuum or evaporator-crystallizer	Potassium carbonate Sodium Nitrate Potassium chloride

ratio of any particular dimension of the crystals, L, to the screen size, D,

$$\alpha \Delta D = \alpha(D_2 - D_1) = \Delta L$$

D_1 is the screen size of a particular seed and D_2 its size after complete development, while ΔL is the actual linear increase. This is the same for all crystals regardless of size since the total growth depends exclusively on the exhaustion of supersaturated solution. As seed crystals grow they will be retained between successively larger screen sizes, their number being related to the weight fraction by

$$dN = \frac{dW}{\rho b L^3} = \frac{dW}{\rho \alpha^3 b D^3}$$

where ρ is the density and b a geometric factor. The total number of crystals too large to pass through a screen of size D is

$$N = \frac{1}{\rho \alpha^3 b} \int_0^W \frac{dW}{D^3}$$

when N^1 is defined as $N^1 = a^3 \, b \, N$

$$N^1 = \frac{1}{\rho} \int_0^W \frac{dW}{D^3}$$

and

$$dN^1 = \frac{dW}{\rho D^3}$$

If no additional centers of growth are formed during the crystallization,

$$dN_s^1 = dN_p^1$$

where s and p refer to seed and product respectively, so that

$$\frac{dW_s}{D_s^3} = \frac{dW_p}{(D_s + \Delta D)^3}$$

TABLE 5-4. TYPES AND MANUFACTURERS OF CRYSTALLIZERS[24,126]

Type	Modification	Manufacturer*
Cooling	Tank	16
	Agitated batch	1, 2, 5, 9, 11, 16
	Continuous cooling (Swenson-Walker)	3, 5, 6, 7, 9, 10
	Double-pipe	3, 5, 12, 13, 14
	Dual-worm crystallizer	13
	Wulff-Bock	18
	Lafeuille rotary	4
	Buflovak grainer	3
Evaporator	Crystallizing evaporator	3, 8, 9, 15, 16, 17
Vacuum	Batch	1, 3, 5, 9, 16
	Continuous	1, 3, 5, 9, 16
Circulation	Cooling—krystal	8
	Evaporator—krystal	8
	Vacuum—krystal	8
	Crystallizing evaporator	15
	Classifying crystallizer	9
Salting Out		16

* Manufacturers:

1. Acme Coppersmithing & Machine Co., Oreland, Pa.
2. Frank L. Allen, Inc., New York 5, N. Y.
3. Buflovak Equipment Division of Blaw-Knox Co., Buffalo 11, N.Y.
4. The Dorr Co., New York 22, N.Y.
5. Industrial Process Engineers, Newark 5, New Jersey.
6. L. O. Koven & Brother Co., Jersey City 7, N.J.
7. The Patterson Foundry and Machine Co., East Liverpool, Ohio.
8. Struthers-Wells Corp., Warren, Pa.
9. Swenson Evaporator Co., Division of Whitling Corp., Harvey, Ill.
10. M. H. Treadwell Co., Inc., New York 6, N. Y.
11. Turl Iron and Car Co., Inc., New York 7, N. Y.
12. Henry Vogt Machine Co., Louisville 10, Ky.
13. Welding Engineers Inc., Norristown, Pa.
14. Worthington Pump & Machinery Corp., Harrison, N. J.
15. Zaremba Co., Buffalo 2, N. Y.
16. Many equipment manufacturers will construct these crystallizers to customer's specifications.
17. Many evaporator manufacturers will construct these crystallizers.
18. Not manufactured in U. S. A.

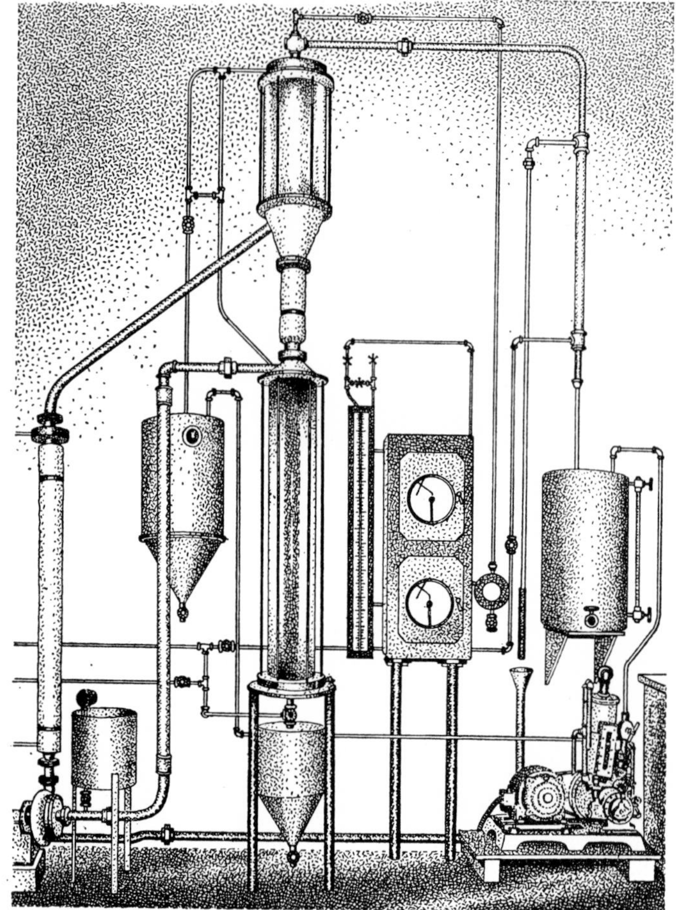

Figure 5-27. Struthers Wells Laboratory crystallizer unit.[121]

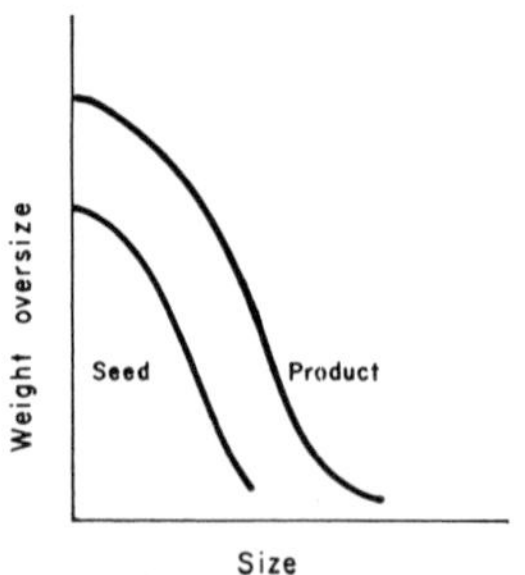

Figure 5-28. Screen analysis.

and

$$W_p = \int_0^{W_s} \left(1 + \frac{\Delta D}{D_s}\right)^3 dW_s$$

Since ΔD is independent of D_s and W_s, the value of W_p can be obtained by graphical integration inasmuch as the screen analysis of the seeds provides a relationship between D_s and W_s. This is the most convenient practical way of predicting the screen analysis of the product from that of the seed and is expounded in detail by McCabe in his various papers.[68 to 70]

Considerable attention has been directed to the analytical relationship between W and D.[A-11,30,104,107,127,135] When a metastable system is allowed to adjust itself spontaneously it may be expected that the necessary nuclei and the resultant crop of crystals should be distributed according to chance. In this case the Gauss or normal arithmetic probability equation describes the frequency of occurrence, n, of particle of diameter, x:

$$n = \frac{\sum n}{2\pi\sigma} \exp \frac{-(x - M)^2}{2\sigma^2}$$

$\sum n$ is the total number of observations and M the arithmetic mean of the diameters. M can be regarded as a constant which fixes the position of the frequency-size curve in appropriate linear coordinates, and σ is the standard deviation or a measure of the slope of the curve. It is numerically equal to the difference between the 84.13 or 15.87 % of x and the 50 % value.

Most commercial granulated sugars are produced by methods of graining which are equivalent to a complete random assortment of nuclei sizes, and the distribution is accordingly Gaussian in type.[105,136b] Table 5-5 and Figures 5-28 and 5-29 illustrate the details of only one particular case of the pattern which is generally observed with this substance.[57,88,98] When logarithmic coordinates are used in place of Cartesian values the log normal distribution curve results:

$$n = \frac{\sum n}{\log O_g \sqrt{2\pi}} \exp \frac{-(\log x - \log M_g)^2}{2 \log^2 O_g}$$

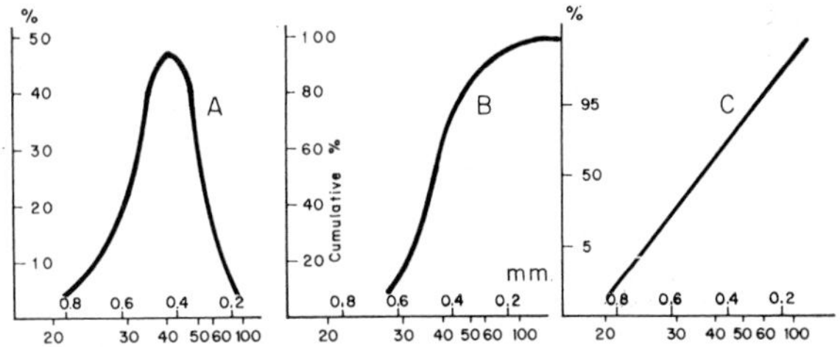

Figure 5-29. Graphical representation of screen analysis of Table 5-5.

TABLE 5-5. TYPICAL SCREEN ANALYSIS OF A GRANULATED SUGAR

Size-mesh	% On Screen	Cumulative %
20	0.3	0.3
30	16.7	17.0
40	48.0	65.0
50	24.0	89.0
60	6.0	95.0
70	2.5	97.5
80	1.0	98.5
100	1.0	99.5

where M_g is now the geometric mean of the values of x, and O_g is the geometric standard deviation. M_g is the value of x at the 50% level, and

$$\sigma = \frac{x \text{ at } 84.13\%}{x \text{ at } 50\%} = \frac{x \text{ at } 50\%}{x \text{ at } 15.87\%}$$

This distribution has been found to be much more general than the normal one and has been applied in great detail by Loveland and Trivelli[72] and by Kottler.[65] One of its chief properties is that, when applicable, it is valid for both weight and count, and both plot as parallel lines on log probability paper. The conversion from number by count (unprimed) to frequency by weight (primed) is given by:[9]

$$\log \frac{Mg}{M'g} = -6.097 \log^2 Og$$

The Rosin-Rammler empirical equation

$$R = 100 \exp -\left(\frac{x}{\bar{x}}\right)^b$$

has been used to represent the variation of sizes of NaCl crystals and a few others[A-11] but is more widely applicable in other directions.

Agglomeration, Recrystallization, and Caking

Uncontrolled development of a crop of crystals often results in a variegated collection amongst which may be identified individuals, loose as well as consolidated clusters of individuals, and distinct couplets which very clearly result from the continued growth of one crystal into another. This diversity of forms usually increases with the crystal population and often appears to be aggravated at certain points particularly when the growth occurs in an undisturbed fashion. The situation also changes with time according to conditions. Figure 5-30 only hints at these three general varieties as commonly observed in the spontaneous crystallization of sugar

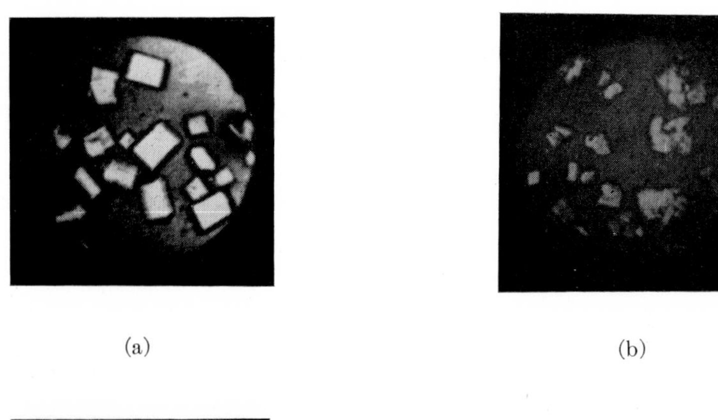

(a) (b)

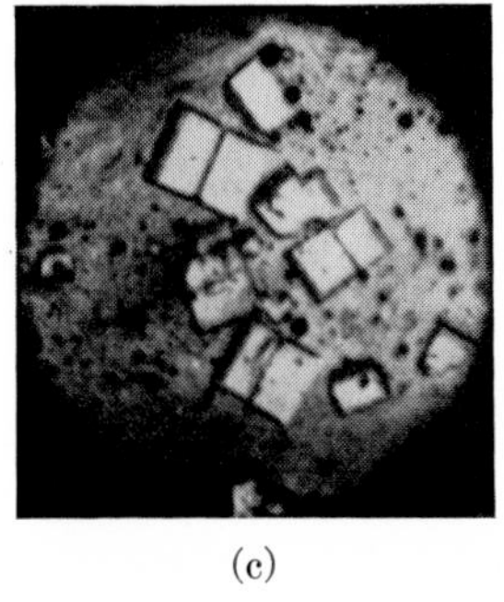

(c)

Figure 5-30. Sugar crystals. (a) Individuals, from gently stirred syrup. (b) Conglomerates, from unstirred syrup. (c) Twins, from impure syrup.

syrups. The crystals pictured in Figure (a) and (b) were grown from the same slightly supersaturated pure sugar solution, the former while the solution was gently agitated, the latter when formed spontaneously upon an undisturbed microscope slide. Figure (c) represents crystals grown from cane sugar syrup whose unknown composition apparently stimulated the production of almost all twinned crystals.

Obviously these variations are the result of interaction between growing crystals. The formations probably originated at the very beginning of crystallization and continued throughout the development of the mass of crystals. At the same time, and even continuing after the nutrient liquor is exhausted, various crystallites recrystallize, forming modified arrangements, or amplifying existing single entities.[A-1,46] This aging process has been studied in great detail by the chemist in the case of ordinary precipitation (*vide infra*), and by the petrologist[101] and the metallurgist. It is also a most important factor in the development of the structure of ceramics and building materials, to mention only one more of many other theoretical and practical applications.

Considerable looseness exists in the use of terms designating mechanically consolidated crystals. Glomerate, agglomerate and conglomerate are all employed somewhat indiscriminately to describe the more or less compactly clustered groups of crystals that are observed. The mineralogist, however, uses the term conglomerate to infer some degree of uniformity in kind or size, in contradistinction to agglomerate for heterogeneous collections. Aggregates imply looser or less compact collections of particles which readily disperse into separate components. Twinned crystals, on the other hand, are well-defined crystallographic entities, consisting of two or more crystals of the same (or isomorphous) crystals joined together at a definite mutual orientation. The two or more lattices comprising the twin result from the deposition on opposite sides of a common sheet of atoms in the nucleus so that the combination may be regarded as an unsuccessful attempt to establish a symmetry higher than that of the simple single crystal itself. In many cases the structure of the two parts can be made to coincide by by rotation of one of them relative to the other through a half-turn about a common axis. Twins are liable to show considerable variation in their structure and Figure 5-31 sketches only a few of the many illustrated in Vavrinecz's many papers[137] on the crystallography of sucrose. A few typical single crystals and conglomerated spikes are also included. The seams of the twins are mostly visible as a sharp line. There is, generally speaking, no set ratio between the height and the breadth of twins. In the case of sucrose twins experience has shown that beet sugar twins are usually elongated in form whereas cane sugar twins are mostly broader in shape.[137] Conglomerates, on the other hand, show a much different form. They generally show no or little arrangement.* In the simplest case the crystals grow together in irregular clumps of individuals of about the same size, or consist of two or more individuals growing together at corners. A fine secondary grain may often be seen on the surface of the crystals. The clusters occur in different ways. Some originate through the growing together of the primary crystals, which thus contribute to the conglomerate formation. More rarely conglomerates may consist of only a few crystals, these concentrated in clusters. The clusters belong mainly to two types; the first consisting of primary crystals upon which some after grain has grown, the second, more unusual, comprises only clumps of after grain grown together to an unusually large mass. These comprise the greater part of the sample and are readily distinguished from the primary grain by their opacity.

F. G. Donnan[32] concluded that there are four factors which tend to cause the agglomeration of granular masses:

1. Unequally distributed stresses

* The clusters which form about a string of rock candy usually are directed to the string at the left poles of the crystal.

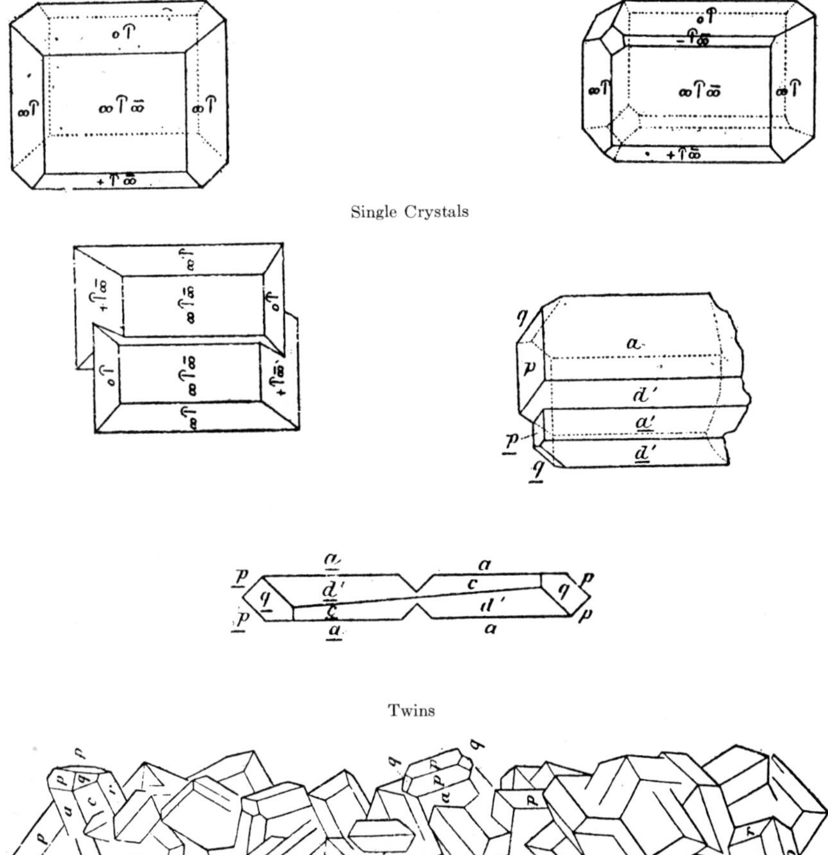

Single Crystals

Twins

Conglomerate

Figure 5-31. Drawings to illustrate growth and twinning habits of sucrose crystals.[137]

2. Unequal size of granules
3. Unstable or metastable forms
4. Sheared or "flawed" crystal surfaces which result in the Beilby effect

Tammann and Kordes[58,125] observed that oxide and sulfide particles commenced to aggregate at temperatures equivalent to 57 per cent of their absolute melting temperatures and the sintering continued at an accelerated pace and in an irreversible manner as the temperature was increased beyond this level. Balarev and Kolavor,[14] however, found that the temperature of agglomeration depended upon the previous history of the particular system. This could vary as much as 215°C for the same powder. They also regarded the region of contact of aggregated crystals as being in more or less of a fused condition rather than possessing any particular crystalline structure. Such sintering considerations are discussed in detail in the many fine books which are now available on solid-solid reactions.

Starodubtsev and Timokhina[119] observed that NaCl and KCl grains were joined together, upon heating, by bridges of circular cross section. These connections consisted of thread-like outgrowths, some of which were only 20 microns in diameter and 300 microns long. Contrary to what might have been expected, conglomeration did not occur primarily at points of contact but rather only between crystallographically identical faces. Surface-tension forces most likely dictate this preferred action and the fact that twinning occurs readily while dendrites are being formed suggests a common origin[20] in high growth rates.

Kolthoff, in his investigations of the aging of precipitated (*loc. cit.*), finds that this process may be accomplished by agglomeration. Some primary particles may share their water jackets and form loose agglomerates which can be easily repeptized. When the perfection process occurs in such an agglomerate, lattice ions may form in the liquid canals between particles, thus cementing them together. This cementing process is irreversible. The factors which promote perfection will also promote agglomeration, so that experiments on crystal perfection are extremely difficult to carry out in actual practice due to the ever-present possibility of agglomeration.

Grove, in his reviews (*loc. cit.*), repeatedly points out that agglomeration accompanies non-uniform conditions of supersaturations at the growing crystal face, and Kopelman and Greggs[64] emphasize two cogent factors in the agglomeration of powders:

1. Sintering.
2. Flocculation due to electrical forces. The degree of flocculation increases with a decrease in particle size and dielectric constant of the medium.

To return to twinning, Vladimerskii[134] has described this process thermodynamically as a mechanical equilibrium corresponding to a minimum of free energy. Stepanov[120] formulates the same state in terms of elastical anisotropism which can be eliminated only by a rearrangement in one-half of the crystal.

J. Beckenkamp[15] discusses the role of pressure in the formation of twins and aggregates. He concludes that the general condition for twinning is the presence of partial lattices, or net lines, which extend beyond the boundary of junction either in a straight line or approximately so. Fullman and Fisher[40] discuss twinning in accordance with the quasi-thermodynamic basis of modern theories of crystal growth. Annealing twins occur at the corners of contiguous grains according to the principle of a corresponding reduction in the interfacial free energy.

The references on these extremes of twinning and conglomeration are voluminous and no pretention of completion is intended in the above mention of a few leading references. The subject of conglomeration of sugar crystals has been considered superficially in the writer's laboratory[16,26] and results are in agreement with those of Vavrinecz. This author includes a complete catalogue of the known twinning forms of sucrose many of which are also described in the crystallographic discussions of other writers.[90] Vavrinecz recognizes three common types of sucrose crystal twins:

(1) Those twinned by the left pole and encountered in cane and refined products; (2) co-crystallized on the α-pinacoid faces and very common in beet products; and (3) individuals joined by the right pole, found principally in the slow crystallization of impure beet molasses. The ratio of height to width of twins is characteristic of many products, i.e.:

Cane sugars	0.5 to 1.0
Refined sugars	0.8 to 1.2
Beet sugars	1.0 to 2.5 and higher.

The technologist has been concerned with the factors which promote the growth of other than definite single crystals. Rabe,[99] for instance, from observations in actual pan boiling, concludes that poor circulation fosters conglomerate formation, while Moller[84] emphasizes the occurrence of conglomerates at high growth rates. The design of the vacuum pan[103] has a great effect upon the formation or absence of conglomerates and, presumably, circulation is most significant. It is a well-known fact in boiling sugar liquors that impure syrups tend to form agglomerates much less than high purity syrups under otherwise constant conditions. It has been observed in laboratory experiments[26] that this marked tendency in pure solutions is reduced by the addition of surface active agents. The tendency of crystal to stick to the walls of the container and other surfaces is also reduced by small concentrations of surfactants.[136d] Viscosity appears to play only a minor role in conglomerate formation but the dielectric constant of the medium is important. The lower the dielectric constant the greater is the number of agglomerates.[26] The size of the crystals is also important in this respect. In liquids of high dielectric constant (i.e. water) large crystals did not agglomerate as readily as small crystals, whereas the increased agglomeration observed in liquids of lower dielectric constants (alcohol, dioxane, etc.) appeared to be independent of size. This may very well depend upon a matter of charge. The few electrophoretic experiments performed in this connection were inconclusive but warrant repetition and elaboration.

Caking

The caking of water soluble crystals involves the formation of a film of saturated solution on the surface of the crystals either by absorption or by migration of mother liquor incompletely removed in the separation of the crystals. This saturated solution will concentrate at the contacts of the crystals due to capillary forces and subsequently crystallize to form a solid bridge upon cooling or evaporation.[55,73,142] The continuation of this surface recrystallization produces a hard cake or cement which often leads to great difficulties in manipulating and handling both bulk and package materials.

Obviously, the humidity of the environment is the most significant factor in deciding whether or not a mass of dried crystals will cake and cement together. The crystals will deliquesce and subsequently recrystallize upon a change of conditions only when the humidity exceeds the vapor pressure of the solution saturated at the appropriate temperature. The Dühring rule, when applied to saturated solutions, suggests that the vapor pressure of such solutions varies with temperature in such a way that the vapor presence is approximately a constant fraction of the vapor pressure of water at the same temperature. In the case of NaCl this humidity is approximately 80%. For pure sucrose it is 86% but much lower values (60% or less) are observed even for refined sugar on account of the concentration of impurities in the adhering surface syrup.[1,89,90] Adams and Ross[3] discuss the relative caking tendencies of fertilizers on this same score.

While humidity is probably the most important single factor in the caking of crystals other conditions probably also contribute. An immediately evident factor is the number of point contacts in the mass of crystals, and some of the preventives attempt to minimize caking by minimizing this item. The fact that type and rate of growth depends upon stress[85,96] is also probably significant, as is most certainly the purity of the crystals also.

Many means are employed to prevent and rectify caking of crystals:

1. Conditioning of the storage space. In principle the humidity of the environment must be maintained below the critical humidity of deliquescence. Such conditioning is widely practiced in the sugar industry especially with the increased practice of bulk handling and silo storage.

2. Large crystals of uniform size. This minimizes the number and area of contacts and provides large void spaces.

3. High purity. $MgCl_2$ in NaCl, invert sugar in sucrose, etc., lower the critical humidity and therefore promote caking. On the other hand, small concentrations of impurities may lead to habit modifications which are beneficial in this respect. Whetstone[144] has shown that several dyes promote the recrystallization of NH_4NO_3, $(NH_4)_2SO_4$, KNO_3, and $NaNO_3$ in a fragile condition so that the hardness of the solidified product remains low even after recrystallization. Traces of surface active agents in super-phosphate fertilizers may also reduce the tendency to cake and stick to process equipment.[116]

4. Various coatings are employed to absorb moisture preferentially and prevent intimate intergrowth of the base crystals. $Ca_3(PO_4)_2$ on NaCl and starch on sugar and confections are well-known examples. Anhydrous $CaCl_2$ is often dusted on flake hexahydrate to delay caking when humidity fluctuations are not severe.

5. In the case of sugar, a caked condition can be alleviated by exposure to a damp temperature and redrying while being tamped. Otherwise, the points of contact will be reunited.[79]

The setting of plaster of Paris and similar cements is similar in mechanism to the caking of crystals except that different hydrate and metastable modifications are involved. Aragonite, for instance, has a higher solubility in water at ordinary temperatures than the more stable calcite so that a finely ground slurry of the former will set slowly to a cement of the calcite form. Additives may improve and either accelerate or retard these reactions in the usual way[27] of promoting preferred habits or by providing nuclei for the final crystalline form.[70]

REFERENCES

1. Abe, S., *Proc. Res. Soc. Japan Sugar Ref.*, **6,** 7 (1957).
2. Abrams, R. K., *Proc. Australian Chem. Inst.*, **6,** 181 (1939).
3. Adams, J. R., and Ross, W. H., *Ind. Eng. Chem.*, **33,** 121 (1941).
4. Alexander, A. E., *J. Chem. Ed.*, **28,** 128 (1951).
5. Anon., *Chem. Week*, **76,** 21 (1955).
6. Anon., *Int. Sugar J.*, **53,** 210 (1951); *Z. Zuckerind.*, **94,** 128 (1944).
7. Anon., *S. African Min. and Eng. J.*, **62,** 707 (1951).
8. Aston, J. G., and Mastrangelo, S. V. R., *Anal. Chem.*, **22,** 636 (1950).
9. Austin, J. B., *Ind. Eng. Chem.*, **11,** 334 (1939).
10. Avakyan, S. V., and Lashko, N. F. L., *Doklady Akad. Nauk (USSR)*, **64,** 827 (1949); *C.A.*, **44,** 10426.
11. Badger, W. L., and Banchero,
    (a) "Unit Operations," p. 520, New York, McGraw-Hill Book Co., 1955.
    (b) "Elements of Chemical Engineering," p. 457, New York, McGraw-Hill Book Co., 1936.
12. Baker, C., and Smyth, C. P., *J. Am. Chem. Soc.*, **61,** 2798 (1939).

13. Bailey, A. E., "Melting and Solidification of Fats," New York, Interscience Publishing Co., 1950.
14. Barlarev, D., and Kolarov, N., *Kolloid Z.*, **101**, 277 (1942).
15. Beckenkamp, J., *Neues Jahrb. Mineral Geol.*, Beilage Ed., **48**, 1 (1923).
16. Bergan, R. W., B.S. Thesis, College of the Holy Cross, 1952.
17. Bergener, E., *Z. Ver. deut. Ing. Verfahrenstecknik*, **5**, 137 (1940).
18. Booth, A. H., *Trans. Faraday Soc.*, **47**, 633–45 (1951).
19. Bouchet, C., and LaFont, R., *Compt. rend.*, **226**, 1823 (1948).
20. Buerger, M. J., *Am. Mineral*, **30**, 469 (1945).
21. Caldwell, H. B., *Chem. Met. Eng.*, **42**, 213 (1935), *Ind. Eng. Chem.*, **53**, 115 (1961).
22. Cavallo, L., and Mantovani, G., *Ind. Sacc. Ital.*, **46**, 188 (1953).
23. Chatterji, A. C., and Rastogi, R. P., *J. Indian Chem. Soc.*, **29**, 485 (1952); *C.A.*, **48**, 12517.
24. "Chemical Engineering Catalog," New York, Reinhold Publishing Corp., 1959.
25. Comer, J. J., *J. Coll. Sci.*, **14**, 175 (1959).
26. Cosgrove, J. F., M.S. Thesis, College of the Holy Cross, 1952.
27. Cunningham, W. A., and Antes, L. L., *Ind. Eng. Chem.*, **44**, 2402 (1952).
28. Davies, C. W., and Nancollas, G. H., *Trans. Faraday Soc.*, **51**, 823, 1232 (1955).
29. Davion, M., *Compt. rend.*, **243**, 1222 (1956).
30. deAlves, L. A., *Tecnica*, **195**, 645 (1949).
31. Demmerle, R. L., *Ind. Eng. Chem.*, **39**, 126 (1959).
32. Donnan, F. G., *Trans. Faraday Soc.*, **14**, 12 (1919).
33. Dunning, W. J., in Garners "Chemistry of the Solid State," III, 19, p. 79, Chap. 6, London, Butterworths (1955).
34. Edwards, R. T., *Ind. Eng. Chem.*, **49**, 750 (1957); *Chem. and Eng. News*, **33**, 1647 (1955), **35**, 78 (1957).
35. Fehlner, F. P., *J. Chem. Ed.*, **33**, 449 (1956).
36. Fieldner, L., *J. Chem. Ed.*, **18**, 44 (1941).
37. Findlay, R. A., and Weedman, J. A., "Separation and Purification by Crystallization," in "Advances in Petroleum Chemistry and Refinery," Chap. 1, p. 118, New York, Interscience Publishing Co., 1958.
38. Friend, J. N., "Inorganic Chemistry," Vol. 4, London, C. Griffin and Co.
39. Fullerton, Hodgart, and Barclay, Ltd., Paisley, Scotland.
40. Fullman, R. L., and Fisher, C. F., *J. Appl. Phys.*, **22**, 1350 (1951).
41. Garrett, D. E. and Rosenbaum, G. P., *Chem. Eng.*, **65**, 116–41 (1958).
42. Gopal, R., and Rastogi, R. P., *J. Indian Chem. Soc.*, **27**, 401 (1950).
43. Griffiths, A., *J. Soc. Chem. Ind.*, **44**, 71 (1925).
44. Gruse, W. A., and Stevens, D. R., "Chemical Technology of Petroleum," p. 574–94, New York, McGraw-Hill Book Co., 1942.
45. Guelin, E. J., "Inclusions as a Means of Gemstone Identification," (1953) Gemol. Inst. Am., Los Angeles, Calif., 1956.
46. Haber, F., *Ber. deut. Chem. Ges.*, **55**, 1717 (1922).
47. Haines, H. W., *et al.*, *Ind. Eng. Chem.*, **47**, 1096 (1955).
48. Hatch, G. B., and Rue, O., *Ind. Eng. Chem.*, **31**, 51 (1939).
49. Heinz, D. M., and Banks, E. J., *J. Chem. Phys.*, **24**, 391 (1956).
50. Hildebrand, J. H., "Solubility," 1st and 3rd eds. New York, Reinhold Publishing Corp., 1924 and 1950.
51. Hilditch, T. P., *J. Chem. Soc.* (*London*), 3147 (1950).
52. Holden, A. N., U.S. Pat. 2,459,869 (1949); 2,484,829 (1949); A-37, p. 312.

53. Horbe, R., Knacke, O., and Prescher, K. E., *Z. Erzbergbau u. Metallhuttenw.*, **11,** 3831 (1958); *C.A.*, **25,** 19270.
54. Horn, F. H., in "Boron," ed. by Cohn, J. A., Nye, W. F., and Gaule, G. K., New York, Plenum Press, Inc., 1960.
55. Irani, R. R., Callis, C. F., and Lieu, T., *Ind. Eng. Chem.*, **51,** 1285 (1959).
56. Jerimiassen, F., and Svanoe, H., *Chem. and Met.*, **39,** 594 (1932).
57. Johnson, J. R., and Newman, J. S., *Anal. Chem.*, **26,** 1843 (1954).
58. Jost, W., and Oel, H. J., *Faraday Soc. Disc.*, **23,** 137 (1957).
59. Joy, E. F., and Payne, J. H., Jr., *Ind. Eng. Chem.*, **47,** 2157 (1955).
60. Keane, J. C., Ambler, J. A., and Byall, S., *Ind. Eng. Chem.*, **27,** 30 (1935).
61. Kirk, R. E., and Othmer, D., "Encyclopedia of Chemical Technology," New York, Vol. 7, Interscience Publishing Co., 1954.
62. Kjellgren, B., U. S. Pat., 1,906,757 and 1,906,758.
63. Komandin, A. V., *Uchenge Zap. Moskov. Gosudarst. Univ. M.V. Lommosoven*, **164,** 123 (1953); *C.A.*, **49,** 12068.
64. Kopelman, B., and Greggs, C. C., *J. Phys. Chem.*, **55,** 557 (1951).
65. Kottler, F., *J. Frank Inst.*, **250,** 339, 419 (1950), **251,** 499, 617 (1951); *J. Phys. Chem.*, **56,** 442 (1952).
66. Kunzl, J., *Chemie* (Prague), **8,** 5 (1952).
67. Lacklan, D., and Christiensen, C. J., *Rev. Sci. Inst.*, **23,** 306 (1952).
68. Lane, F. C., "Earth's Grandest Rivers," New York, Doubleday, 1949.
69. LeClerc, E., *Rev. Univ. des Mines (Liege)*, **8,** #31, 1943.
70. Leininger, R. K., Conley, R. F., and Bundy, W. M., *Ind. Eng. Chem.*, **49,** 818 (1957).
71. Lipsett, F. R. L., *Can. J. Phys.*, **35,** 284 (1957); *C.A.*, **51,** 7794; **53,** 66.
72. Loveland, R. P., and Trivelli, A. P. H., *J. Phys. Chem.*, **51,** 1004 (1947); *J. Frank Inst.*, **204,** 193, 377 (1927); **246,** 459 (1948).
73. Lowry, T. M., and Hemmings, F. C., *J. Soc. Chem. Ind.*, **39,** 101 (1920).
74. Matz, G., *Chem. Ing. Tech.*, **27,** 18 (1955); *Fortsch Vertahrenstech.*, 280 (1952/3).
75. Mayers, D. E., *Rev. Sci. Inst.*, **21,** 891 (1954).
76. McCabe, W. L., in Perry's "Chemical Engineers Handbook," p. 1780, New York, McGraw-Hill Book Co., 1941.
77. McCabe, W. L., and Smith, J. C., "Unit Operations," p. 804, McGraw-Hill Book Co., 1956.
78. McCabe, W. L., and Stevens, R. P., *Chem. Eng. Prog.*, **170,** 168 (1951).
79. McGinnis, R. A., "Beet Sugar Technology," New York, Reinhold Publishing Corp., 1951.
80. McKay, D. L., Dale, G. H., and Weedman, J. A., *Ind. Eng. Chem.*, **52,** 197 (1960).
81. Mellor, J. W., "Treatise on Inorganic and Physical Chemistry," Vol. 5, p. 588, New York, Longmans-Green Co., 1924.
82. Michaels, A. S., and Colville, A. R., Jr., *J. Phys. Chem.*, **64,** 13 (1960).
83. Milone, V. M., and Cetini, G., *Ann. Chem. Roma*, **32,** 180 (1950); **41,** 325 (1951); *Gazz. Chem. Ital.*, **84,** 133 (1954); **77,** 348 (1947); *C.A.*, **45,** 9927; **49,** 10697.
84. Moller, C., *Int. Sugar J.*, **49,** 182 (1947).
85. Mosebach, R., *Z. Naturforsch.*, **5a**, 508 (1950).
86. Mukhergie, N. R., *J. Imp. Coll. Chem. Eng. Soc. (London)*, **2,** 68 (1946); *Engineering* (U. Washington), **4,** #4, 8 (1952).
87. Nacken, R., *Z. Instrumentenkunde*, **26,** 12 (1916).
88. Nees, A. R., *Proc. Am. Sugar Beet Tech.*, **4,** 572 (1946).

89. Nelson, T. J., *Food Tech.*, **3**, 347 (1949).
90. Neuhaus, A., *Chem. Ing. Tech.*, 155, 350 (1956).
91. Nicholson, A. M., *Trans. Am. Inst. Elec. Engrs.*, **38**, 1467 (1919).
92. O'Rourke, J. D., and Johnson, R. A., *Anal. Chem.*, **27**, 1699 (1955).
93. Ossadtschew, J., *Zapiske Vsen. Minerol. Obs.*, **75**, 238 (1946).
94. Packter, A., *J. Phys. Chem.*, **59**, 1140 (1953).
95. Palmer, W. G., "Experimental Physical Chemistry," Cambridge Press, 1941.
96. Partington, J. R., "Treatise on Physical Chemistry," Chap. III, p. 16, London, Longmans-Green Co., 1952.
97. Pfann, W. C., "Zone Melting," New York, John Wiley & Sons, 1958.
Parr, N. L., "Zone Refining and Allied Techniques," New York, St. Martin's Press, Inc., 1960.
98. Powers, H. E. C.,
(*a*) *Tate and Lyle Times*, July and Aug. (1955); *Z. Zuckerind.*, **5**, 557 (1955).
(*b*) *Int. Sugar J.*, **53**, 25 254 (1951); **50**, 149 (1948); **52**, 194, 283 (1950).
(c) in Honig's "Sugar Technology," Vol. II, Chap. 1, Amsterdam, Elsevier Co., 1959.
99. Rabe, A. E., *Int. Sugar J.*, **53**, 309 (1951).
100. Ralston, A. W., "Fatty Acids and their Derivatives," New York, John Wiley & Sons, 1948.
101. Ramberg, R., "The Origin of Metamorphic and Metasomatic Rocks," Chicago, University Press, 1952.
102. Res, I. S., Rusahov, L. S., and Stoidov, G. N., A-42.
103. Rieger, E., *Deut. Zuckerind.*, **65**, 585 (1940).
104. Robinson, J. N., and Roberts, J. E., *Can. J. Chem. Eng.*, **35**, 105 (1957); *C.A.*, **52**, 1697.
105. Roginskii, S. Z., and Todes, O. M., *Compt rend. acad. sci.* (*U.S.S.R.*), **27**, 677 (1940); *C.A.*, **35**, 1296, 5010.
106. Ross, E. T., *Pacific Chem. and Met. Ind.*, 9–20 (1938).
107. Saeman, *Trans. Am. Inst. Chem. Eng.*, **2**, 107 (1956).
108. Sauchelli, V., "The Chemistry and Technology of Fertilizers," Chap. 18, New York, Reinhold Publishing Corp., 1960.
109. Schaller, W. T., *Bull* **#610**, *U. S. Geol. Survey*, (1916).
110. Schlain, D., Prater, J. D., and Ravitz, S. F., *Ind. Eng. Chem.*, **41**, 834 (1949).
111. Schwab, F. W., and Wichers, E., *J. Research. Natl. Bur. Standards*, **32**, 253 (1944).
112. Sears, G. W., *J. Chem. Phys.*, **33**, 1068 (1960).
113. Seavoy, G. E., and Caldwell, H. B., *Ind. Eng. Chem.*, **32**, 627 (1940).
114. Seifert, H., *Chem. Ing. Technik.*, **27**, 135 (1955).
115. Seitz, F., and Turnbull, D., "Solid State Physics," Vol. 3, p. 225, New York, Interscience Co., 1953.
116. Semenchenko, V. K., *J. Phys. Chem.* (*USSR*), **19**, 289 (1945); **21**, 613 (1947); *C.A.*, **41**, 6788; **54**, 21909.
117. Sheftal, N. N., *Kristallografia*, **2**, 193 (1957); *Trudy Inst. Krist* (*USSR*), #3, 55 (1947); *C.A.*, **44**, 9172.
118. Shoen, H. M., "Crystallization—The Unit Operation," Univ. Microfilm, Ann Arbor, Mich., Dissertation #20829, 243, 1957.
119. Starodubtsev, S. V., and Timokhina, N. I., *Doklady Akad. Nauk. SSSR*, **62**, 619 (1948); *C.A.*, **43**, 1622.
120. Stepanov, A. V., *Neues Jahrb. Mineral. Geol.*, **17**, 713 (1947).

121. Struthers-Wells Co., Warren, Penn.
122. Sugihara, J. M., and Newman, S. R., *J. Organic Chem.*, **21**, 1445 (1956).
123. Suzuki, K., *J. Chem. Soc. Japan, Ind. Chem. Sect.*, **55**, 652 (1952).
124. Svanoe, H., *Ind. Eng. Chem.*, **32**, 636 (1940); *J. Chem. Ed.*, **27**, 549 (1950).
125. Tammann, G., and Kordes, E., *Z., anorg. Chem.*, **149**, 58 (1925).
126. Thompson, A. R., *Chem. Eng.*, 127 (1950).
127. Tipson, R. S., in Weissberger's "Techniques of Organic Chemistry," Chap. 6, New York, Interscience Co., 1950.
128. Tipson, R. S., *Anal. Chem.*, **22**, 628 (1952).
129. Tovbin, M., and Krusnova, S., *Zhur. Fiz. Khim.*, **23**, 863 (1949); *C.A.*, **43**, 8805; Tovbin, M., and Boevudskaya, Z. L., *Ukrain Khim. Zhur.*, **22**, 173 (1956); *C.A.*, **50**, 14322.
130. Trey, F., *Berg u huthenmann Monatsch. Hochschule Leoben*, **94**, 100 (1949); *C.A.*, **43**, 8229.
131. Turkevich, J., and Smyth, C. P., *J. Am. Chem. Soc.*, **62**, 2468 (1940); **64**, 737 (1942).
132. Ubbelohde, A. R., *Trans. Faraday Soc.*, **33**, 1198 (1937); *Sci. J. Roy. Coll. Sci.*, **15**, 40 (1945).
133. Vahl, L., Private Communication.
134. Vladimerskii, K. V., *J. Exptl. Theor. Phys. (USSR)*, **17**, 530 (1947); *C.A.*, **42**, 6599.
135. VanGoler and Sachs, *Z. Phys.*, **77**, 281 (1932); **43**, 227 (1935).
136. Van Hook, A., *et al.*,
    (a) *Proc. Am. Soc. Sugar Beet Tech.*, **6**, 570 (1950).
    (b) *Sugar J.*, 20 (1953); *J. Coll. Sci.*, **5**, 315 (1950); *Int. Sugar J.*, 298 (1950); *Ind. Eng. Chem.*, **44**, 1306 (1952); *Proc. Am. Soc. Sugar Beet Tech.*, **9**, 590 (1957).
    (c) *Z. Zuckerind.*, **6**, 25 (1956).
    (d) Unpublished observations.
137. Vavrinecz, G., *Deut. Zuckerind.*, **3**, 107 (1938); *Int. Sugar J.*, **41**, 345 (1939); "La Cristallisation du Sucre," p. 15, C.I.T.S., Bruxelles, 1953.
138. von Weimarn, P. P., *Kolloid Z.*, **27**, 4 (1909).
139. Walker, A. C.,
    (a) *J. Frank Inst.*, **250**, 481 (1950); *Bell. Lab. Records.*, **25**, #10 (1947);
    (b) *J. Am. Cermic Soc.*, **30**, 250 (1953); *Ind. Eng. Chem.*, **46**, 1680 (1954).
140. Walker, A. C., and Buehler, E., *Ind. Eng. Chem.*, **42**, 1369 (1950).
141. Walker, A. C., and Kohman, S. T., *Bell Tel. System. Tech. Pub.*, B 1562; *Trans. Am. Inst. Elec. Engrs.*, 67 (1948).
142. Walker, H. S., *Int. Sagan J.*, **25**, 131 (1923).
143. Wells, A. F., *Phil. Mag.*, **37**, 184, 217, 605 (1946).
144. Whetstone, J., *Trans. Faraday Soc.*, **51**, 973, 1142 (1955).
145. White, A., and Bishop, *J. Am. Chem. Soc.*, **62**, 8, 16 (1940).
146. Yamamoto, T., *Sci. Papers Inst. Phys. Chem. Res.*, **35**, 228 (1939).

Chapter 6

THE PRACTICE OF CRYSTALLIZATION

SUGAR AND THE SUGARS

The sugar industry is the leading practitioner of the art and science of crystallization from solution. It is not the oldest; the production of solar salt by natural evaporation has been performed since the earliest times. Although the total annual production of salt exceeds that of sugar (Chapter 6), the amount actually crystallized is considerably less. Most industrial salt is used directly as brine. Another contender on the weight basis is artificial ice. The production of this commodity on a commercial scale flourished during the first quarter of this century but thereafter declined with the advent of mechanical refrigeration. Production reached a peak of 57 million tons in the United States in 1931[253, 279] while throughout the world during this same year 26 million tons of sugar were produced and consumed.[240]

In technological directions the sugar industry pioneered the development of the vacuum crystallizer as well as many other unit operations and unit processes of modern chemical engineering,[152] and has always fostered scientific and practical investigations of its many operations, especially those involving crystallization. It was originally the intention of the author to develop this theme and the technology of sugar crystallization in considerable detail, but the recent appearance of an entire volume[105] devoted to this subject makes this appear unnecessary. On this account, only a few random comments and some discussion of the preparation of sugars other than sucrose will be presented here.

Layerwise Growth and Spirals

The layerwise growth of sucrose crystals is rather readily observed[192a] in spite of earlier reports to the contrary (A-37, p. 132). Figure 6-1 illustrates the appearance of a growing surface under oblique illumination at relatively low magnification. In a typical examination at room temperature the steps advanced at the rate of about 30 μ/hr when the degree of supersaturation was 20%. Several successive steps pass any given point during this period and the step height is several microns. From such observations the macroscopic growth rate can be computed and it amounts to about 10 mg M^{-2}

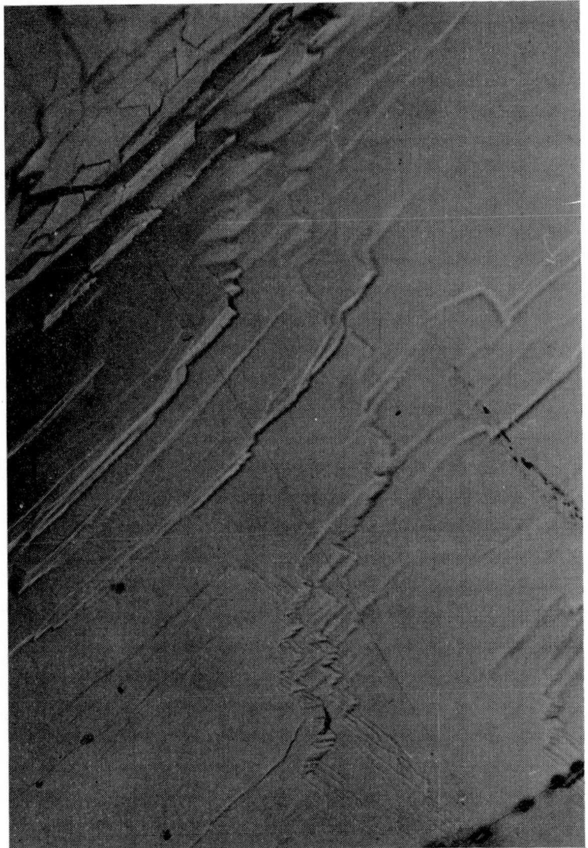

Figure 6-1. Layerwise growth of sucrose crystal.

hr^{-1} in the typical case cited. This is to be compared to the 1500 measured directly by Kucharenko[133] for this concentration and temperature. Dunning[68] has made more exact measurements of this kind. At a degree of supersaturation of almost 5% he finds that the steps of height about 500Å and spacing about 10μ advance at a rate of about 180 μ/hr. This is equivalent to about 2 mg M^{-2} hr^{-1} compared to Kucharenko's value of 188, which is in about the same low ratio as before. It will be necessary to acquire more experimental information about the frequency and distribution of these active points of growth before the results can be reconciled, but in the meantime the method offers a very quick and convenient method for the determination of the rate of growth of crystals. While Powers and the writer have been unable to associate this layerwise growth feature with

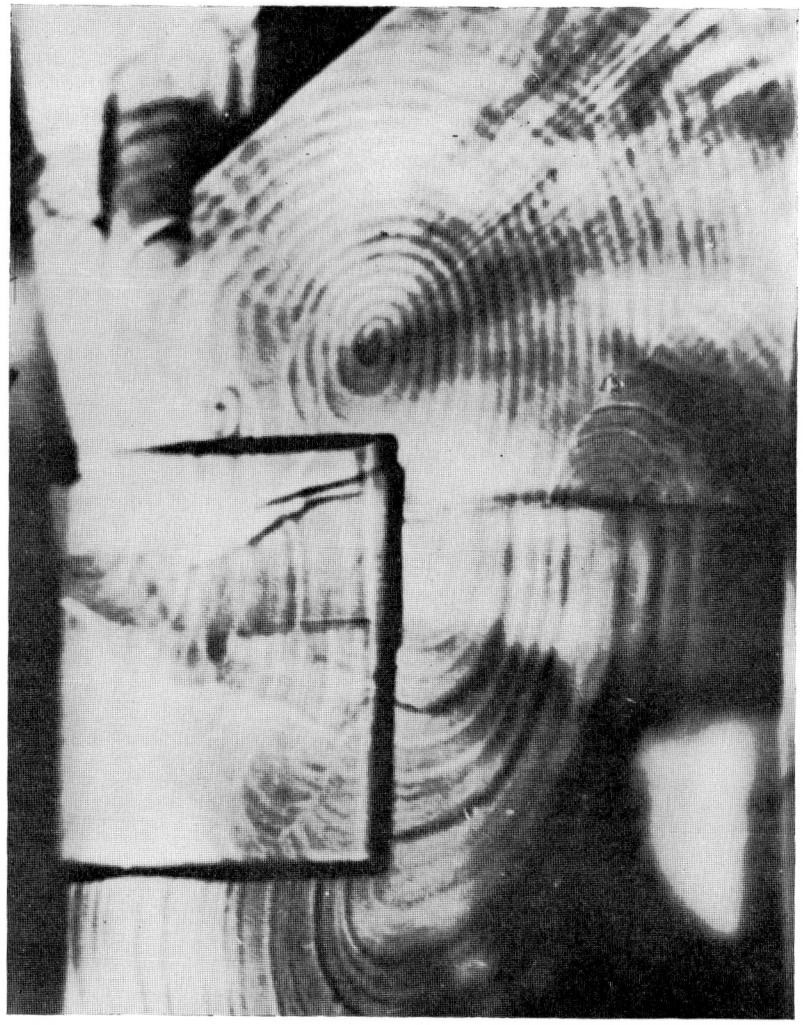

Figure 6-2. Spirals on sucrose crystal.[68]

screw dislocations, Dunning has done so by aluminizing, and Figure 6-2 is a vivid record of such a case.

Growth at Very Low Supersaturations

The kinetics of growth of crystals at very low supersaturations should be most revealing of the mechanism of growth. The two-dimensional nucleation hypothesis, for instance, demands effective stoppage of growth at finite, positive supersaturations. This requirement, however, is moderated considerably by Frank's hypothesis which dictates a change in order of reaction from a first to a higher degree as the supersaturation is reduced (Chapter 3).

Dunning[68] finds a critical representation and a non-linear growth pattern for sucrose crystals and the latter is also reported by Smythe.[227] Smythe's most drastic case at 60°C approximates Dunning's result at 30°C in a relative sense. This is represented in Figure 6-3 where the points have been estimated from Smythe's curve. The slope in the low range approximates a second-order reaction but lower values are estimated at other temperatures; namely 1.4 at 30°, 1.7 at 40°, and 1.3 at 50°C. All of Smythe's curves become nicely linear above a supersaturation of about 1.08. Unlike Dunning, Smythe found definite growth at all supersaturations; his lowest concentrations were estimated as equivalent to 0 = 1.00^5, 1.01, 1.00^8 at the successively increasing temperatures. Dunning reports no measurable growth at his lowest supersaturations of 1.00^7 to 1.01° at 30°C.

Neither a critical oversaturation nor non-linear growth curves have been observed in the writer's laboratory.[229, 260a] Using mostly linear measurements but also, like Smythe, weight increments, positive linear growth of perfected single crystals was observed at all supersaturations to as little as 0.1% (0 = 1.001). Pronounced dissolution also occurred immediately when this concentration was extended into the undersaturated range to an equivalent amount. Experimentation over this minute concentration range is very

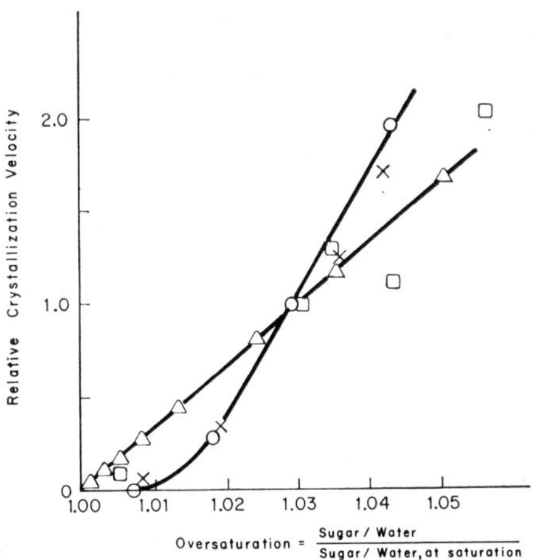

Figure 6-3. Growth rate of sucrose crystals at low supersaturations. ○—Dunning,[68] ×—Smythe,[227], 60°C △—VanHook,[260a], 30°C □—Smythe, 30°C.

difficult and obviously much more investigation is required, at least in this case, to reconcile these differences.

Growth at Very High Supersaturations

These reports on the rate of growth of sucrose crystals at very low supersaturations quite naturally provoke interest in the crystallization behavior at the opposite extremity of the concentration scale. The limiting case here would be that of the melt, for which Tammann-type curves are generally realized, albeit in only a few isolated cases with substances as heat sensitive as sugars.[143, 244] The effect of solvent is to moderate the influence of the temperature potential and to modify the rate of nucleation and growth according to the diffusional characteristics of the solute.[A-1, A-38, 41, 79, 184]

The nucleation and growth of sugar solutions at ordinary concentrations appear to follow normal kinetic laws but drastic abatement sets in as the concentration becomes excessive. This was ascribed in an earlier work on nucleation to (A-37, p. 112) the inevitable degradation accompanying the preparation of solutions stronger than 75–80% by weight. However, a recent publication of Nickik[173] suggests that this might not be so. The relative permanence of carbohydrate glasses and amorphous sucrose[181] also infers a reduction of the crystallization potential at extremely high concentration, and Herrington[98] claims that definite maxima occur in the nucleation frequency-concentration curves of lactose syrups. Some of Waterman and Gentil's[272] crystallization curves for concentrated sugar solutions also display such extremes in the 88% range and Webre[105] describes their occurrence in actual practice.

It seems likely that the methods applicable to the study of the crystallization of glasses, polymers,[A-45] etc. may be suited to the investigation of very strong sugar syrups, candies, etc.[192b, c] However, for exploratory purposes the writer inquired into the behavior of syrups of ever-increasing concentration by ordinary crystallization techniques. These consist essentially of observations on the frequency of nucleation and the rate of growth of single crystals.

Nucleation

As before,[A-37] it was impossible to prepare aqueous sucrose solutions stronger than about 80% ($0 \sim 1.8$ at 30°C) without considerable degradation. Such alteration is evidenced by inversion and formation of color. Nonetheless, the frequency of nucleation increases rapidly in solutions up to about 85% ($0 \sim 2.5$). Beyond this concentration there is a sudden decrease. 87% solutions ($0 \sim 3.0$) are very slow to crystallize spontaneously and are invariably slightly colored and contain at least several per cent invert sugar and some titratable acid. The same impurity combination may be realized in an 81% syrup (0 ~ 2.0) by previously adding about 0.5% invert sugar and heating to match colors. In this case the syrups become virtually uncrystallizable when protected from accidental inoculation. Presumably, the impediment to crystallization is in large part due to the accumulation of impurities even though these syrups are considerably less viscous than the stronger, faster crystallizing ones. However, viscosity is not unimportant in tending to diminish crystallization since additives such as acacia, dextran, etc. considerably extend the crystallization time at all supersaturations.

Growth

Maxima appear in the growth rate-supersaturation curves computed from Kucharenko's formula for pure syrups[51, 278a] as well as being observed in less pure syrups.[151, 170] However, the calculated feature of the first case is not borne out in the English version of Kucharenko's data. The experimental values cited at fixed temperatures increase monotonously to the highest supersaturation even though the formula calls for a decrease. The unique shape in the curves in the second instance may be regarded as incidental to the manner of presenting the data.[91, 260b] At constant impurity level the rate is found to increase steadily with the sugar concentration.

Many workers[62b, 224, 265] have accounted for the velocity of growth of crystals from sugar syrups by relationships of the form

$$R = f\left(\frac{S}{\eta}\right)$$

where s represents the supersaturation and η the viscosity but the author has been unable to rationalize simple forms of this functional relationship with the published data.[105] It, therefore, appeared appropriate to examine anew the rate of growth behavior of pure syrups at every-increasing concentration and constant temperature, irrespective of the viscosity influence.

In Table 6-1, we are immediately confronted with the fact that at supersaturations above 20–30% the growth becomes polycrystalline by virtue of false-grain formation. With reasonable assumptions regarding the kinetic aspects of this complication, it had been demonstrated refractometrically that the growth rate increases more or less regularly out to $S = 2.6$ at 30°C (85.5%). This limit is also now indicated by single crystal measurements. These results are not pretended to be exact even though they are essentially the same at low concentrations as those established in more precise investigations. The values above $S = 1.2$ have been estimated from the early part of the growth curve in order to eliminate the exhausting effect of the

TABLE 6-1. REPRESENTATIVE SINGLE CRYSTAL RESULTS 30°C

Wt %	Super-saturation	CV (μ/hr. *C* axis)	Invert on Sucrose	Type of Growth
71	1.1	30	none	Single crystal
72.5	1.2	80	none	Single crystal
75.5	1.4	200	none	False grain
80	1.8	300	0.1%	False grain and changing habit!
85	2.5	(650)	0.3%	Spherulitic growth
88	3.0	(280)	>0.5%	Spherulitic growth
90	4.0	(75)	>3%	Spherulitic growth

unavoidable false grain. At the highest concentration they probably include the effects of aggregation and polycrystalline growth. The over-all pattern of an increase up to about 85 % concentration and thereafter a rather rapid decline has been confirmed by direct microscopic measurements. The numerical rates must be considered as only indicative since the growth is overwhelmingly polycrystalline at the high concentrations. This feature itself presents an attractive field for intensive study. The apparent decrease at the highest concentrations is probably the result of this type of growth as well as the depressing effect of the inevitably increasing impurity (this is less than similar solutions studied in the first part). Ordinary linear crystallization velocity (L.C.V.) measurements were also attempted in this exploratory survey but these were futile since spontaneous nucleation occurred throughout the tubes and no steady, advancing crystal front could be established.

It may be concluded from this preliminary summary that the apparent decrease in the rate of crystallization of sugar at very high concentrations is primarily the result of unavoidable products of decomposition and of polycrystalline growth.

Activity Theory

Many properties of aqueous sucrose solutions suggest very extensive solvation,[69, 105, 121, 135, 185, 192d, 222, 259, 264, 290] the extent of which is sometimes expressed as equivalent to the formation of a hexahydrate.[61b, 159, 209] This designation of a particular hydrate is probably an over-simplification even in the purely chemical sense.[160] The necessity for an exact model may be circumvented by expressing concentrations as thermodynamic activities rather than actual molecular concentrations. This procedure rationalized the kinetics of sucrose crystallization with some success,[51, 105] although the hypothesis requires re-examination in view of Wise's[285] criticism.

Glucose, like most of the sugars, is highly solvated in solution[182] so that we might expect an activity representation to be useful here also. The thermodynamic properties of glucose and sucrose solutions are very similar[246] (Figure 6-4) so that we expect the crystallization-rate gradient to increase with higher supersaturations. This increase is evident in some of Sadovgi's[203] data on the crystallization rate of glucose from solution (Table 6-2). ΔC_m is the supersaturation in g/m^3 and K the reduced crystallization rate as grams of glucose deposited from 100 g of solution on 1 g of seed in 1 min. A slight increasing trend is indicated at the two higher temperatures but just the reverse occurs at other conditions. The temperature coefficient at equal supersaturations is notably small.

Habit Modifications

The usual habit modifications of sucrose may be readily described by reference to the normal sucrose crystal pictured in Figure 2-9.[14] The fast-growing bevels and left prisms tend to grow out at high concentrations and/or temperatures, so that such crystals tend to display 10 to 8 faces according to the prominence of the truncations. That is, the more complete forms tend to develop at low rates of development.[222] When grown more rapidly, the crystal tends to an elongated shape.[260c] Impurities promote more drastic modifications; dextrose, for instance, favoring the development of the a faces. Raffinose causes the r' faces to predominate over

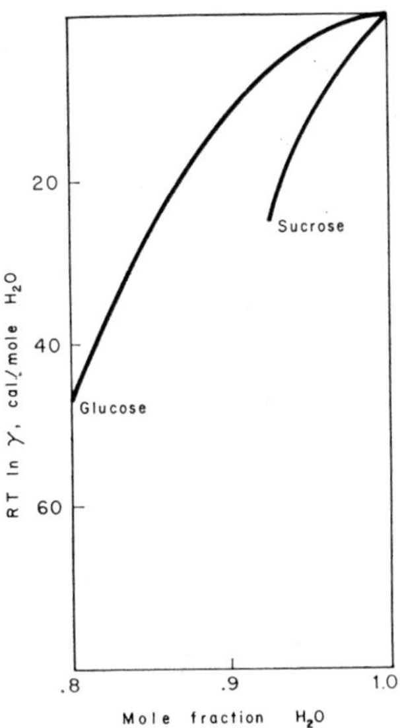

Figure 6-4. Activity coefficient of water (γ_1), in glucose and sucrose solutions. After Taylor and Rowlinson.[246]

TABLE 6-2. CRYSTALLIZATION RATE OF GLUCOSE AT VARYING TEMPERATURES[203]

Temperature (C°)	ΔC_m	K	$\frac{K}{\Delta C_m}$
	0.30	3.20	10.7
25	0.20	2.25	11.2
	0.12	1.40	11.6
	0.31	3.10	10.0
	0.30	3.20	10.7
30	0.23	2.40	10.4
	0.15	1.90	12.6
	0.15	1.80	12.0
	0.30	3.00	10.0
	0.304	3.18	10.4
35	0.160	1.95	11.8
	0.15	1.93	11.8
	0.12	1.32	11.0
	0.301	3.51	11.6
	0.30	3.44	11.4
40	0.23	2.39	10.4
	0.17	1.15	9.0
	0.12	1.35	11.2
	0.23	2.71	11.5
43	0.20	1.92	9.5
	0.15	1.50	10.0

c and the formation of long, slender needles.[110] This is illustrated in the data of Table 6-3. Degradation products that form in sour cane tend to minimize the development of the *C*-pinacoids and bevels and emphasize the truncations. This leads to triangular-shaped crystals such as illustrated in Figure 6-5.

It seems evident that adsorption of some kind must precede and cause habit aberrations. That this is preferential in the development of plates in the presence of dextrose is suggested by the radioautograph of Figure 6-6. In this single experiment a sucrose crystal was grown in a syrup containing some radioactive C_{14} invert sugar. The presence of that material on the pinacoid faces and not on the prisms is evident. Similarly, preferential adsorption of raffinose on the appropriate faces of sucrose crystals grown in its presence has been indicated by methods of paper chromatography.[120]

TABLE 6-3. RELATIVE INCREASE IN DIMENSIONS OF SUCROSE CRYSTALS GROWN IN SOLUTIONS CONTAINING 245 G SUCROSE PER 100 OF WATER AT 25°C[110]

Raffinose % on Sucrose	Growth of $B - B'$ (mm/day)	Ratio of Increase to Increase of $(B - B')$	
		$A - A'$	$C - C'$
0.00	1.00	0.56	0.80
0.10	1.18	0.47	0.74
0.30	0.89	0.45	0.71
0.50	0.74	0.47	0.97
0.75	0.58	0.50	1.00
1.00	0.51	0.57	0.16
2.00	0.38	0.42	0.92
3.00	0.43	0.07	0.67
4.00	0.38	0.08	0.61
5.00	0.45	0.06	0.50

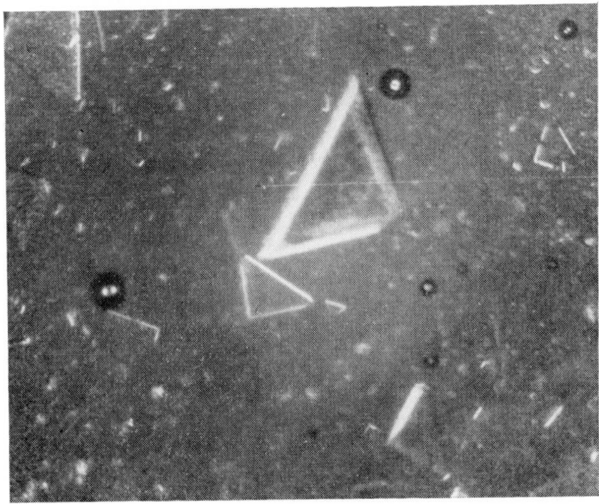

Figure 6-5. Triangular sucrose crystals. (*Courtesy D. Foster, Sugar Research Institute, Mackay, Queensland, 1958.*)

Conglomerates

Conglomerates are very common in sugar boiling. Conglomerates make it difficult to finish the massecuite, delay exhaustion of the syrup, increase the danger of false-grain formation, and result in a yield of non-uniform sugar crystals.[161] The decrease in surface area resulting from the formation of agglomerates also decreases the net crystallization velocity of the sucrose. The presence of agglomerates causes the crystal yield to be unnecessarily

Figure 6-6. Radioautographs of sucrose crystal grown in the presence of tagged invert sugar.[13]

1. syrup control
2. prism face contact
3. α-pinacoid face contact
4. c-pinacoid face contact

bulky and results in higher costs in packaging and difficulties in storing. Several factors have been suggested as the cause of this phenomenon. The most significant ones seem to be viscosity, surface tension, and dielectric constant of the liquid, and conditions of temperature, concentration, purity, intensity of agitation, crystal size, and size distribution also exert effects. Probably no one of these alone determines the net effect. This is more likely the result of the combined influence of two or more of these variables and, probably most important of all, the uniformity of the conditions while the crystal is growing or recrystallizing.

It has been suggested[30, 260d] that viscosity plays a part in the formation of sugar agglomerates, aside from the question of its role in the boiling process.[105] If crystals are to twin or agglomerate they must first come into contact. Since the syrups on which the crystals are grown are kept constantly in motion the crystals have ample opportunity to come together. Furthermore, they must remain in contact long enough for them to grow together. In a viscous medium they would be apt to stay together long enough for a growth process to be initiated between them whereas in a medium of low viscosity the crystals would tend to separate after colliding.

Starodustev and Timokhina[234] propose that surface tension is a dominant factor in the formation of agglomerates. The surface tension at the liquid-gas interface can be related to the surface tension at the solid-liquid interface by the following equation:

$$\sigma_{sl} = \sigma_{sg} - \sigma_{lg} \cos \theta$$

where σ_{sl} = surface tension at the liquid-solid interface
σ_{sg} = surface tension at the solid-gas interface
σ_{lg} = surface tension at the liquid-gas interface
θ = angle of wetting

Differentiating the above equation with σ_{sg} and θ remaining constant, we obtain

$$d\sigma_{sl} = -\cos \theta \cdot d\sigma_{lg}$$

This means that as the surface tension at the liquid-gas interface increases the surface tension at the liquid-solid interface decreases and vice versa. Take, for example, an impure syrup. Decreasing the surface tension means that more of the impurities or colloidal matter will go into the liquid-gas interface and less into the liquid-solid interface. Thus the capacity of the liquid-solid interface for sugar is increased and the film is relatively undersaturated. Agglomeration of the crystals will be inhibited since there is no crystallizable sugar present to form the bridge between the crystals when they come into contact. This elementary explanation is in agreement with the well-known fact that impure sugar syrups, which are surface active, exhibit much less tendency to form agglomerates than pure syrups of higher surface tension. It has also been observed that surfactants greatly reduce the formation of aggregates of all kinds in spontaneously nucleating syrups.[105]

The dielectric constant of the medium is also said to have an effect on agglomerate formation. Kopelman and Gregg[129] determined the agglomerating tendency of tungsten powder in liquids of varied dielectric constant. They found that agglomeration takes place in liquids with a dielectric constant below two and to a minimum extent in water which has a dielectric constant of about eighty. The difference was ascribed to the charge which was acquired by adsorption of either hydrogen or hydroxyl ions. Similar results were observed by Cosgrove[49] when single crystals of sucrose were suspended in media of varying dielectric constants. Clustering was extensive in CCl_4 and dioxane (dielectric constants 2.24 and 2.2, respectively), moderate in ethyl alcohol (25.8) and least in saturated water syrup (ca. 80). Cosgrove also observed that small crystals agglomerated more than large ones in liquids of high dielectric constant but that the difference was obliterated in the more extensive aggregation at low levels. In either case coalescence was more pronounced as the crystals were less uniform in size.

Continuous Crystallization

The crystallization of sugar on a commercial scale is still essentially a batch process even though the equipment has changed from that depicted in Figures 6-7 and 6-8 to such as illustrated in Figures 6-9 and 5-22. Pro-

Figure 6-7. Old sugar mill "Mon Loisir," Mauritius. Closed about 1875. (*Courtesy Dr. P. O. Wiehe.*)

Figure 6-8. "Batterie a la Malartic." This battery was connected to the smaller stack in Figure 6-7. (*Courtesy Dr. P. O. Wiehe.*)

Figure 6-9. Vacuum pan station. Labourdonnais raw sugar factory, Mauritius. (*Courtesy Mr. A. Wiehe.*)

duction rates, of course, have multiplied tremendously; from probably only hundreds of pounds per day in the old units to as much as 40 tons or more per strike which takes only a few hours in a refining pan such as illustrated in Figure 6-10. It is generally not feasible economically to exhaust completely the sugar-bearing mother liquor in the pan, so that it is general practice to withdraw the charge to crystallizers. The remaining 25 per cent or so of crystallizable sugar is recovered by regulated cooling in such equipment. The crystallizers also serve as holding reservoirs to feed the centrifuges.

"In most branches of chemical engineering, the ultimate aim is to design a perfect continuous system of production."[192d] A great deal of effort has been expended to this end by the sugar industry but none of the proposals have yet succeeded commercially. Continuous operation of crystallizers is possible[258] and this has led Proskowitz[194] to suggest that pan boiling may be eliminated altogether if wider cooling temperatures were employed. With continuous centrifuges a truly continuous process can be visualized on this score. Conventional vacuum crystallizers do not work with sugar solutions since the key to the effective operation of such units is the proper grading of the growing crystals[179] and this is very irregular in sugar massecuites presumably on account of high viscosity and the rapid accumulation of impurities.

Nonetheless, the relatively slow crystallization rate of sucrose makes continuous operation all the more attractive and the search for an effective design goes on at an ever-increasing pace as judged by the numerous papers

Figure 6-10. Refinery vacuum pan. Prymont Refinery, Colonial Sugar Refining Co., Sydney.

and patents on this subject. The few references cited[23, 24, 26, 51, 62a, 64, 205, 228, 241, 254, 278b, 284] are considered to be only representative.

The slow speed of growth of sucrose is illustrated by the following examples: linear growth rates of electrolytes such as KCl, $CuSO_4 \cdot 5H_2O$, E.D.T., etc. from aqueous solutions are frequently one hundred or more times those of sucrose at comparable supersaturations and temperatures. The same disparity is displayed by a comparison with NaCl. The (110) face of this material advances at a rate of about 100 μ/day when a solution saturated at 30°C is cooled one degree. This is equivalent to approximately 10^{20} molecules/cm^2 day. Under the same conditions sucrose crystals extend themselves at the rate of about 6 μ/day or only 10^{18} molecules/cm^2 day. Incidentally, this ratio of about 100-fold is approximately the same as the difference in growth rates of melts and solutions,[A-11, 245] the former commonly much faster than the latter.

Sugars other than Sucrose

Dextrose, lactose, and maltose are the only crystalline sugars other than sucrose which are commercially important; while fructose, xylose and various hexitols are produced in smaller amounts. The crystallization of other sugars and derivatives on a laboratory scale is also an important matter to the carbohydrate chemist since this accomplishment assures the separation, purification, and identification of a single unique entity.

Dextrose (*d*-glucose, corn or grape sugar) is made by the acid hydrolysis of starch under pressure. After neutralization and decolorizing the liquors are concentrated by vacuum evaporation to about 75% solids, but are reluctant to crystallize. The presently used process is largely the development of W. B. Newkirk[172] of the Corn Products Refining Co. and consists, in principle, of the crystallization of the dextrose upon a very heavy seed base. As much as 25% of a finished strike is left in the crystallizer to serve as a footing for the succeeding batch. With this tremendous growing area, exhaustion is rapid so that supersaturations are never excessive and false grain is avoided. When the crystallization proceeds below 50°C the monohydrate is formed while above this temperature the anhydrous form is obtained.[60] At still higher temperatures and concentrations (100°C, 90% solids) an isomer, β dextrose, forms and will continue to crystallize even as the temperature is lowered, provided seed crystals of the α form are excluded. A similar case[3a] is reported in which the crystallization of β-melibiose had been proceeding smoothly for over a year when suddenly the α form appeared. It was subsequently impossible to avoid formation of this isomer, so that the manufacture of the β form had to be discontinued. Apparently, a new virgin location will be necessary. Other similar incidents have already been mentioned (Chapter 1). In fact, the rates of crystallization and solution of these and other sugars which exist in several isometric forms are controlled entirely by the rate of conversion of one form into the other.[14, 107]

The rate of crystallization of dextrose is directly proportional to the supersaturation and is virtually independent of the temperature over the range of 25–43°C (Table 6-3). This means that diffusion is the rate-controlling step, which is not so in the case of sucrose.[165] This difference is emphasized in Figure 6-11 in which the monomolecular velocity constants of crystallization of several sugars are represented. Sucrose is the only one of those represented in which isomeric changes are not involved. Impurities in glucose syrups impede the crystallization tremendously[231] and the removal of those of an ionic nature by means of ion exchange agents improves the yield by 6 to 10% and increases the rate of crystallization as much as 30%.[90] Other factory data are available in the reports of Lebedev,[138] Gamannoto,[81] etc.[115, 262]

Lactose is made from milk whey. After deproteinating, the thin liquor is evaporated to 60% solids and then crystallized in water-cooled troughs. Roughly two-thirds of the lactose is obtained as very small pure crystals.

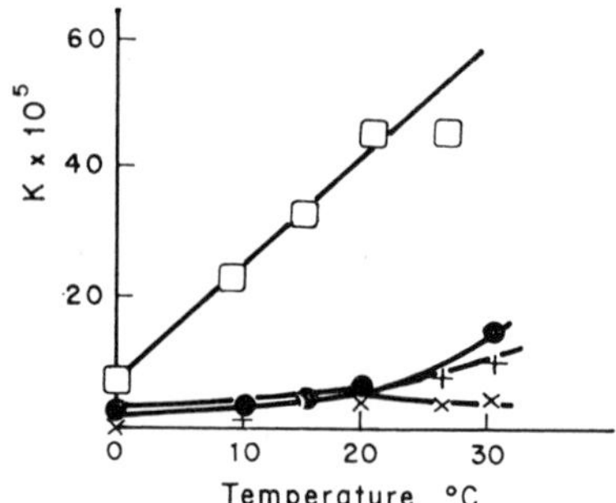

Figure 6-11. Monomolecular rate constants of crystallization.[282] □ Sucrose; ● Lactose; + Galactose; × Glucose.

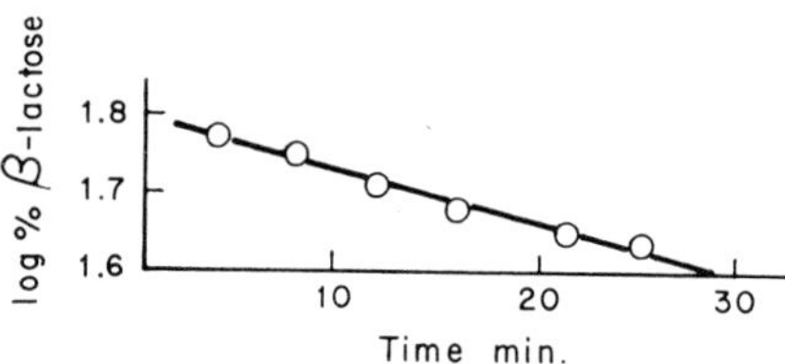

Figure 6-12. Monomolecularity of crystallization of β-lactose, After Choi, Tatter, and O'Malley.[43]

A second, relatively impure crop, amounting to another 15–20%, is obtained after concentration. Refining is effected by ion exchanging and recrystallizing in stainless steel equipment.[142, 198] Mutarotation of lactose solutions is pronounced and equilibration of the several isomers is sluggish. Choi, Tatter, and O'Malley[43] make use of this fact to determine the composition of dry milk products. Figure 6-12 illustrates the monomolecular crystallization of the β-form from a mixture with the α type.

Maltose, or malt sugar, may be made commercially by the carefully regulated hydrolysis of starch but is more generally produced on a large scale by the use of the enzyme maltase.[176] Levulose is another reducing sugar for which feasible commercial methods have been worked out on a pilot-plant scale. It is difficult to crystallize* in the presence of impurities but the use of ion exchange agents has greatly improved the recovery. In fact, these agents, and other intensified methods of purification, have been a great boon to the organic chemist who so often purifies and separates complex mixtures by the process of crystallization.

Crystalline D-fructose may be prepared by adding absolute alcohol to

* Levulose was known for a long time as "Uncrystallizable sugar." The proper chemical name is D-fructose.

the concentrated syrups obtained from the acid hydrolysis of inulin or inulin-bearing plants, such as Jerusalem artichoke. Alternatively, calcium levulate may be precipitated by adding calcium hydroxide to an approximately 10% solution of invert sugar. This is the product of hydrolysis of ordinary sucrose and consists of equimolar parts of D-fructose and glucose. The calcium compound of the latter is relatively soluble. The free sugar is freed from lime by carbon dioxide and, after concentration, the syrup is crystallized by adding alcohol. The details of this preparation, which are common to the production of many other sugars, are given in C 440.[14] The crystallizability of xylose syrups (wood sugar) has been studied by Nakhamanovch and co-workers,[168] while another Russian group[86] reports the production of single crystals of L-rhamnose hydrate as large as 285 grams.

Sorbitol and mannitol are made by electrolytic reduction of glucose and mannose respectively, or by hydrogenation over nickel catalyst. If invert sugar is used hexol is produced. This is a mixture of sorbitol and mannitol in 3/1 ratio and is used as such or is separated by crystallization of the mannitol (Table 6-4). Similarly, fructose alone gives 50–50 mixtures of the hexols. Sorbitol is quite difficult to crystallize from aqueous solutions due to the ease with which supersaturated solutions form and the relatively high viscosity of saturated solutions. The normal tendency is to form an amorphous or gelatinous precipitate when attempting to crystallize aqueously. These difficulties are overcome by crystallizing from an alcoholic solution. Good crystals are obtained in high yields.

A recommended procedure for alcoholic crystallization is to evaporate the sorbitol solution, using vacuum and a temperature of 70–80°C, until the water content is less than 5%. The syrup is then mixed with sufficient methyl or ethyl alcohol to obtain a 12% sorbitol solution and cooled slowly from 50 to 35°C with continuous agitation. If the solution does not self-seed add a small amount of sorbitol crystals. Allow to cool to room temperature overnight with continuous agitation. After filtration, the wet

TABLE 6-4. SOLUBILITY IN WATER OF MANNITOL AND SORBITOL

Temp (°C)	Solubility (g/100 g H_2O)	
	Mannitol	Sorbitol
10	13.8	179
20	18.6	222
30	25.3	275
40	34.2	335

filter cake should be vacuum dried at an initial temperature of about 25°C. This may be increased to about 65°C after most of the alcohol is removed.

Mannitol may readily be crystallized from aqueous solutions in the form of needles.

SALT

Production

The salt industry is the oldest, and next to the sugar industry, the greatest practitioner of the art of crystallization from solution. Caldwell[38, 141] mentions a Chinese print dated 2700 B.C. which shows the production of salt by the evaporation of natural brine. Schoen, Grove, and Palermo[214] in their "Early History of Crystallization" sketch many of the early developments in the production of salt.

While the current annual world production of salt greatly exceeds that of sugar—77,400,000 short tons[257] vs. 58,267,000[3b] in 1957—it is likely that at least half is used directly as brine (Figure 6-13). On the other hand, practically all the world's sugar is crystallized at least once.

Solid salt is produced as rock salt[91, 116, 283] by direct mining or by evaporation of brines. The performance of the latter by natural means is probably the oldest of the crystallization arts and is still conducted widely in different parts of the world (Figure 6-14). A recent improvement[17] consists of the addition of a green dye to increase the solar energy absorption. This has enhanced the evaporation efficiency as much as 19%. Free[78] discusses in detail the present-day production of solar salt, and Meyers and Bonython[157] the theory involved. Evaporated salt is produced in grainers or vacuum evaporators, or by the Alberger process. Submerged combustion[3c] has also been applied to the concentration of the brines by evaporation of water. In these processes the brines are usually first purified by aerating to remove dissolved gases and alkalized to remove or at least reduce sus-

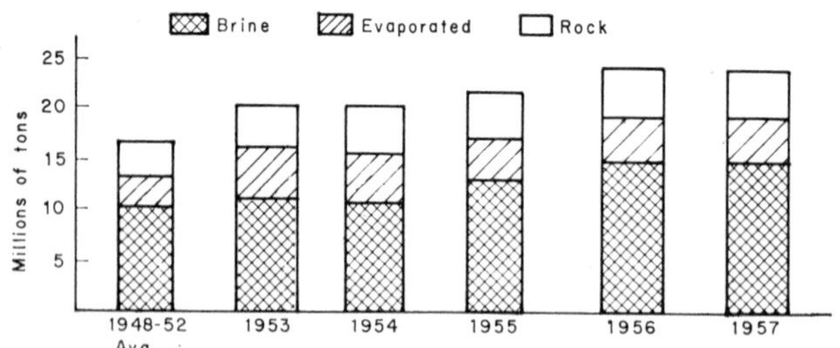

Figure 6-13. Salt sold or used by producers in the U.S. Compiled from data in Ref. 257.

Figure 6-14. Solar salt evaporation. Mauritius.

pended iron sols and dissolved alkaline earths. In any case, the crystallization itself effects the major purification.

The grainer process consists of evaporation in long shallow pans, often 180 ft long, 18 ft wide, and 18 in. deep. The heating coils are close to the surface of evaporation and below them is a slowly moving reciprocating rake which removes the salt which settles out. A pan of the above size will produce 80 tons of salt a day. Brine is fed in continuously so that impurities accumulate and eventually the operation must be terminated for purging. The characteristic feature of grainer operation is that evaporation occurs below the boiling point of the solution and crystallization commences and proceeds in the relatively undisturbed surface. The freshly formed crystals are retained in this surface by surface-tension forces and grow principally in this plane since the submerged zone is slightly undersaturated and the top of the cube is not wetted by the brine. A plate or flake-like aggregate thus accumulates until its weight exceeds the buoyant force. It then drops to the bottom. Should the crystal sink only slowly, typical hopper-shaped crystals result. Fragmentation of these rather delicate structures gives rise to the flat plates which are a characteristic component of grainer salt.[124] The hollow square pyramidal components are the same as commonly obtained by the quiet evaporation of salt solutions in shallow vessels with no special regulation. Grainer salt is consumed largely by the dairy and pickling industries. Only about 400,000 tons were produced by this method in the United States in 1957. The remaining approximately 3.5 million ton production of evaporated salt in that year was produced by vacuum pans and solar evaporation in the ratio of about 2 to 1.

Figure 6-15. Vacuum pans in Watkins Glen plant of International Salt Company.

Triple-effect vacuum evaporators fed with fresh brine to each effect are the usual practice for concentrating salt solutions. Vertical units are the universal choice for the salting-out operation. Agitators promote crystallization and minimize caking on the tubes. There is little or no corrosion with cast iron or copper. Alloy steel plate is a satisfactory substitute with considerable reductions in weight and cost. A representative size would be 18–22 ft in diameter × 36–45 ft high (Figure 6–15). The crystals formed in these units are freely suspended in the circulating brine and grow uniformly as perfect cubes. When sufficiently large to settle, they are withdrawn in various ways: (1) A salt-catcher. This consists of a receiving vessel with valves above and below. By opening the upper valve with the lower closed, the salt collects and may be removed after reversing the valve positions. This method is little used except when small amounts are involved. (2) Another passing method consists essentially of a barometric leg through which wet salt is withdrawn by means of a pump or bucket elevator. (3) A centrifugal pump is attached to settling tanks or screen filters from which solution is returned to the evaporator and salt to the centrifuges.

The Alberger process is a unique system[8, 201] in which superheated brine is flash evaporated. The resulting slurry is sent to grainer pans. The final crystals are a mixture of fine needles and characteristic hollow grainer pyramids and present a very high specific surface.

Growth Characteristics

Some details of the forms of NaCl crystals and their modifications have already been described (Chapter 2). Honigmann[106a] describes many others. The nucleation of NaCl solutions is similar to that of the other alkali halides and can be adequately accounted for by the Volmer theory as developed by Turnbull. Nucleation is facilitated by many foreign bodies. Galena, for instance,[178] reduces the effective supersolubility limit considerably. The influence of conditions and impurities are discussed by Neuhaus[171c] who points out that the low temperature coefficient of solubility of NaCl means that practical supersaturations will be small and, therefore, growth rates slow. Copious nuclei form at even very small degrees of supersaturation so that the production of good single crystals is difficult. However, the addition of even a few ppms of Pb^{++} to the solution inhibits the spontaneous formation of nuclei so that good, clear, and even brilliant crystals may be obtained[A-37, 70] (Figure 6-16). In fact, recent Russian workers[154] claim that 40–50 g crystals of KCl, KBr and KI grown from aqueous solutions in the presence of Pb^{++} and Zn^{++} are superior to those usually grown from the melt. The improvement is the result of a slower growth rate due to absorption of the impurity. Analysis shows that these impurities are incorporated in part in the crystal, and Figure 6-17 demonstrates a marked reduction in the growth rate. The benefits of such "mineralizers" are not unique to the alkali halides.

Other Alkali Halides

The crystallization patterns of the other alkali halides are similar to that of NaCl with benefits accruing from higher temperature coefficients

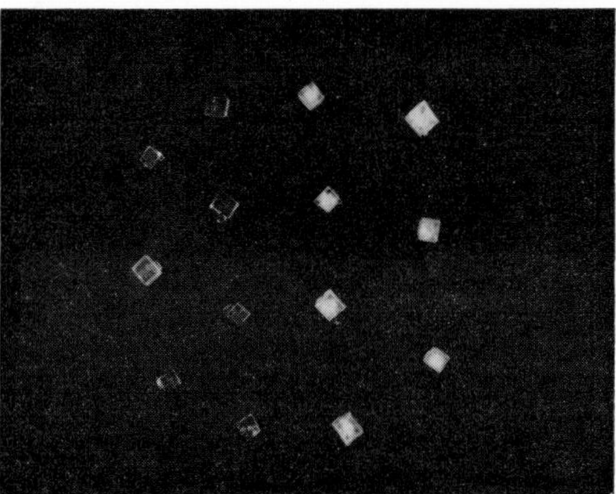

Figure 6-16. NaCl crystals grown from pure brine (right) and same containing 1 ppm Pb^{++} (left).

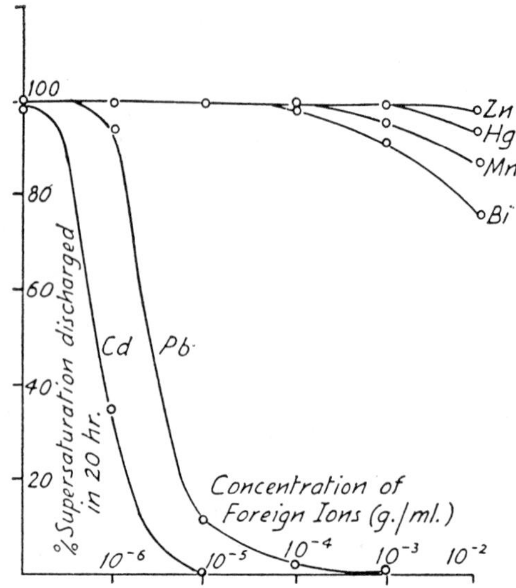

Figure 6-17. Effect of foreign ions on the crystallization rate of NaCl.[21]

of solubility. General conformation with the Volmer expectations have been found and most recently elaborated by Chatterji and Singh.[42] Sears[217] also reports that the growth of KCl from aqueous solution is consistent with the Frank theory while Schnerb and Block[213] investigated several mineralizers in this system.

KCl is the most important of these salts as a heavy chemical and a comprehensive discussion of its recovery from crude salts by crystallization is given by Autenrieth, Rieke, and Dust[6, 169] and others.[5] Pozin, and Muratova[193] also discuss the kinetic features of the same process, while Moriyama and Yawataya[163] do the same for NH_4Cl.

HEAVY AND FERTILIZER CHEMICALS

Many important heavy chemicals such as sodium carbonate, bicarbonate and hydroxide, ammonium and calcium chloride, sodium sulfate, hydrochloric acid, etc. are derived from sodium chloride as a raw material. Na_2CO_3, $NaHCO_3$, $CaCl_2$, Na_2SO_4, and other products are also recovered from natural deposits by crystallization. There are many other important inorganic chemicals which are won by crystallization, for example: Ammonium nitrate and sulfate, boric acid, copper sulfate, the sodium phosphates, copperas, magnesium chloride and sulfate, the alums, potassium and sodium nitrate, sodium thiosulfate, zinc sulfate, etc. The following sections will describe only superficially the production of a few of these "tonnage" crystalline materials together with pertinent theoretical interpretations.

Sodium Sulfate

Somewhat more than two-thirds of the million and a half tons of salt cake produced in the United States in 1957 came from Mannheim hydrochloric-acid plants and the balance from natural sources.[257] The manufactured product is the residue from heating salt and sulfuric acid together to give hydrochloric acid as the primary product. Rayon and cellophane factories and other chemical plants also produce by product sodium sulfate.

Natural sodium sulfate occurs as lake brines and crude beds of Glauber's salt ($Na_2SO_4 \cdot 10H_2O$) in extensive deposits in the western part of this continent and abroad. A 95 per cent anhydrous product may be realized from some of the crude materials by merely crushing, washing, and drying.[190] Purification and recovery from saturated brine on a large scale may be carried out most effectively in the Oslo-type of crystallizer[113] such as illustrated in Figure 6-18.

The heated brine (*H*) is supersaturated by flashing in chamber *V*, from which it circulates downward and then upward (*C*) through a bed of anhydrous crystals. These crystals are maintained in a state of limited suspension and are grown large enough to stay in the crystal body and not circulate. As they grow still larger they settle and are removed by a trap *T*.

Sodium sulfate exhibits retrograde solubility above 32.38°C and this causes rapid scaling in the heating tubes. Methanol and ethanol reverse this solubility relationship and the saturation concentration remains almost

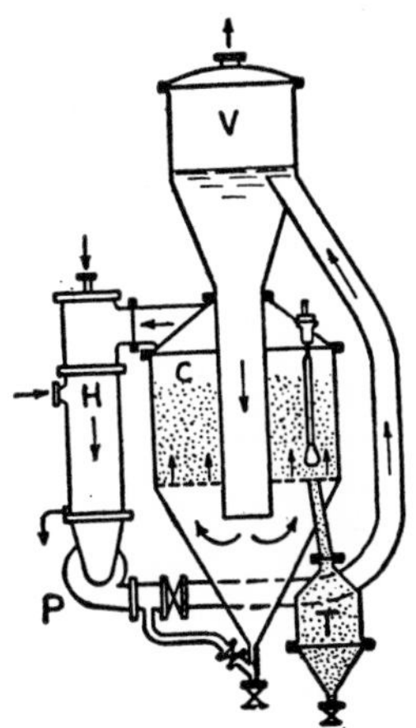

Figure 6-18. Oslo crystallizer.[113]

invariant with temperature in the presence of ethylene glycol.[263] Accordingly, scaling may be avoided by crystallization in the presence of these agents.[84] The product is obtained in a variety of forms, ranging from fluffy fine grains to large, well-formed and uniform crystals, depending upon the degree of agitation and concentration of the salting-out agent.

Many of the very early experiments on supersaturation were performed with sodium sulfate, probably because it was readily available and supersaturates and supercools very easily. This behavior presents no particular difficulty in the usual commercial production of the solid salt since sufficient footings of seed material are usually present during the crystallization process. However, the possible supercooling of 14°C or more, in the case of the melt, could be an impediment to the use of this reversible transition as a reservoir in the storage of solar heat. The possibility may be avoided by adding small amounts of sodium tetraborate decahydrate.[248] Many of the salt hydrates isomorphous with Glauber's salt have considerably lower transition temperatures but borax is eminently suited in the 90°F working range. Borax is not only just slightly soluble in supersaturated sodium sulfate solutions but also is well within a 5 per cent epitactic tolerance (Table 6-5). It catalyzes the nucleation of $Na_2SO_4 \cdot 10H_2O$ very well, reducing the sustained supersaturation to 2°C. On the other hand, Pb WO_4, for instance, does not relieve the usual supercooling of Glauber's salt.

Salt Lakes and Deposits

A wide variety of inorganic salts is derived from numerous salt lakes. The classic phase-rule study of such salt deposits is van't Hoff's[261] "Zur Bildung der Ozeanischen Salzblagerungen." Books like those of Teeple, Curtis, and Turrentine[256] describe the commercial application of these principles.

The chief salt in the Stassfurt deposit is carnallite, $MgCl_2 \cdot KCl \cdot 6H_2O$.

Table 6-5. Materials with Crystallographic Data within the 15% Rule[248]

Salt	Crystallographic Data			
	a (Å)	b (Å)	c (Å)	β
$Na_2SO_4 \cdot 10H_2O$	1.116	1	1.238	107°45′
$Na_2B_4O_7 \cdot 10H_2O$	1.114	1	1.159	106°35′
$PbWO_4$ (Raspite)	1.344	1	1.114	107°33′
	Deviations (per cent)			
$Na_2B_4O_7 \cdot 10H_2O$	−0.2	—	−6.3	−1.1
$PbWO_4$	20.5	—	10.0	−0.2

This comprises about 55 per cent of the crude material, another 25 per cent being NaCl, and the balance chiefly kieserite, $MgSO_4 \cdot H_2O$. About 80 per cent of the KCl crystallizes directly upon cooling a hot purified solution. Upon further concentration and cooling the balance of the KCl crystallizes as carnallite. This is returned to the incoming fresh solutions of raw material. Sylvinite (NaCl, KCl) deposits are extracted with hot saturated NaCl solution. This leaves most of the NaCl component and insolubles behind. Alternatively, either component may be separated from the other by means of appropriate flotation operations. KCl crystallizes from these liquors upon cooling and the mother liquor is returned to the leaching lines. A brief outline of the Searles Lake potash operations will illustrate the general mode of working American salt deposits. This dry lake is a bed of solid salt of very complex composition. It is permeated with a saturated brine containing chiefly K, Na, Cl, CO_3, B_4O_7 and PO_4 ions. This brine is first concentrated in multiple-effect evaporators with the separation of sodium chloride and burkeite, $Na_2CO_3 \cdot 2Na_2SO_4$, until saturated with respect to KCl. At this stage it is almost saturated with respect to borax. Upon rapid cooling only pure KCl crystallizes and no borax, since supersaturated solutions of borax are rather stable and crystallize slowly.[83, 101] Upon further cooling in vacuum crystallizers crude borax crystallizes after heavy seeding.[19] This is purified by recrystallization. The water condensed from the crystallizers is refluxed to prevent KCl from crystallizing. The CO_3/SO_4 ratio in the first evaporator feed is controlled by addition of mother liquor from the first borax crystallization in order to avoid precipitation of glaserite, $K_3Na(SO)_2$, instead of burkeite. The essential features of this process are represented in Figure 6-19.

"Raw brine is represented by point B and plant mother liquor by point M. A mixture of these two solutions in the proportions of about three parts brine to one part of mother liquor is represented by point F.

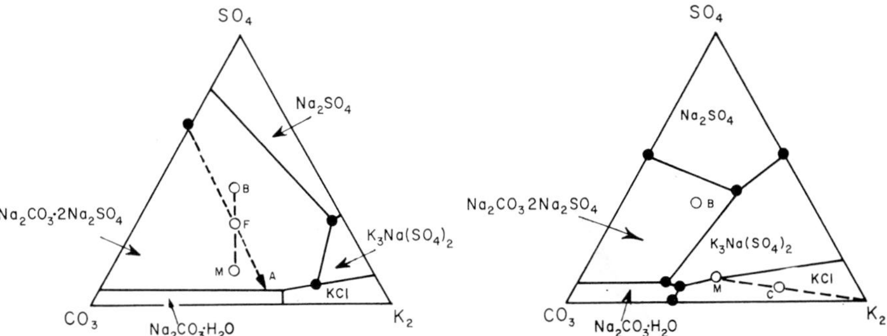

Figure 6-19. Phase diagram, Searles Lake brine.[80] 100°C and 35°C, respectively.

This is the mixture fed to the triple-effect evaporator. These operate in countercurrent fashion so that the concentration is finished at the highest temperature. During this evaporation sodium chloride and burkeite crystallize and are removed continuously. The composition of the liquor travels along the line *FA*, the path of crystallization of burkeite, until point *A* is reached. At this point the mother liquor reaches saturation with respect to $Na_2CO_3 \cdot H_2O$ which also precipitates with burkeite and sodium chloride from *A* to *C* as the liquor approaches saturation with potassium chloride in the high temperature effect. This concentrated liquor, freed from suspended salts and containing about 19 to 20 per cent KCl, is sent to the potash-crystallizing house where it is cooled for crystallization of KCl. Point *C*, at 35°C represents the composition of the hot concentrated liquor. This is near the center of the KCl field and upon cooling to this temperature only KCl crystallizes out along the line *CM*. The mother liquor *M* is thus regenerated for use in the next cycle, insofar as the potash content is concerned."[80, 201]

Soda may be leached from those Searles salts rich in that component. Burkeite is left behind and the soda is recovered as decahydrate by chilling the liquors. The burkeite may be resolved into its component salts with water at 20°C, whereby the soda is extracted and sodium sulfate left. Another possibility is to carbonate the appropriate brine. $NaHCO_3$ precipitates and is calcined to soda ash. At high alkalinity, sodium sesquicarbonate, $NaHCO_3 \cdot Na_2CO_3 \cdot H_2O$, precipitates rather than the straight bicarbonate, and the rate of crystallization of this salt from Lake Owens brines is represented in Figure 6-20.

Epsom Salts

Magnesium sulfate is a common constituent of many natural brines and mineral waters. It also occurs as the mineral kieserite, $MgSO_4 \cdot H_2O$. How-

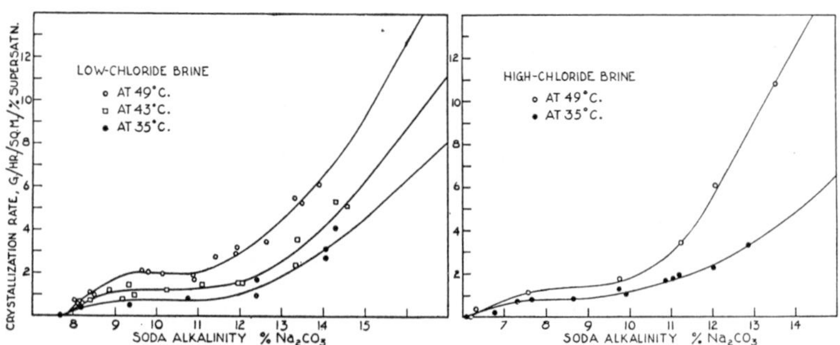

Figure 6-20. Crystallization rate of sodium sesquicarbonate during carbonation of brines.[65]

TABLE 6-6. THE SEVERAL HYDRATES OF $MgSO_4$

Form	Equilibrium Temperature (°C)
Ice and $MgSO_4 \cdot 12H_2O$	−3.9
Ice and $MgSO_4 \cdot 7H_2O$	−5.0
$MgSO_4 12H_2O$ and $MgSO_4 \cdot 7H_2O$(I)	1.8
$MgSO_4 \cdot 7H_2O$(I) and $MgSO_4 \cdot 6H_2O$	48.1
$MgSO_4 6H_2O$ and $MgSO_4 \cdot H_2O$	67.5
$MgSO_4 \cdot 6H_2O$ and $MgSO_4 \cdot 5H_2O$	77.5
$MgSO_4 \cdot 7H_2O$ and $MgSO_4 \cdot 6H_2O$	23

ever, it is most commonly produced by crystallization of the sulfuric acid leachings of natural or burned magnesia minerals. The procedure is simple in principle and consists essentially of concentrating in vacuum evaporators and crystallization upon cooling in shallow iron tanks, troughs, or vacuum crystallizers. There are, however, complications due to polymorphism, metastable phases and slow rates of adjustment.

Of the first, there are two forms of the heptahydrate: a stable rhombic one (I) and an unstable monoclinic one (II). (I) is the form which usually crystallizes from aqueous solutions at normal temperatures while the second comes down below 21°C. The equilibrium temperatures of the several hydrates which can form are listed in Table 6-6. The interconversion of these in the metastable condition is apt to be slow.

Much epsom salts is used as a pharmaceutical. For this purpose a needle-like product which dissolves quickly is demanded. This has restricted the use of continuous crystallizers for this product since such equipment tends to produce symmetrical granular crystals rather than needles. Under controlled conditions, however, needles are possible.[252] Mokievskii[160] finds that concentration currents and motion of the solution affect the form of Epsom salt crystals, as well as temperature, supersaturation, and impurities.

Alums

The alums are illustrative of another product which is still produced in elementary ways even though improved and continuous processes have been worked out. The sodium alum, for instance, is made by evaporating a solution of Na_2SO_4 and $Al_2(SO_4)_3$ to such concentration as forms a hard cake of alum, $NaAl(SO_4)_2 \cdot 12H_2O$, in cooling pans. Better crystals are obtained by controlled crystallization in shallow ponds, troughs, or other equipment. Copperas, $FeSO_4 \cdot 7H_2O$, another common coagulant for water treatment, is processed similarly from "pickle" liquors. Perry[189] gives some data on the tank crystallization of copperas (Table 6-7).

TABLE 6-7. TANK CRYSTALLIZATION OF COPPERAS[189]

Total Time of Cycle (hr)	Solution Received (gal)	Sp Gr of Solution Received	$FeSO_4 \cdot 7H_2O$ in Solution lb	Crop (lb)	Mother Liquor (gal)	Sp Gr of Mother Liquor
48	1,630	1.400 at 62°C	11,171	7,275	835	1.240 at 15°C
60	1,630	1.395 at 60°C	11,085	7,365	945	1.247 at 19°C
72	1,630	1.935 at 53°C	10,994	8,550	815	1.210 at 10°C
96	1,660	1.400 at 51°C	11,254	8,787	950	1.201 at 9°C

Phosphates

Of the various phosphates the trisodium salt is the most important tonnage-wise. This is made by the neutralization of phosphoric acid with soda ash and caustic soda, the excess of the latter being carefully adjusted since it greatly influences the size distribution of the final crystals. Additives are also helpful for this purpose.[3d] Size distribution is an important specification since much of this product is packaged for domestic use. The hot alkaline solution is usually crystallized in tanks or in continuous equipment. The crystallization of phosphoric acid as such is described by Waggman.[269]

Fertilizer Chemicals

Many fertilizer chemicals are crystalline products. The production of ammonium nitrate may be taken as typical and representative of vacuum crystallization in a continuous way. The flow diagram for the process as practiced at the TVA plant in Wilson Dam, Alabama, is illustrated in Figure 6-21 and the crystallization plant features in Figure 6-22.

Each of five units produce 105 tons of NH_4NO_3 per day. Supersaturation is induced by evaporation and cooling in the vaporizer. Scaling on the wall

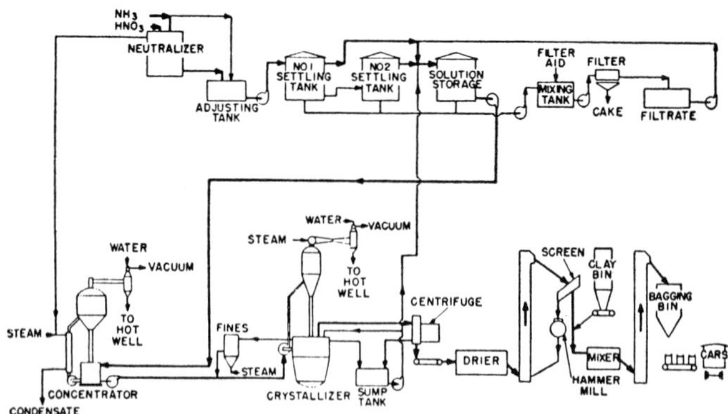

Figure 6-21. Flow diagram of TVA vacuum crystallizer plant for ammonium nitrate.[204]

is prevented by directing the circulating suspension against the wall in a continuous, circular sheet. The liquor velocity of 5 to 7 ft per second prevents the crystals from settling out. Fines and heavies are removed continuously for redissolving. The supersaturation of about 14 pounds of ammonium nitrate per 1000 gallons is completely exhausted by the 40 tons of suspended crystals. The product averages 65% on 20-mesh and 97 on

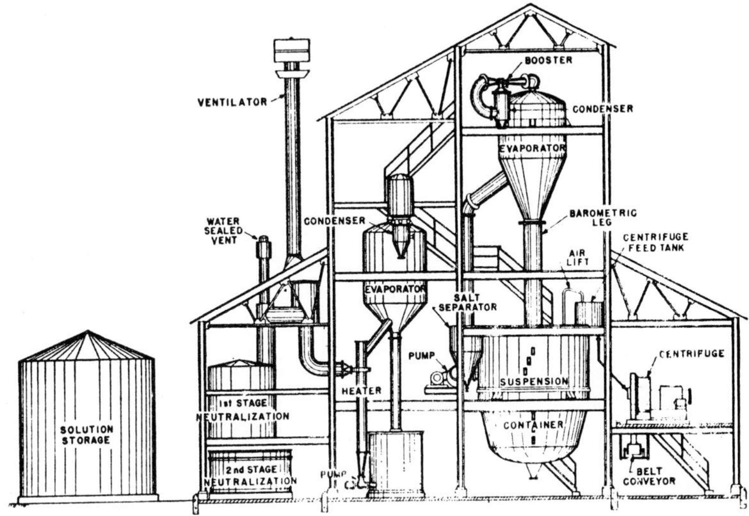

Figure 6-22a. Cross-sectional view of crystallizer building.[204]

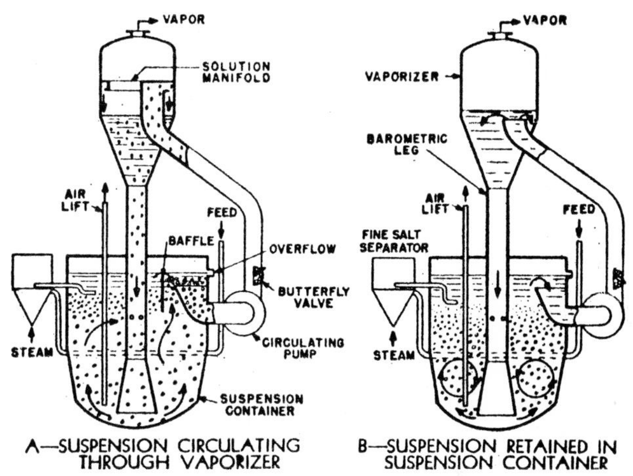

Figure 6-22b. Cross-sectional views of vacuum crystallizers for ammonium nitrate.[204]

35-mesh screens. The crystallizers are operated above 90°F for greater heat economy and because the crystals produced at this temperature have better drying characteristics and strength than the polymorphic forms produced at lower temperatures.

Saeman, Miller, *et al.*[204] found no special effects of pH and impurity content of the solution, but it has since been reported[220] that as little as 0.05% of surface active agents in the liquor, or even smaller amounts of habit-modifying dyestuffs such as Acid Magenta,[281] obviate caking of ammonium nitrate and other fertilizer chemicals upon storage. Other reports[3f] indicate that surfactants are no panacea for caking troubles (*vide infra*, Chapter 5). A common method of combating this difficulty in fertilizers is to "prill." This consists in pelleting by dropping molten NH_4NO_3 or other materials through high towers. The spheres are then coated with paraffin, rosin, or Vaseline, and a parting agent such as clay.

Metallurgy

The principles of crystallization theory are most certainly of cardinal significance in the science of metallurgy. This has long been realized, and many of the early theoretical ideas and practical technics of crystallization have stemmed from investigations in this field. This is especially true regarding polycomponent systems and complicated mechanisms. The subject is so vast that only a few of its pertinent aspects will be indicated here in the form of some leading introductory references.

Older theories of phase transformations by nucleation and growth are presented in standard works such as those of Burger,[36] Cottrell,[50] etc.[55, 57, 218, 237b] The formal theory of the kinetics of transformations is covered in the numerous publications of Mehl and co-workers,[153] Avrami,[7] Cahn,[37] etc. This same subject in all its complexities has also been considered in detail in several recent symposia.[A-45, 243a] The application of modern theories of growth to metal systems is presented in a number of readily available books and reviews on solid state physics and chemistry.[32, 40, 126, 219, 243b]

Single Crystals

The revival of crystallization investigations may be ascribed at least as much to the search for new piezoelectric materials as to metallurgical and meteorological interests. There was a continuing interest in the production of large single crystals ever since the turn of the century and this reached a peak during World War II in view of threatened insufficient supply of natural quartz crystals. Since that time many other materials have been produced in the form of large single crystals for various applications and the methods employed truly involve as much art as science.

TABLE 6-8. COMMON SINGLE CRYSTALS PRODUCED SYNTHETICALLY

Use	Examples
Piezo crystals	Quartz, ammonium and potassium dihydrogen phosphates (EDP, KDP), Rochelle or Seignette Salt (potassium sodium tartrate, KNP), Ethylene diamine tartrate (EDT), Lithium sulphate monohydrate (LSH).
Optical crystals	Alkali halides, calcium fluoride, silver chloride, thallium bromide iodide.
Luminescent crystals	Anthracene, napthalene, stilbene, terphenyl, Na and KI activated with thallium iodide, ZnS-silver activated Ca and Cd tungstates.
Gemstones	Sapphires, rubies, emeralds, etc.
Miscellaneous	Diamonds (abrasive), mica, asbestos (insulator), Silicates (ceramics).

In addition to primary use in piezo and other electrical and magnetic applications, good single crystals are used in optical apparatus, radiation counters, gemstones, etc. The following list, Table 6-8, is an enumeration of those most commonly produced on more than a laboratory scale.

There is a prolific literature on the subject of single crystals. As in many sections of this monograph no pretense is made to cover these references completely but, rather, an indication of those reviews and leading references which may be useful for those approaching the subject anew. In the first instance, the best general account, to the writer's knowledge, is Chapter 2 in Buckley's book. Then, there are the reviews of Walker,[270a] the O.T.S. reports,[177] Lawson and Nielson, and others,[171, 245] in addition to the general papers mentioned in the appendix.

Piezo crystals are manufactured mainly by crystallization from solution; optical, and luminescent materials from the melt or vapor; and gemstones by the Verneuil flame process.

Crystallization from the Melt

Zerfoss[282] classifies crystal-growing methods from the melt in three simple categories: a) Crucible methods; b) Withdrawal methods; and c) Flame fusion. In the first, a cone-tipped cylindrical crucible filled with the melt is lowered through a furnace in which a temperature gradient is maintained. This region extends from above to below the melting point of the material. A nucleus usually forms at the tip as this passes through the solidification point and continues to grow and fill the crucible as a single crystal. The thermal gradient and speed of movement are critical. These are the essential features of the Stockbarger method (Figures 6-23, 6-24, 6-25), which form

Figure 6-23. Experimental furnaces, Harshaw Chemical Co.

Figure 6-24. String saws, Harshaw Chemical Co.

Figure 6-25. Typical single sodium chloride crystal, Harshaw Chemical Co.

of equipment has also been operated as a vacuum furnace for producing superior fluoride crystals. In the older Tammann and Bridgman modifications[28a] the tip of the crucible or tube is drawn out into a capillary, or extended beyond a constriction. Polycrystalline growth starts in this section but a single crystal extends itself and continues to grow in the main part of the crystallizer, as illustrated in Figure 6-26. Kapitza and others have used this design also with many variations (A-1). For instance, Stöber[235, 238] keeps the crucible stationary and varies the gradient; Cinnamon's[45] crystallizing tube was fixed in a horizontal position, Palibin and Froiman[180] adjusted the angle of the tip according to the orientation of the single crystal, etc.

The Kyropoulos and Czochralski methods are typical of the withdrawal technique. In these, a relatively cool tube or rod is lowered into a crucible of melt. Crystals form but a single crystal dominates as the stock is slowly withdrawn. Alternately, a properly orientated single seed crystal may be used. The seed crystal is then gradually developed by regulated withdrawal. These methods have an advantage in that the crystals produced are relatively strain free and the troublesome detail of separating the solidified product from the container is avoided. Dislocation-free silicon[56] crystals and many others have been produced in this way.

In the flame-fusion technique powder is dropped or injected into the stream of an oxygen-hydrogen or other high-temperature burner. The powder melts as it emerges from the flame and builds up a cone-shaped deposit of sintered solid upon a pedestal which is inserted in the stream. A single crystal is usually favored at the tip of the polycrystalline mass and is developed as a boule by careful manipulation and control of operating details. Annealing of the finished boule is especially critical. The method is generally used with refractory materials, especially as first developed by Verneuil in 1891 for synthetic rubies and sapphires.[158]

The synthesis of sapphires probably constitutes the most important commercial application of the Verneuil process even though the limited production of high-quality gems by this same method is much more spectacular.[223] World production of ordinary grade sapphires now amounts to several million carats.[32] These are utilized for bearings, abrasive, phonograph needles, drawing dies and optical windows. Drost and Kebler[66] have grown 2¼-inch diameter sapphire disks at the rate of 150 to 200 ct/hr in about 2½ hr by rotating or reciprocating the boule transversely to the flame. The boules are built up of a succession of very thin layers. This structure is not observed in the product made by hydrothermal methods.[137]

Figure 6-27 pictures the development of a ruby boule produced in the apparatus represented in Figure 6-28. Figure 6-29 compares the elegance of this product with the natural stone. Rubies, sapphires, rutile, and many other fine quality gems (as distinct from bogus stones) are made by this method, but the famous Chatham emeralds are probably produced hydro-

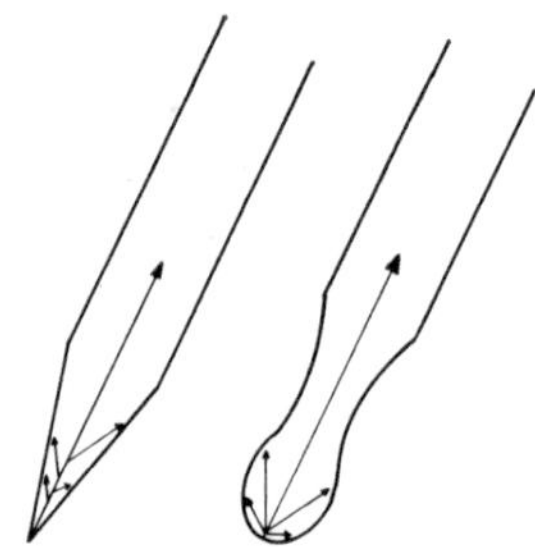

Figure 6-26. Domination of one single crystal.

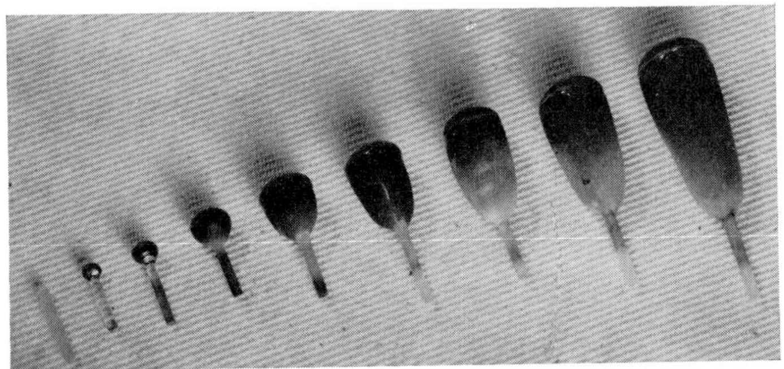

Figure 6-27. Development of a ruby boule. (*Courtesy Linde Air Products Co.*)

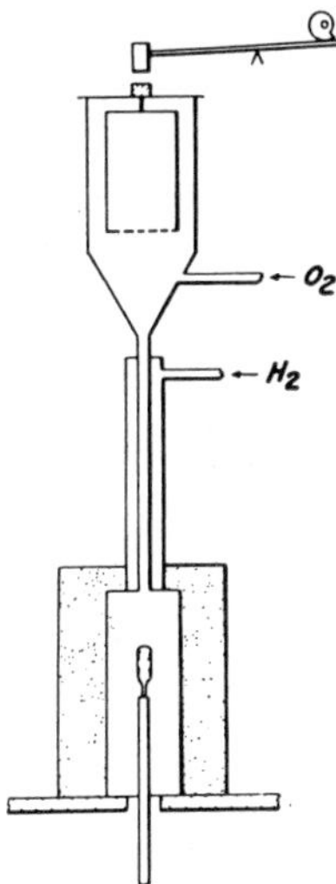

Figure 6-28. Schematic Verneuil furnace. (*Courtesy of the Linde Air Products Co.*)

thermally.[274] The natural and synthetic stones are practically identical and only the expert can distinguish them (Table 6-9).

Crystallization from Solutions

Buckley traces the development of apparatus for crystallization of single crystals from solutions—most often aqueous. These methods have been considerably improved in recent years for the commercial and semi-commercial production of most of the crystals listed as piezo crystals in Table 6-8. The hydrothermal production of quartz calls for special consideration.

Holden (A-37, 103) describes many of the guiding rules as well as fine points of the art of crystal growing. It is, for instance, more satisfactory

Figure 6-29. "Linde" synthetic "star" ruby (right); natural "star" ruby (left). (*Courtesy of the Linde Air Products Co.*)

to grow crystals by slowly cooling the solution than by evaporation. The rate of cooling should be regulated so that fast-growing faces advance no faster than 0.05 in. to 0.10 in. per day (100–200 molecular layers per second). Inclusions are apt to appear in faster-grown crystals. These inclusions often assume the form of threadlike veils and appear to be the result of inhomogeneities of concentration in the immediate neighborhood of the growing crystal. Reciprocal agitation of the crystal itself dissipated these irregularities. It must be gentle to avoid generating grain in the main body of the mother liquor. A proven laboratory crystallizer is best described in Holden's own words:

"A cylindrical jar of Pyrex glass, a foot in diameter and a foot-and-a-half high, acts as a container for about 24 l of mother liquor and as its own thermostat. It sits on an enclosed annular air space about an inch

TABLE 6-9. EMERALDS[274]

Origin	Refractive Index	Specific Gravity
Finest Muzo, Columbia	1.570–1.580	2.71
Finest Chiro, Columbia	1.569–1.577	2.69
Synthetic American	1.565–1.570	2.65
Synthetic German (Igmerald)	1.561–1.564	2.67

deep containing unsheathed Nichrome-coil heating elements. One set of coils, below the center of the jar, continuously dissipates 30 W. Another coil, beneath the periphery of the jar, dissipates 100 W under control of a heavy-duty relay and a thermal regulator of the sealed-contact mercury-in-glass type.

"The lid of the jar is drilled in the center to clear a shaft which carries and moves the crystals. Commonly the shaft is 1 in. polymethyl methacrylate rod, 15 in. long, turned down to $\frac{1}{2}$ in. for an inch projecting through the lid, and the crystals are supported on spoke-like cross arms of $\frac{1}{16}$ in. stainless steel rod, carried in tightly fitting holes drilled in the shaft, and projecting about 3 in. from it. The lid is also drilled to take rubber stoppers, one carrying a thermometer, and another the thermal regulator, if it is adjustable, or a test tube in which a fixed thermal regulator will loosely fit so that it can be removed for resetting without exposing the solution to the dust outside, and in which a little water or oil improves thermal contact between regulator and solution.

"The crystals are carried through the solution at the ends of the cross arms by rotating the central rod at rates of from 15 to 30 rpm depending on the viscosity of the solution and its stability to supersaturation. If spurious crystals are formed, they find their way to the bottom of the jar and are carried to the centre of the bottom by the vortical motion of the solution. That section of the bottom is slightly warmer than the bulk of the solution, because of the continuous heater beneath it, and the spurious crystals are either dissolved or much slowed in growth.

"Unless the direction of rotation of the shaft is reversed at least once a minute, the solution rotates with the crystals and relative motion declines, and the crystals show veils on the "wake" side, evidencing dead spots. Midget motors, reversed by relays controlled by clock motors through cams operating micro-switches, afford elegant driving units of the required type. Simpler, and adapted to driving several crystallizing units, is belting from pulleys on a jack shaft driven as follows. A continuous motor turns, through a reducing gear, a crank at the rate of about 4 rpm, from which a crank shaft drives a large bicycle sprocket, rotating it about one-third revolution forwards and back. From this sprocket a roller chain drives a small sprocket on the jack shaft, one-third revolution of the former providing three revolutions of the latter."

Temperature control is important and schedules may be automatic or approximated by regularly resetting the regulators by small decrements of a few tenths of a degree. At temperatures above about 50°C, heaters and insulation are required and precautions must be taken to avoid loss by evaporation.[74, 239] In general, any fragment of crystal is a possible seed, but commonly one showing natural faces is best. The seed may be mounted in many ways; most simply by glueing to a hair, glass fiber or wire, or by clamping or inserting in appropriate plastic tubing. The seed must be purged of extraneous surface nuclei. This is accomplished most readily by previously warming the mother liquor to slight undersaturation before inserting the seed. The operation must be performed so that spurious seed is dissolved without complete loss of the parent seed. If the finishing temperature is far different from the ambient, the crystals should be again tempered before removal. This may be accomplished most easily by drawing off the solution and allowing the crystals to cool slowly in the still warm crystallizer.

A serious limitation of the batch-wise operation described is that only the crystallizable solute content of the solution is available for deposition during a single cycle. This led to the development[44, 270b, c] of the constant temperature apparatus sketched in Figure 6-30.

"Tank A is the saturator. Solution is stirred constantly at a fixed temperature in contact with an excess of the finely divided salt. Because the rate or flow in the system is only 10 to 15 gal per hour, the solution is practically saturated in A before it flows through the filter B, and the heated insulated pipe line, into the superheater tank C. The liquid is

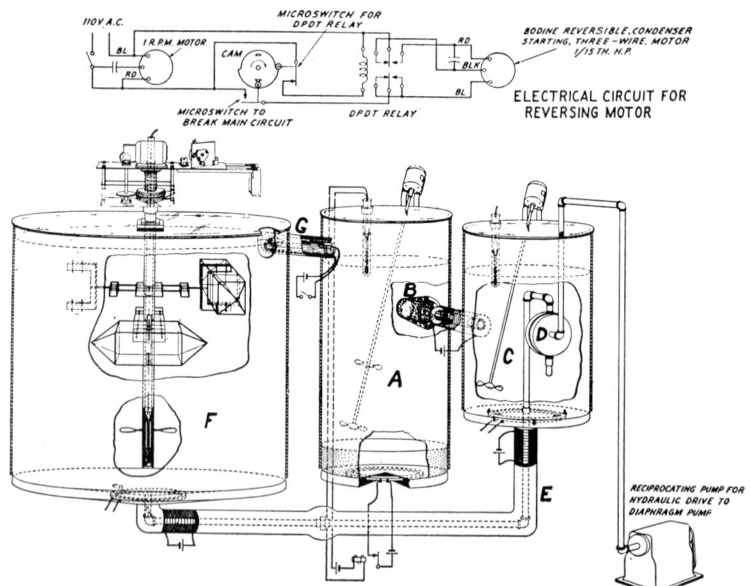

Figure 6-30. Sketch of constant temperature crystallizer.[270a]

maintained in C at a temperature several degrees above that in A. No matter how fine are the pores in B, some particles of salt will dissolve to a size where they get through the filter into tank C. It is the function of this superheater to maintain a large volume of solution for a sufficient time above the saturation point so that the fine particles of solid will be dissolved before they enter the pump D.

"The solution is delivered by this pump through the heated insulated pipe line E, into the crystallizer tank F. This tank is controlled at a temperature about 1°C below that in A, and this temperature difference determines the degree of supersaturation in which the crystals grow. Radiation of heat from the bare, stainless steel walls of F cools the entering liquid rapidly enough so that it mixes with the solution in F without raising the tank temperature. Partially depleted solution overflows by gravity through the line connecting F and A. Different solution levels are maintained in A, C and F by the pump, the slight resistance of filter B, and the position of the overflow in F."[270a]

The rocking tank crystallizer[270b] has been used to grow large crystals, but is not as satisfactory as the circulating equipment. In the first type, crystals are grown in covered stainless steel tanks each 48 inches long by 25 inches inside by 12 inches deep. The seed crystals are mounted on racks which rock back and forth. The whole is assembled in an air-conditioned room where temperature is slowly lowered a fraction of a degree per day. More than a month is required to grow the crystals to lengths of 10–12 inches and cross section approaching 2 inches although much longer ones (22 inches long, 6 inches square, 40 pounds) have been grown over longer periods of time in the circulating equipment. Res, Rusakov and Stoikovz' summary of "The Growth of Piezo Electric Crystals in USSR" given at the Montreal Congress of the International Union of Crystallography in 1957 (A-42) is generally indicative of the present state of the industry, and is given below for that purpose.

"1. KNT is grown by the dynamic method in 10 l glass crystallizers, arranged in groups of 100–130 in thermostatic chambers. The seeds have the dimensions of $3 \times 1.5 \times 6.0$ mm (x,y,z) and are mounted on stainless crystal holders having the form of a tapered rod. During the growth period the temperature is reduced from 46 to 27°C. The crystals rotate at a rate of 26 rpm. The duration of the growing cycle averages 22 to 23 days. The crystal crop is 60 kg m^{-2} of floor area per month. Rates of growth on the x, y, and z axes amount to 3.1 to 3.6, 4.3 to 4.8, and 3.3 to 4.4 mm day^{-1}, respectively. The mean weight of the KNT crystals is about 4 to 5 kg. Additive to the solution: KOH + NaOH (1:1), 2.0 g $l.^{-1}$

"2. DKT crystals are grown by the dynamic method in group crystallizers, 180 l stainless steel tanks, 32 crystals in each. Growth of single crystals starts from bar-shaped seeds of $100 \times 5 \times 5$ mm with their length along the y axis, fixed in groups of eight on a flat crystal holder of polymethyl methacrylate. The common shaft is oscillated through an angle of 90 to 120°, 30 reversals per minute. During the growth period the temperature drops from 55 to 25°C. The duration of growth cycle averages 43 to 45 days. Additive to the solution: KOH, 9–10 g l^{-1}. Weight of 'half' crystals amounts to 0.6 to 0.7 kg (weight of 'full' crystals is about 0.9 to 1.2 kg); crystal crop 30 kg m^{-2} floor area per month. Rates of growth on the x and z axes are -0.3 and -0.7 mm day^{-1}, respectively.

"3. ADP crystals are grown by the dynamic method in group crystallizers, 180 l stainless steel tanks, 12 crystals in each. Growth is achieved from bar-shaped seeds of $100 \times 3 \times 3$ mm, oriented along the (111) faces. The seeds are fixed on individual crystal holders, mounted on a common shaft. The shaft is oscillated through an angle of 90–120°, 30 reversals per minute. The temperature is reduced from 60 to 40°C. The duration of growth cycle is 27 to 29 days. The solution is prepared from chemically pure ADP without any additives. The weight of individual crystals amounts to 1.7 to 2.3 kg. Crystal crop is about 60 kg m^{-2} floor area per month. Rate of growth on the z axis is 3.3 to 3.7 mm day^{-1}; on the x and y axes it is negligible.

"4. Growth of oriented ADP crystal blocks is carried out from solutions with pH 5.7. The rectangular seeds, cut in the y and z plane, are arranged to allow growth in the x direction only. The seeds are submerged in an array of crystallizers connected with saturating and filtering tanks. The temperature in the saturator is 8–10°C higher than in the crystallizers of the battery. Convection circulation secures perfect growth of crystalline blocks at the rate of 2 to 2.5 mm day^{-1}.

"5. EDT crystals are grown from flat seeds, oriented along the short diagonal of plane (010). The method used is isothermal, with a constant temperature difference between the saturator and crystallizer tanks of 42–39°C. The solution is continuously saturated with fresh salt and circulates through the closed system by means of a pump. The rate of growth on the y axis is 2.5 to 4 mm day^{-1}. The presence of Fe'' ions causes tapering of the EDT crystals.

"6. LSH crystals are grown isothermally from bar-shaped seeds, oriented on the z axis. The LSH solutions are acidified with 2 to 3 g l^{-1} sulphuric acid. The rate of growth is equal to 1.3 mm day^{-1}.

"7. GASH (guanidine aluminium sulphate hexahydrate) is grown isothermally from water solutions, saturated at 40–45°C. The seeds are pointed; supersaturation is regulated by controlled evaporation. The growth is static. The rate of growth is 1.5 mm day^{-1}. A perfect GASH monocrystal, weighing 234 g was grown in 28 days.

"8. SHA (sorbitol hexaacetate) is grown dynamically from solutions in 96% ethanol with the addition of 5 g l^{-1} KOH. The seeds are bar-shaped and oriented parallel to the z axis. During growth the crystals are oscillated. The rate of growth on the y and z axes is about 2 to 3 and 0.4 to 0.6 mm day^{-1}, respectively. The temperature of saturation of the alcoholic SHA solution is about 60°C."

Hydrothermal Methods

The successful production of quartz on a commercial scale is a relatively recent development which has served to revive interest and activity in all aspects of single crystals. Attempts to grow quartz in the laboratory date well back into the nineteenth century,[11, 12, 119, 195] but the real first success was attained by Spezia in 1905.[230] Spezia was able to grow a few millimeters of clear quartz on the end of a natural crystal in alkaline solutions under pressure. Several months were required. Nacken,[167] during the time of the last war, succeeded in growing discrete crystals in a similar way but under much higher pressure and temperature. The improved methods of Hale,[93a] Wooster,[287] Walker,[270] Kohman,[128] and others,[164] have evolved from these pioneer works. The hydrothermal method has since been adapted to the production of ferrites,[127] sapphires,[137] and other minerals.[233]

In essence, pieces of quartz are placed in the bottom of an autoclave such as illustrated in Figure 6-31. Above this section is a bubble plate or cup which impedes full circulation. The seed or seeds are mounted near the top and the whole is partially filled with alkali solution. The closed bomb is heated in a furnace from 300 to 450°C in such a way that the growing zone is 20–100°C cooler than the nutrient section. Pressures attained are a thousand or more atmospheres, well above critical. Under these conditions quartz dissolves to saturation in the lower region and the solution formed is supersaturated near the cooler seed so that growth ensues. One of the main problems in the development of the process was the control of the excess saturation so that spontaneous nucleation would not occur. In general, 5 per cent supersaturation can be tolerated without excessive deposition on the walls and redeposition in the nutrient solid. Laudise[A-45, 137] lists the following parameters to be of paramount importance:

1. Orientation of seed crystal
2. Temperature of growth zone
3. Temperature difference between growth and nutrient zone
4. Ratio of the area of the quartz available for dissolving to the area on which growth is taking place
5. Per cent of fill of the vessel

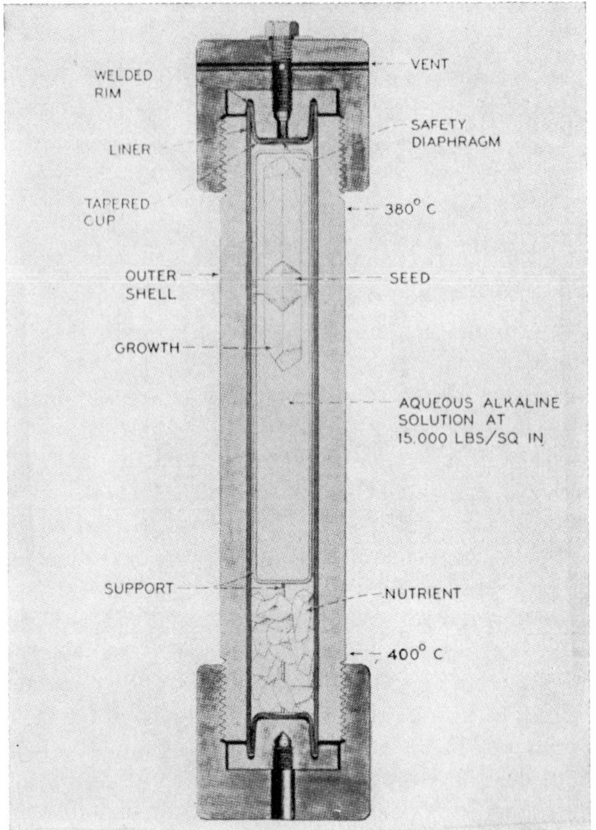

Figure 6-31. Sketch of liner type autoclave for high pressure temperature gradient method of growing quartz.[270a]

6. Per cent of baffle left open
7. Concentration of sodium hydroxide

The order of growth rates normal to various planes is: basal (0001) $\gg$ minor $(01\bar{1}1)$ > major $(10\bar{1}1) \gg$ prism $(10\bar{1}0)$. The dependence of rate of growth is given in Figure 6-32. The Arrhenius plot of Figure 6-33 displays the effect of temperature, which same factor is displayed as supercooling in Figure 6-34. At very high temperatures rates of growth as high as 0.5 cm/day have been attained for good quality quartz, and as much as double this for flawed product. If the area of the quartz dissolving is much greater than that growing, the rate of growth remains independent of the area ratio but is nearly linearly dependent on the degree of fill. The uniformity of conditions in the growing section improves with small baffle openings.

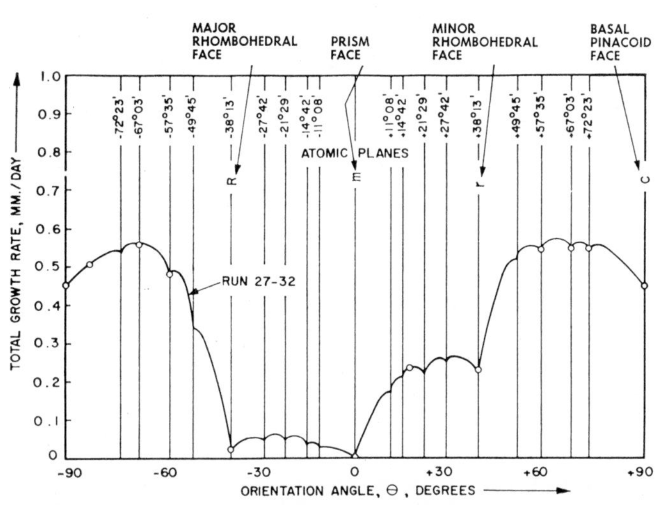

Figure 6-32. Growth rate as related to orientation of growing surfaces.[93b]

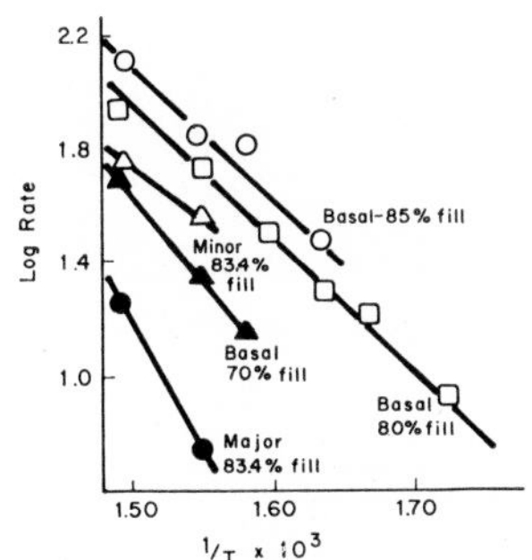

Figure 6-33. Arrhenius plot of rate of growth of quartz crystals in 0.50*M* NaOH.[137]

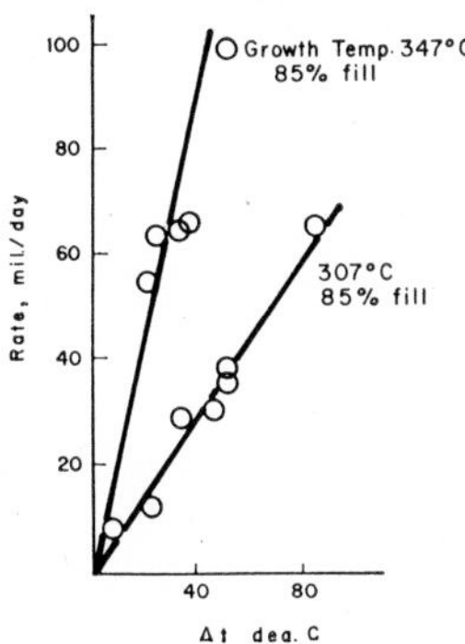

Figure 6-34. Rate of growth on basal planes *vs.* supercooling.[137] 0.50*M* NaOH.

Increasing the alkali concentration increases the rate slightly, up to a point. The simplest empirical relationship consolidating these data and observations is

$$R = k\alpha\Delta S$$

where R is the linear rate of extension per day of a particular face, k is a velocity constant, ΔS the supersaturation, and α a dimensional conversion factor. The activation energy corresponding to this law is 19.9 Kcal/mole for the basal plane. This is considerably greater than the 1.3 Kcal/mole observed for the solution process. This leads Laudise to suggest that the rate-determining step is surface migration, although the possibility that transport through the solution is important should not be neglected. Growth most likely proceeds via dislocations.[20, 93b, 293]

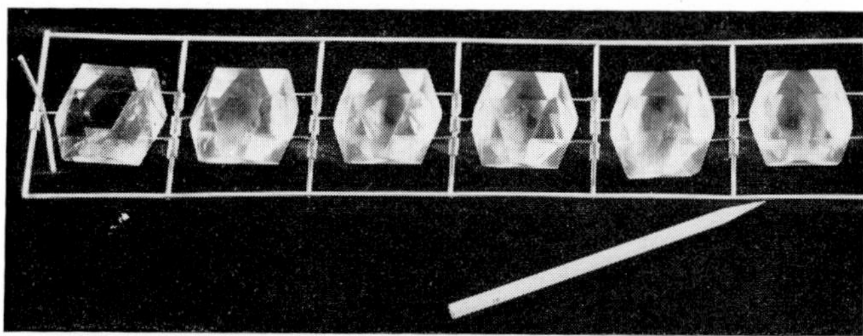

Figure 6-35. Quartz crystals grown from seed quartz under extreme pressure in an autoclave. (*Courtesy Bell Telephone Laboratories.*)

Figure 6-36. Synthetic quartz crystal, 1014 grams. Grown by Clevite Research Center for U.S. Signal Corps.

Synthetic quartz is entirely equivalent to Brazilian quartz as oscillator plates[93] and even superior in terms of usable volume since preferred cuts can be promoted by proper solution and orientation of seed crystals. The morphology of the synthetic product closely follows that of the natural one although the prism faces of the former are rarely striated, as are frequently those of the latter kind. Artificial crystals are also rarely twinned if developed on twin-free seeds. In general, more solid inclusions are found in synthetic quartz,[48] but additives often reduce this defect. The refractive index, interfacial angles, and other properties of the two kinds are practically identical and minor variations are ascribed to lattice defects.

Figures 6-35 and 6-36 are examples of synthetically grown quartz, the latter one having been exhibited at the Brussels World Fair in 1958. A larger one, weighing 1393 grams but having two areas of poor quality growth is probably close to as large a synthetic product as has been produced.[93c]

Growth from Vapors, etc.

The formation of crystals from the gaseous state occurs upon direct condensation (i.e.: Se, I_2, hexamethylene tetramine, etc.) or upon reaction with deposition of the solid (i.e: Cd (g) + H_2S = Cd S(s) + H_2(g)). Usually only small crystals result (5 to 10 mm) since control of the supersaturated state is difficult. Table 6-10 summarizes information available on

TABLE 6-10. CRYSTAL GROWTH FROM VAPOR[106b]

Substance	Temperature (°C)		Pressure	Crystal Type	Size (mm)	Reference
	Source	Crystal				
Se	~270	~210	Vac	Poly	10 × 0.2–0.3	31
I_2, P, -Napthalene	0	−0.037 to −0.07	Vac	Single	1.5–3	266
Cd, Zn	MP	—	Vac and H_2	Poly	<1	237
Mg	~600	~550	—	Poly	3	206
As_4O6	130–300	—	Vac	Poly	3	196
I_2	38	70–80	Air	Poly	<1	237a
		27–30	Air	Poly	<1 (?)	237a
Zn	409–419	410	N_2	Poly	—	117
Cd	310–321	305	N_2	Poly	—	117
BaO	1400	1380	Vac (?)	Single	10 × 10 × 1	232
$(CH_2)_6N_4$	30–100	Δ = 0.5–6.0	Vac	Single	10 × 10 × 3	106b

crystals condensed directly from vapor. Deposition by means of reaction is exemplified in the papers of Czyzak,[54] and others.[59, 207, 233]

Proper annealing of metals often produces well-developed single crystals which in the case of wires (Pintsch method; W, Fe, etc.) often extend for many yards of length. Many solid-solid reactions lead to crystalline products[3g, 22, 280] (Si C, diamond, ferrites, mica, minerals, ceramics), and the old question whether such reactions proceed directly in the solid state or via an intermediate vapor state has been examined[22] anew with conclusions in favor of the former. Many of the present theories on sintering and growth of crystallites in polycrystalline solids[47] are due to studies of metals[122] and their application to recrystallization in refractory oxides such as Al_2O_3 ,[46, 134] MgO, and Fe_2O_3.[243c] A very interesting extension of existing theories has been made in experiments on the sintering behavior of ice.[122]

The successful synthesis of diamond involves a recrystallization. This transformation has had a long and stormy history which is outlined here in only barest form. Current developments are catalogued completely in *Industrial Diamond Abstracts*.[112] The early attempts of Hannay and Moissan to make diamonds were outstanding, and created the greatest confusion. Hannay[95] obtained purported diamonds in 1880 by heating paraffin and bone oil with metallic lithium under extremely hazardous conditions. His conclusive test of the identity of these microscopic diamonds was endorsed by reputable colleagues, but doubt was expressed by others.[155] Later X-ray examination[10] of these reputed stones showed them to be true diamonds of a rare type. Moissan prepared his diamonds by dissolving sugar carbon in molten iron and quenching to generate the high pressure required for the transformation. His tests were also conclusive and endorsed by some but rejected by others. This situation, like Hannay's, preceded the days of the unequivocal X-ray test. Unfortunately, none of Moissan's stones could be found for reexamination when this proof was suggested.

This history is outlined in greater detail by A. L. Marshal[85] who summarizes the situation by stating that "The statements of the very eminent authorities cited are quite confusing, but the modern consensus is that successful synthesis of diamonds has not yet been reported in the literature." Many other writers[18, 73, 275] have come to the same conclusion. Neuhaus'[171] theoretical considerations amount to the same negative result, namely:

"(1) Metastable nucleation and growth of diamond is practically excluded for reasons of reaction kinetics. Its formation can be attempted only within its range of stability.

"(2) The initial phase must be as free as possible from aromatic or graphitic groups, including C_2 molecules.

"(3) Even in the stable formation range of diamond, the metastable formation of graphite nuclei is the kinetically preferred process. Diamond seeding or other inoculations for diamond formation are therefore necessary.

"(4) Sufficient atomic migration has to be provided without unnecessary increase in temperature. Consequently suitable mineralizers have to be found.

"This shows that thermodynamically, as well as kinetically, diamond synthesis is fraught with quite unusual difficulties, though these are certainly not insuperable. These difficulties, the full magnitude of which has only recently been realized to an ever-increasing extent, fully explain the failure of all attempts known up to the present."

It was just at this time that the General Electric Research Laboratories in Schenectady announced the production of synthetic diamonds under conditions of high pressure and great heat.[34] Shortly after this announcement other inventors claimed to have achieved the diamond synthesis and it appears that the first truly synthetic diamonds were those produced in 1953 by the Swedish ASEA Electric Co. in Vasteras.[58, 140] The rapid developments of and since that time are reviewed in a number of places.[2, 3h, 28b, 118, 125]

The conditions for the reversible transformation of graphite to diamond are defined by the phase diagram[202] and are experimentally possible. However, the rate of the desired transformation is extremely slow and the secret of the GE process appears to be the maintenance of high pressure and temperature simultaneously for relatively long times, minutes rather than seconds. Catalysts may also be important.[89] The apparatus is pictured in Figure 6-37 and the product in Figure 6-38. The ultimate proof of these being diamonds was supplied by X-ray diffraction patterns (Figure 6-39). The process* is now a commercial reality.[15, 72] Consumption will probably also increase steadily, unless the still harder Borazon (Boron nitride) proves more satisfactory.[92] No immediate prospects are held for simulating gem-quality stones,[162] although this is not an impossibility.[35] Synthetic stones may be distinguished from natural by means of growth spirals and dendritic features[251] as well as the nature and amount of impurity.[3k] The growth characteristics result from the rapidity with which the crystals are formed.

This section should not be closed without some reference to single crystal whiskers. Filamentary growth of metals and salts has been known for a long time but interest in these fine structures has been stimulated recently

* *Chem. and Eng. News* (Jan. 9, 1961, p. 41) reports the production of diamonds up to 1 carat that are dark in color but not *yet* strong enough for industrial applications.

Figure 6-37. GE's 1000-ton press for achieving high pressure, 1.6 million psi. (*Courtesy General Electric Research Laboratory.*)

in three connections: (1) the trouble they cause in co-axial cables and electric relays, (2) their exceptional high strength and, (3) their manner of growth. Eighteen papers, covering 290 pages of the Cooperstown Conference,[A-45] are devoted to the growth and properties of whiskers and constitute a complete account of recent interest and activity in this subject. Only an outstanding feature of each of the three factors mentioned will be stated here; the published record of the conference is recommended for a complete account and references.

1. Figure 6-40 illustrates the way in which tin whiskers on a relay can cause a short circuit. Ellis, Gibbons, and Treuting, (A-45, p. 102) describe this development as a process of grain growth or recrystallization and growth entailing mass transport.

2. The strength of whiskers approaches that calculated theoretically,[97] thus suggesting crystallographic perfection.

Figure 6-38. A group of carat-sized synthetic diamonds. (*Courtesy General Electric Research Laboratory.*)

3. The generation of whiskers by individual screw dislocations has been unequivocally confirmed[27, 273] and the Frank theory has been extensively applied to account for their formation and development.

GLASS AND CERAMICS*

Glass is distinguished from other states of matter by the fact that it is a transparent non-crystalline solid, produced by fusion of inorganic oxides. Most of the effort of glass-makers for several centuries has been centered on preventing glass from crystallizing, or "devitrifying." For these reasons it may seem paradoxical to discuss crystallization of such an unlikely substance.

However, some glasses make use of controlled precipitation of small quantities of crystals from the melt as it cools or is reheated. These include

* Contributed by S. D. Stookey, Corning Glass Works.

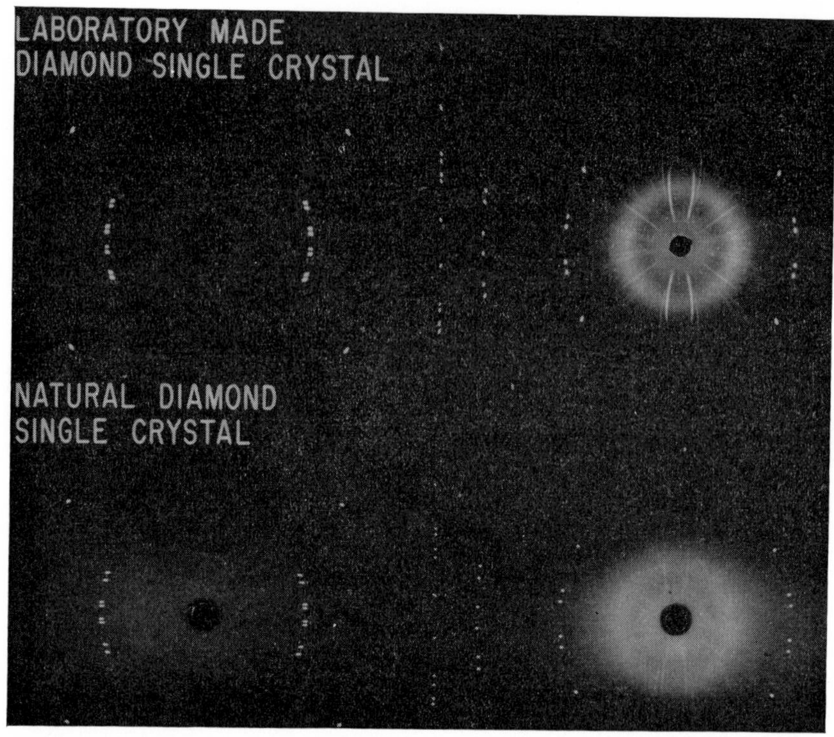

Figure 6-39. X-ray diffraction patterns of natural and manmade diamonds.[85] (*Courtesy General Electric Research Laboratory*).

"ruby" glasses, in which colloidal gold, copper, or cadmium sulfoselenide are the coloring agents; and translucent or opaque "opal" and "alabaster" glasses, which precipitate crystals of CaF_2 or other fluorides, phosphates or sulfides as the glass is cooled or reheated.

Within the past few years, the currently, controlled nucleation and crystallization have found new uses in the glass industry. Several types of photosensitive glass have been developed in which nucleation is initiated by a photochemical process, and the principles of nucleation have been extended and applied to produce completely new crystalline materials called Pyroceram,* from glass.

Nucleation and Crystallization in Glass

Tammann's[244] experimental studies of crystallization in undercooled organic liquids and inorganic glasses are the classic basis of much of our

* Corning Pyroceram is a trademark applied to fine-grained crystalline products made by controlled crystallization of glass.

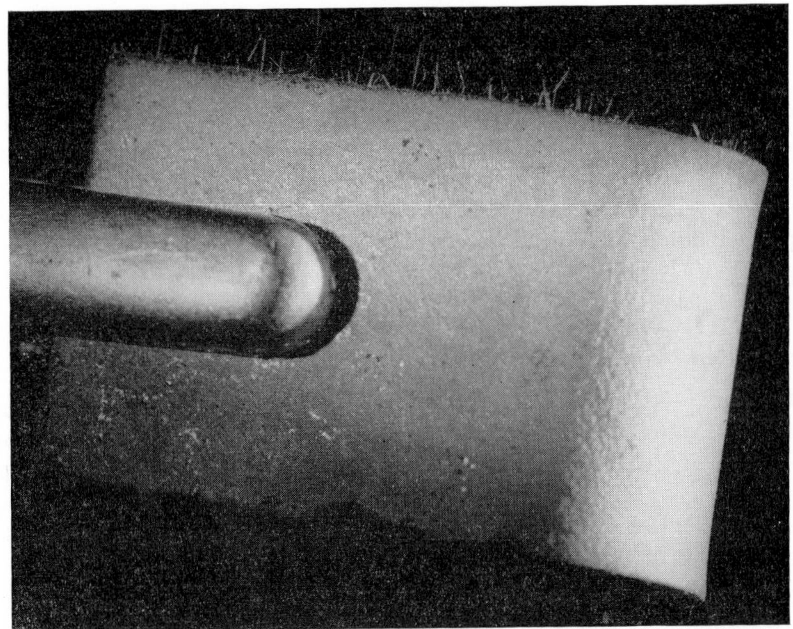

Figure 6-40. Whiskers on tin-plated metal. (*Courtesy Bell Telephone Laboratories.*)

knowledge of nucleation and crystallization from undercooled melts. By making counts of the number of crystals, and measuring their growth rates, as functions of the degree of undercooling below the equilibrium melting temperature, he showed that there is a metastable zone below the melting temperature, in which nuclei do not form at any measurable rate but in which crystals, once nucleated, can grow; and that at lower temperatures the crystallization is controlled by two essential factors, rate of spontaneous formation of crystal nuclei and rate of crystal growth. He also showed that melts which increase rapidly in viscosity during cooling have maxima in the crystal growth and nucleation rates. At low temperatures, increasing viscosity decreases these rates.

Recent studies have extended our knowledge of these phenomena in the special case of glass.

It is now known that the resistance to crystallization of most or all commercial glasses, such as soda-lime-silica[139] or borosilicate glasses, is due to the virtual absence of crystal nuclei at all temperatures.

The recent developments in controlled crystallization all involve controlled heterogeneous, rather than homogeneous nucleation. This is successful in glass because of the absence of both homogeneous nucleation and accidental foreign nuclei. The latter results from the extreme melting temperatures, such that foreign particles are either evaporated or dissolved in the melt.

We may classify the crystallization found in glass into two categories, "solute" crystallization, in which minor ingredients dissolved in the glass crystallize without materially altering the glass structure; and "solvent" crystallization, in which the glass structure itself is altered by crystallization involving the ions in the structural network. Examples of the "solute" type include the ruby and opal glasses, and some of the photosensitive glasses. The "solvent" category is exemplified by the glass-ceramics to be described below.

Controlled Nucleation of Gold, Silver, and Copper

Photosensitive Glasses. Until a few years ago it had been thought that the metals gold, silver, and copper dissolve in molten "ruby" glass as colorless atoms and that they decrease in solubility so that nuclei are formed as the glass cools. It was furthermore thought that the nuclei are prevented from growing because of the high viscosity, so that the glass remains colorless, and that subsequent reheating permits the metal nuclei to grow to colloidal colored crystals. Actually, we now believe the process is somewhat more complex. It has been found that limited quantities of these metals dissolve as ions rather than atoms, and that the nucleation step must be preceded by a reaction between the metal ions and other ions which become reducing agents as the glass cools.

Also, it was found that by substitution of an optical sensitizer (cerium ions) for the reducing ions (Sn^{+2}, Sb^{+3}, etc.) it is possible to control the concentration of metal atoms, and thereby the number of nuclei, by a photographic process. This is the basis of photosensitive glasses.[236] These glasses, when they are first made and cooled to room temperature, are colorless and transparent. Exposure to ultraviolet light or X-rays results in formation of nuclei whose concentration may be controlled from zero to billions per cubic millimeter. Reheating the glass permits these nuclei to grow to larger colloidal particles, resulting in a colored photograph.

The kinetics of this photo-nucleation process have been studied by R. D. Maurer,[149, 236] using a new theoretical and experimental approach. The sizes and numbers of the metal particles were determined by solving simultaneous equations involving functions of optical scattering and optical absorption measurements. One interesting result of this work was evidence that the smallest stable gold nucleus is 3 to 5 atoms.

Nucleation of Sodium Fluoride Crystals in Glass

Photosensitive Opal Glass. Sodium fluoride dissolves readily in a molten soda-alumina-silica glass. Its solubility-temperature curve is relatively steep, so that the glass becomes a strongly supersaturated solution of NaF as it is cooled.

When a glass of this type is made photosensitive by introduction of gold or silver and cerium compounds, as described in the preceding section, a photosensitive opal glass results. In these glasses exposure to ultraviolet light and subsequent heat treatment causes controlled precipitation of the colloidal metal crystals. Further heat treatment then causes heterogeneous nucleation of NaF crystals by the metal crystallites to produce a white opaque photographic image. The crystallization occurs at such a high viscosity that each crystal remains *in situ*. The crystallization does not propagate at random throughout the glass.

Sodium fluoride, gold and silver all have cubic crystal structures. The interatomic lattice parameter for NaF is 4.62 Å; for Ag, 4.08 Å; and for Au, 4.07 Å. Thus this system obeys the widely accepted empirical rule stating that nucleation can occur if the "disregistry" is less than 15%.

Another fact of interest relates to the critical size of metal nuclei for nucleation of NaF crystals. Increasing the photographic exposure results in progressively more and smaller metal particles, so that a "saturation" exposure produces metal particles too small to nucleate NaF. As yet the critical nucleus size has not been determined but it is believed this can be done by light-scattering, small angle X-ray scattering, and electron microscopic methods. A certain degree of extrapolation beyond the limit of resolution of some of these methods may be required.

Lithium Silicates—Fotoform and Fotoceram

The fluoride opals, although they illustrate the mechanism of heterogeneous nucleation in glass, are not of direct interest in the forming of crystalline ceramics, because the product is still essentially a glass, with only a few per cent of crystals.

However, photographic nucleation of lithium silicate glasses has quite remarkable results. The first is precipitation of a crystalline phase, Li_2SiO_3, producing a three-dimensional crystallized pattern that dissolves many times faster in HF than does the surrounding glass. This makes it possible to "chemically machine" the glass.[236]

The second effect, and the one which is of more direct interest in this discussion, is as follows. Photographic nucleation in this glass, followed by heat treatment at about 850°C, results in progressive crystallization, and final conversion to a crystalline material containing lithium disilicate and quartz. This ceramic is nonporous, very fine-grained (1 micron or less) and uniform; higher than the original glass in mechanical strength, hardness, electrical resistivity, and deformation temperature.

In this case, as in the NaF opal, the nucleating agent may be gold or silver. Typical Fotoform glasses consist essentially of SiO_2, Al_2O_3, Li_2O, K_2O, and small amounts of other oxides in addition to the photosensitive nucleating agent.

Pyroceram

On May 23, 1957, Corning Class Works announced a new family of crystalline products made from glass, and designated by the trademark Pyroceram. These products may be produced from a wide range of compositions to obtain many combinations of new and useful properties.

Glass-ceramics are made by incorporating nucleating agents in special glass batches; melting and forming the glass by conventional methods; cooling and reheating on a precisely controlled cycle to precipitate subcolloidal nuclei uniformly throughout the glass article; and final heating at a higher maturing temperature to cause precipitation of the major crystal phases on the crystal nuclei.

Properties of Glass-Ceramics

The process by which glass-ceramics are made takes advantage of the versatile glass-forming methods, and produces articles having a wide range of properties. These depend on control of chemical composition, size and concentration of the crystal phases.

Glass-ceramics have been made having high mechanical strength, high deformation temperatures, and greater hardness than glass and most metals (Table 6-11). Some compositions possess superior resistance to thermal shock. Expansion coefficients can be varied from slightly negative to 200×10^{-7} per degree centigrade. Some compositions are transparent, although most are opaque; and some are resistant to chemical attack.

It appears certain that controlled crystallization will have an important future in the glass industry.[236]

ORGANICS

Many organic and fine chemicals are finished by crystallization processes.[242] The following random comments are meant to be only indicative of the practices which are followed.

Crude citric acid is crystallized in vats from the hot, concentrated liquors obtained by acidulating calcium citrate. This salt is the form in which the acid is recovered from citrus fruits and pineapple wastes, or by fermentation. Two or three crops of small white crystals are obtained in the "granulators," after which the impure mother liquors and washings are returned to the process at the point of calcium citrate precipitation. Vacuum crystallizers are also used for producing the crude acid. The crude acid is clarified with active carbon and recrystallized in the same type of equipment. Large crystals, for which a particular demand persists, are obtained by running the hot concentrated liquor into cone-shaped vats. Crystallization ensues on planted seeds while slowly cooling for several days. Crystallization at ordinary temperatures produces the monohydrate product, while the anhydrous material is obtained above about 50°C. Alternatively, the hydrate loses its water of crystallization upon drying at 40–50°C. The transition temperature is 36.6°C.

The kinetics of crystallization of citric acid, and the similar itaconic acid, has been studied by Cartier[39] and co-workers, who find that the rate is independent of the degree of agitation and the viscosity of the solution, and, therefore, presumably surface reaction controls rather than diffusion.

Tartaric acid and its salts are produced by methods similar to those employed for citric acid, but on a smaller scale. The acid is extracted from the marc, lees, and argols left in wine making, and separated as the calcium salt. This is decomposed with sulfuric acid and the liquors evaporated in acid-resistant equipment until crystallization ensues. The heavy magma is then cooled in stirred granulators until exhausted. Second and third crops can be won after repeated concentration before the impure mother liquor must be returned to the process for separation of calcium tartrate. Purifications are effected by carbon treatment, etc., and recrystallization in vacuum pans. Large crystals are obtained by the quiet crystallization of relatively small batches.

The crystallization of oxalic acid[187] is exceptionally simple and straightforward. Solutions are concentrated to somewhat less than saturation. Quick cooling and rapid stirring give fine crystals, while gentle conditions give larger crystals. Purification may be affected by recrystallization.

Glutamic acid, nitroguanidine, dicyandiamide, sodium salicylate, and phthalic acid are just a few more of the many organic chemicals which are produced by crystallization processes and for which satisfactory manufacturing processes have been worked out. Unfortunately, in most instances, this information is not readily available for reference, and in only a few cases (citric acid,[39] insulin,[212] etc.), have details such as the crystallography, effect of additives on nucleation and growth, and growth rates been published.

POLYMERS

The crystallization of polymers and related materials is another subject about which a prolific literature exists. Fortunately, this has been reviewed and consolidated in a number of places.[35, 76, 102, 146, 175, 216, 286] The unique feature of the polymeric state is that part of the extended monomolecule

Table 6.11. Com

	Pyroceram				Glass			
	8605 (Opaque)	8606 (Opaque)	8607 (Clear)	8608 (Opaque)	Fused Silica 7940	Vycor 7900	Pyrex 7740	Lime (008
Specific Gravity Room Temp. (25°C)	2.62	2.60	2.40	2.50	2.20	2.18	2.23	2.47
Water Absorption (per cent)	0.00	0.00	0.00	0.00	0.00	0.00	0.00	0.00
Porosity (gas permeability)	Gas tight	Gas tight	Gas tight	Gas tight	Gas tight	Gas tight	Gas tight	Gas ti
Thermal								
Softening Temp. (°C)	1350	1250			1584	1500	820	696
Specific Heat (25°C)	0.185	0.190		0.190	0.176	0.178	0.186	0.200
Mean (25°C–400°C)	0.230	0.232		0.240	0.223	0.224	0.233	0.235
Thermal Conductivity (CGS) 25°C mean temp.	0.0100	0.0073		0.0037	0.0028	—	0.0026	—
Linear Coef. of Thermal Expansion × 10^7 (25° to 300°C)	14	57	−7	2 to 3	5.5	8	32	92
Mechanical								
Modulus of Elasticity (PSI × 10^{-6})	19.8	17.8			10.5	9.6	9.5	10.2
Poisson's Ratio	—	0.24			0.17	0.18	0.20	0.24
Tensile Strength (PSI × 10^{-3}) (For metals: Ultimate Strength)	—	—			—	—	—	—
Modulus of Rupture (PSI × 10^{-3})	37	32			10	10	10	10
Strength to Weight Ratio M. R. strength/spec. gr. (PSI × 10^{-3})	14.1	12.3			4.55	4.59	4.48	4.05
Hardness:								
(1) Brinell 500 Kg	—	—			—	—	—	—
(2) Knoop 50 gm	1100	940			644	030	550	520
500 gm	720	570			—	—	—	—
(3) Abrasion (sand blast)—plate glass-1.0	27	20			3.60	3.53	3.10	1.23
Electrical								
Dielectric Constant								
(1) Freq. 10^6								
25°C	6.1	5.62			3.78	3.8	4.6	7.2
300°C	6.3	5.80			—	3.9	5.9	—
500°C	—	—			—	—	—	—
(2) Freq. 10^{10}								
25°C	6.1	5.53			3.78	3.8	4.5	6.71
300°C	6.1	5.53			3.78	—	—	—
500°C	6.1	5.54			3.78	—	—	—
Dissipation Factor								
(1) Freq. 10^6								
25°C	0.0017	0.0024			0.0002	0.0005	0.0046	0.009
300°C	0.014	0.013			—	0.0042	0.0130	—
500°C	—	—			—	—	—	—
(2) Freq. 10^{10}								
25°C	0.0002	0.0003			0.00017	0.0009	0.0085	0.017
300°C	0.0008	0.0006			0.00008	—	—	—
500°C	0.0025	0.0018			0.00009	—	—	—
Loss Factor								
(1) Freq. 10^6								
25°C	0.0102	0.013488			0.0008	0.0019	0.0212	0.065
300°C	0.0782	0.07540			—	0.0164	0.0566	—
500°C	—	—			—	—	—	—
(2) Freq. 10^{10}								
25°C	0.0012	0.001659			0.0007	0.0036	0.0282	0.114
300°C	0.0049	0.003318			0.0003	—	—	—
500°C	0.0153	0.009972			0.0003	—	—	—
Volume Resistivity—Log 10 (ohm-cm)								
250°C	10.1	10			12.0	9.7	8.1	6.4
350°C	8.7	8.6			9.7	8.1	6.6	5.1

Courtesy, Corning Glass Works.

Ceramic			Metal					
Aluminas	Steatites $MgO \cdot SiO_2$	Forsterite $2\ MgO \cdot SiO_2$	Aluminum (99.0) 2 S Alloy Annealed	Aluminum 75 S Alloy Annealed	Gray Cast Irons	Stainless Steel Type 302 Annealed	Titanium (99.9) Iodide Tit.	Note
.61 to 3.67	2.65 to 2.92	2.8	2.71	2.80	7.0 to 7.7	7.93	4.50	
.00	0 to 0.03	0 to 0.01	—	—	—	—	—	
as tight	—	Gas tight	—	—	—	—	—	
700 to 1745	1349	1349	—	—	—	—	—	
.181	—	—	0.23(100°C)	0.23(100°C)	0.131(100°C)	0.118(100°C)	0.053(100°C)	1
.241	—	—	—	—	—	—	—	
.052 to 0.058	0.0062 to 0.0065	0.010	0.53	0.29	0.110	0.052	—	
3 (20°C to 500°C)	81.5 to 99 (20°C to 500°C)	99 (20°C to 500°C)	256	232	100(25°C)	95(−18 to 316°C)	82	
)	15	—	10	10.4	11.6	29	15.9	
.32	—	—	0.33	0.33	0.17	—	—	
5	13	10	13	40	20 to 60	80	36	
8	20	19	—	—	—	—	—	
3.1 to 13.3	6.85 to 7.56	6.75	4.8	14.3	2.67 to 8.0	10.1	8.0	2
-	—	—	23	30	163–269	135–185	76	3
800	—	—	—	—	—	—	—	
-	—	—	No. conv.	No. conv.	180–300	147–201	100	
-	—	—	—	—	—	—	—	
.81	5.9	6.3						
-	—	—						
.03	—	—						
.79	5.8	5.8						
-	—	—						
.03	—	—						
.00035	0.0013	0.0003						
-	—	—						
.012	—	—						
.0015	0.0014	0.0010						
-	—	—						
.0021	—	—						
.0031	0.0077	0.0019						
-	—	—						
.108	—	—						
.0132	0.0082	0.0058						
-	—	—						
.019	—	—						
4.0(100°C)	14(20°C)	14(20°C)						
2.95(300°C)	—	—						

Note 1
Softening temp. method of evaluation:
(a) Pyroceram—comparable to ASTM C 24-46
(b) Glass—ASTM C 338-54T
(c) Ceramics—ASTM C 24-46

Note 2
Strength to weight ratio:
(a) Pyroceram, ceramic and glass based on modulus of rupture per specific gravity
(b) Metal based on tensile strength which is actually ultimate strength

Note 3
Knoop number for metal was obtained by converting Brinell to Knoop number

Figure 6-41. Schematic representation of morphology of a semicrystalline polymer.[14]

is capable of distinct ordering while the other part remains amorphous. This is represented schematically in Figure 6-41. The degree of crystallinity may be determined by X-ray diffraction, light scattering, infrared absorption, dilatometer, microscope, calorimeter, or refractive index.[174] Flory has developed a statistical thermodynamic description of this state. The temperature dependence is given by the equation:

$$\frac{1}{T} - \frac{1}{T_m^o} = \frac{R}{\Delta H}\left[\frac{1}{x\lambda} + \frac{1}{x - \zeta + 1}\right]$$

in which T is the absolute temperature, T_m^a the melting point or temperature at which crystallinity disappears, ΔH is the heat of fusion per structural unit, x the number of configurational segments per molecule in which there are ζ repeating units, and $1 - \lambda$ the degree of crystallinity. This equation indicates that crystallinity of a polymer will decrease more or less continuously as the temperature increases due to the extension of the amorphous ends. The encroachment is complete at what is conventionally called the melting point, T_m, and is clearly indicated on the typical dilatometric curves in Figure 6-42. The thermodynamic theory accounts for the effects of chain length, diluent, and pressure, and applies also to polymorphs and co-polymer formation. However, the proper transformations are more often than not extremely sluggish in these viscous and even plastic systems so that kinetic considerations become of primary importance.

The rate of development of crystallinity is found to be determined by the rate of formation of crystallization centers and the simultaneous growth

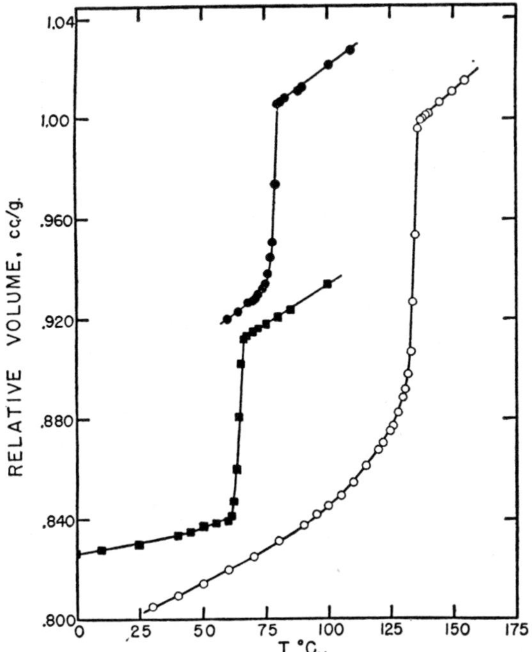

Figure 6-42. Plot of relative volume *vs.* temperature: ○, polymethylene; ■ polyethylene oxide; ●, polydecamethylene adipate.[146]

of nuclei. The former is time dependent[144] and if, for instance, it is first order, can be represented by:

$$\frac{dN_t}{dt} = k(N_o - N_t)$$

where N_o is the initial number of unnucleated particles and N_t the number nucleated at time t. Each nucleation center grows, usually as a spherulite, only to a finite size on account of end effects, impingement on other growing areas, or exhaustion of the environment in the case of an amorphous solution or solvated plastic. If the time for completed growth is r and the particle grows at a rate C, the rate of disappearance of amorphous material is then

$$\frac{dM_t}{dt} = -C(N_t - N_{t-r})$$

The solution of this set of differential equations demands a linear semi-logarithmic plot which is found to be the case in the example illustrated in Figure 6-43. Observed crystallinity data, Figure 6-44, for this particular

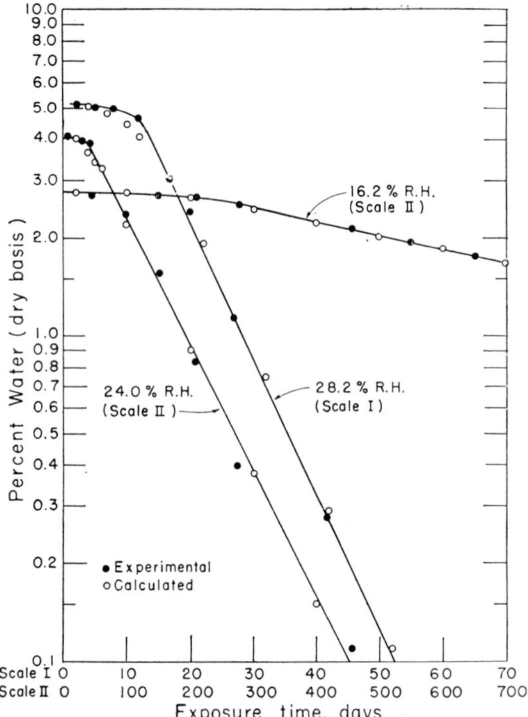

Figure 6-43. Log (% H_2O) *vs.* time for amorphous sucrose at three relative humidities at 25°C.[144]

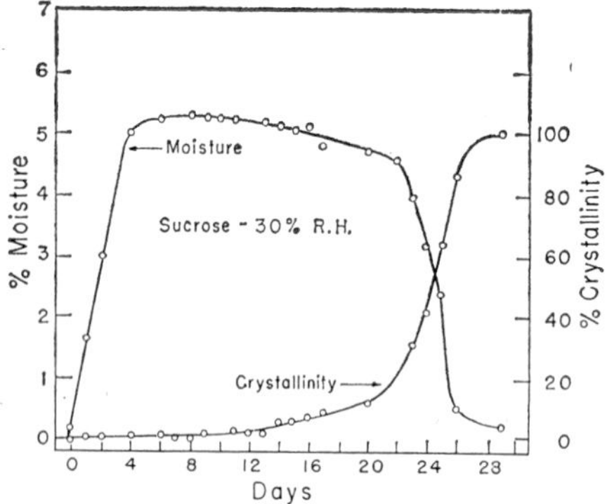

Figure 6-44. Effect of time of exposure on water content and crystallinity at relative humidity of 30.0% at 24°C.[144]

TABLE 6-12. VARIATION OF $t½$ WITH CRYSTALLIZATION TEMPERATURE T FOR BULK POLYETHYLENES AND A DILUTE POLYETHYLENE SOLUTION.
(Mandelkern in Ref. A-45, p. 478)

(a)		(b)		(Solution of b)	
T(°C)	$t_{\frac{1}{2}}$ (min)	T	$t_{\frac{1}{2}}$	T	$t_{\frac{1}{2}}$
120	5.3	122	8.8	97	20
123	13.8	123	12.5	98	34
124	23.0	124	18.0	99	60
125	38.5	125	26.0	100	115
126	76.0	126	57.0	101	270
127	225	127	190	102	550
128	780	128	580	103	1,300
129	3,400	129	3,300	104	3,200
130	17,000	130	19,000	—	—

case display the usual incubation period during which, essentially, nuclei are formed; then an accelerating period of active growth; and finally a decline as the supply of amorphous material becomes depleted.[16] These are the common features of almost all polymer and related systems. Kinetic details of more complicated cases are worked out in the general references cited.

The temperature coefficient of the rate of crystallization of polymers is generally very large. In Table 6-12, for instance, it is well over 10^3 per 10^0. This is greatly in excess of that associated with diffusional processes and immediately suggests that some other process at the crystallite-amorphous phase interface is the rate-controlling factor. This is borne out by the observation that the diameter of spherulites in many instances increases linearly in time[146] rather than proportional to the square root of the time as demanded by a diffusional mechanism.* When the activation energy of total growth is resolved into its separate components of nucleation and growth respectively, it is found that the two are the same. This emphasizes that growth is essentially governed by some kind of secondary nucleation.

RAIN MAKING

The study of precipitation of water from the atmosphere has been greatly stimulated by the real possibility of catalyzing this natural phenomenon by means of cloud seeding. This is not a new endeavor, "Pluviculture is a

* This same situation has been found in the writer's laboratory in the case of very concentrated sugar syrups and hard candies. The rates are extremely sensitive to temperature, probably as the result of the prolific formation of false grain at these very high concentrations.

never-failing drought crop".[109] One of the more elaborate schemes of the last century involved the setting off of explosive charges from balloons. Even the congress of this country was prevailed upon to make an appropriation for test of this proposal, in view of the persuasive observation that heavy rainfalls appeared to follow great battles. This trial was a failure. The more serious works of men like J. Aitkens[1, 145] and Wilder Bancroft[31] served to preserve scientific interest in the possibility of causing rain to fall, but it was not until 1946 that the first real success was had. Aitkens recognized the role of nuclei as rain promotors, while Bancroft sought to utilize charged particles to promote precipitation. He actually distributed charged sand grains into clouds and fogs from an airplane and was able to disperse them but not form rain. He predicted that "with improved apparatus, we may be able to attack such a problem as the London fogs with some chance of commercial success."

The first incontrovertible artificially induced snowstorm was produced east of Schenectady, New York on November 13, 1946 by the meteorological research team of the General Electric Company.[210] This project had been organized to investigate problems of radiostatic which made communication with aircraft flying in snowstorms difficult, and also the related problem of accumulation of ice on aircraft at high altitudes. These problems led to the study of cloud structure and snow formation and to the discovery that dry ice could transform a fog of supercooled water droplets to ice in the laboratory. The first trial on a large scale was eminently successful even though the snow itself did not actually reach the ground. Succeeding tests (Fig. 6-45) were equally encouraging and the first man-made rain positively to reach the ground was provoked on February 5, 1947 in Australia.[131] Simultaneous with the pioneer works of Langmuir and Schaefer, their colleague, Dr. Vonnegut, observed that silver iodide was an effective nucleating agent for ice formation,[267] and this agent has proven to be the most frequently used catalyst for cloud seeding, at least in this country. Its effectiveness as a heterogeneous nucleus appears to be due to an almost identical epitactic fit with the ice structure.

A hectic period of commercial exploitation of this spectacular process soon ensued and, of course, inevitably controversy over its effectiveness also arose. Official meteorological offices were at times skeptical—as they were in the case of Veraart's dry-ice seeding experiments in Holland in 1930—but eventually recognized the reality of the procedure with its many limitations. There is no doubt that rainfall can be induced over small or large areas when the cloud formations are propitious; thus creating local and/or short-term advantages as well as swelling of reservoirs for irrigation and power use in the drier months. The Australians have been particularly

Figure 6-45. Twenty-mile long straightaways and five-mile long turn formed by seeding a stratus cloud with dry ice. (*Courtesy General Electric Research Laboratory.*)

active in this latter regard and have underway a very ambitious project for assuring sufficient precipitation over the Snowy Mountain water reservation in southeastern Australia.

The incidence of lightning-caused forest fires has been reduced in many areas of the western United States by strategic cloud seeding. The city of New York attempted to fill its depleted reservoirs in this way during the dry summer of 1950 but without success. The sugar planter is only one of the many factions interested in control of rainfall, and the discussion by H. R. Shaw[221] is representative of the status of operations in this and other instances.

Weather control or modification does not now appear to be an impossibility, especially since it is possible not only to cause rain to fall by cloud seeding, but to dissipate threatening showers. Langmuir's own words recording his test flights in Honduras on April 18, 1949, outlined this situation, "In other words, on this day we had beautiful examples of two effects that can be produced by seeding with pellets of dry ice. First, the seeding of the top of the cloud can cause the top to float off from the lower part. However, in this case some of the ice crystals reached the lower part of the cloud and caused rain to dissipate it. In the lower seeded cloud which was much lower and reached only a few thousand feet above the freezing level, the whole cloud rapidly dissipated as the upper part changed to ice and the lower part rained out."[3m]

It is also possible that precipitation can be prevented by poisoning the initial key nuclei. Ethyl amine has been found to be effective in this way and in recent field tests none of the treated clouds snowed while some of the controls did.[3m]

Clouds are formed by the adiabatic cooling of ascending moist air which condenses to myriads of liquid water droplets on the nuclei which are almost invariably present in the atmosphere.[1, 165] The droplets may grow by the continued condensation of water vapor upon them, but this process alone is generally unable to produce droplets sufficiently large to fall to the ground as rain against the updraft forming the clouds themselves. Coalescence is presumably not the rule except in the case of drizzle and tropical rain storms. For this to happen particular combinations of updraft, water content, and cloud depths are required. There must also exist a wide distribution of cloud droplet sizes,[25] which may be introduced for artificial rain formation by spraying water into or just beneath the cloud base.

The usual mechanism by which precipitation occurs is through the initial formation of ice crystals. This is essentially Bergeron's theory (1932) and there appears to be no doubt that most natural precipitation originates in this way from supercooled clouds. The first ice nuclei grow because their vapor pressure is less than that of the neighboring liquid droplets. This growth is accelerated by the immediate addition, as ice, of those liquid droplets with which they collide. Since the growth is rapid, it is usually dendritic. Soon fragments of the parent crystal are broken off in the turbulent environment. These act as new centers of growth and, thereby, a snowstorm has started. This autocatalytic chain reaction[136] continues until the cloud is exhausted. The precipitation may or may not reach the ground as snow or rain according to the temperature of the freezing level and the surrounding meteorological conditions. The original triggering nuclei are provided naturally by the local formation, homogeneously, of ice nuclei at about -40°C or, more commonly, by heterogeneous nucleation at lower supersaturations. The former condition is reproduced artificially by seeding with dry ice, while silver iodide provides the necessary "freezing nuclei" of the latter class. There is almost certainty of producing rain within the cloud by dry ice if its top temperature is at -7°C or colder but the chance falls rather sharply to nothing at 0°C. At temperatures colder than -15°C results lose significance because of the high probability of rain forming naturally. Temperatures at least lower than -4 to -8°C are necessary for nucleating with AgI, according to the particle size.

The above perspective is of necessity very sketchy. An excellent review of current knowledge on the physics of clouds and rain making and an account of both small- and large-scale attempts at weather modifications are contained in reports of the World Meteorological Organizations.[288] Schaefer's review summarizes most of the pioneering laboratory and field work of the General Electric group, while Bowen[25] reports the early Australian experiments. General reviews are numerous, but only a few are indicated here.[A-45, 148b, 188] Latest developments are recorded in voluminous technical papers and in various symposia, reviews, etc.[130, 148c, 243d, 276]

The formation of ice crystals is of considerable interest and importance in several directions other than their spectacular role in rain making. Freezing is an attractive way of purifying water and the method is receiving considerable attention in current water reclamation investigations.[3m, 87] The cost is favorably low but the complete separation of pure ice and mother liquor remains a problem within the cost limitation. In the same way waste pickle liquors have been enriched in sulfuric acid by freezing out water.[3o]

Consumption and process ice are produced on a tremendous scale but as an industry appears to be now dying out as the result of improvements in refrigeration equipment; just as commercial ice supplanted natural ice some fifty years ago. The mechanics of freezing has been considered in connection with the behavior of water in soils at low temperatures, living cells and tissues,[143, 156, 226, 243e] and in food preservation.[289]

MISCELLANEOUS APPLICATIONS

Alumina

Alumina, for preparation of aluminum metal, is commonly purified by the Baeyer process or modifications thereof. The oxide is extracted with a strong solution of NaOH at temperatures of 160–170°C and, after filtering, cooled and diluted. The trihydrate then crystallizes out. This is a notably slow process[71, 77, 96, 147, 208, 268] even though the supersaturations are frequently of the order of 200 per cent. The general American practice for precipitating alumina is as follows:[94, 108, 197]

The solutions fed to the precipitators contain approximately 100g/1 alumina and 120 g/1 NaOH. The quantity of caustic is in excess of that equivalent to the alumina. This excess is necessary to prevent spontaneous decomposition of the sodium aluminate during clarification of the process solution. There has been a tendency in recent years to increase the concentration of both alumina and caustic in process solutions. However, the ratio between the two has remained essentially constant.

The pregnant liquor is cooled to a carefully controlled temperature and is pumped into precipitation vessels which are from 20 to 25 feet in diameter and 60 feet high. A seed charge of previously precipitated alumina trihydrate is added to the liquor and the mixture is agitated for a period of 30 or more hours by means of a central air lift in the tank. After precipitation, the slurry system is separated into coarse material and one or more seed fractions. The coarse material is washed and calcined to become the product alumina.

This precipitation or crystallization process has three major objectives: (1) a maximum yield of product per unit volume; (2) a product fraction sufficiently coarse to filter and calcine well; and (3) maintenance of an equilibrium in the quantity of seed in the process. Since some of these objectives are not compatible with the others, the operating conditions must be compromises.

The two controls for a precipitation system are temperature and the quantity of seed added. In response to these variables, the process behaves like similar crystallization operations. The lower the temperature of the solution, the finer the product will be. Also, the larger the quantity of seed added, the higher the yield per unit volume. The last statement holds only up to a certain point; beyond that point a further increase of seed will not increase yield. Control is based on the fact that the concentration of the liquor coming to the precipitator is virtually constant. A few screen tests on the precipitated material are sufficient for a man experienced in the art to make the necessary control decisions. Advantage is also taken of the inertia of the system, since the quantity of seed and product in suspension at any given time is many times the production rate of a plant.

Experience and experiments have led to several theories about the process:

1. Although the solution is supersaturated with respect to alumina at precipitation temperatures, the presence of certain impurities in the solution prevent nucleation at an appreciably high rate.

2. The rate of precipitation in a solution of a given concentration is a function of the seed area present.

3. Precipitation probably occurs as an amorphous, gelatinous material, which subsequently becomes oriented into a crystalline structure.

4. The surface of the seed can be poisoned by certain inorganic or organic materials so that it will not function to seed a pregnant solution.

5. Virtually all particles larger than 325 mesh are agglomerates of several smaller particles.

6. It is probable that most nuclei are formed by attrition of particles of the newly formed amorphous precipitate from the surface of the larger particles.

Building Materials

The setting of building materials such as gypsum, mortar and cement, involve solid-state reactions which, however, as in the case of gypsum, may involve an intermediate solution stage.[52] Metastable forms may also appear and these, upon recrystallizing, may either consolidate or destroy the structure of the mass. The rate of set of these products is frequently divisible into initial and final periods,[4] both of which are sensitive, positively or negatively, to many additives.[111, 114, 250] The initial setting is usually explained in terms of colloidal coagulation, and the final as a straightforward crystallization. Powell,[191] and others,[277] believe both to be crystallization processes in the case of plaster of Paris. The kinetics of this particular process is found to be first order and diffusion controlled.[150, 199, 211]

Sludge Precipitation

The lime softening of process and consumption waters involves the precipitation of calcium salts. This may be a slow process in terms of the large volumes treated but may be considerably accelerated by providing a sufficient number of growth nuclei. For this purpose it is not unusual to recirculate a portion of the precipitated sludge.[183] The same practice has been suggested for sugar-liquor defecation; in which case the aragonite form of the clarifying precipitate is encouraged in order to promote better filtration rates.[61c]

In some cases it may be desirable to restrict the number of centers of growth, for which purpose homogeneous precipitation is most effective. This is an especially useful technique in analytical precipitations.[88]

Reagent Chemicals

Purity is the ultimate aim in the preparation of reagent chemicals and for this purpose crystallization is frequently employed. Generally speaking, small batchwise processes are used although some recent quality sucrose, for instance, has been prepared by large-scale commercial crystallization of selected syrups.[63] The impression persists in several instances (i.e., sugar, citric acid, tartaric acid) that large crystals are purer than small crystals. This is by no means generally true, for in many instances just the opposite is observed.[75] This impression persists probably because large crystals are easier to separate from the mother liquor and because the initial shower of small crystals may be contaminated with the suspended impurities which they purge from the solution. Large crystals from the sides, false bottom, or crystallization supports, are also less apt to be contaminated with the sludge which gravitates to the bottom of the tank.

Biological Applications

Hollomon and Fisher[104] have made the interesting suggestion that the spontaneous appearance of cancer may be a phenomenon of nucleation and growth, and outline a description of the critical size cell colony according to this concept. In a more purely crystallographic sense, Pauling[186] and others[29] have pointed out the analogies between antibodies and other immunological systems with the crystallization process.

Fractures

Flaws have been recognized for a long time as the seat of rupture in metals. It was quite reasonable to transfer this belief to the dislocation on an atomic scale. In this sense the flow and fracture of metals and other materials may be interpreted in terms of nucleation and growth. This has been done with some considerable success[166, 271, 291] and the interpretation has also been applied by the chemical engineer to the unit operation of size reduction by crushing and grinding.[3p, 225]

REFERENCES

1. Aitkens, J., "Collected Scientific Papers," Cambridge Press, 1923.
2. Anderson, B. W., *J. Gemnology*, **5**, 59 (1955).
3. Anon
   (a) *Ind. Eng. Chem.*, **45**, 11A (1953).
   (b) *Int. Sugar J.*, p. 60, (1958).
   (c) *Chem. Eng. News*, **33**, 2329 (1955).
   (d) *Silicate P&Q's*, 28, #5 (1948), Philadelphia Quartz Co.
   (e) *Chem. Eng. News*, **28**, 1934 (1950).
   (f) *Chem. Eng. News*, **32**, 3840 (1954).
   (g) *Chem. Eng. News*, **35**, 110 (Aug. 5, 1957).
   (h) *Chem. Eng. News*, **37**, 24 (Nov. 23, 1959).
   Diamond News, **22**, 24 (1959).
   Ind. Diamond Rev., **15**, 57 (1955).
   (i) *Deut. Goldschmiede Ztg.*, **56**, 648 (1958); **57**, 139 (1959).
   (j) *Mineralogist*, **26**, 222 (1958); **27**, 158 (1959).
   (k) *New Scientist*, **6**, 1053 (1959).
   (l) *Chem. Eng. News*, March 10, 1923 (p. 844, Feb., 1953).
   (m) *G.E. Review*, p. 8 (Nov. 1952).
   (n) *Chemical Week*, p. 40 (Jan. 4, 1958).
   Chem. Eng. News, **33**, 4169 (1955); **36**, 52 (1958); **37**, 28 (1959); **38**, 35 (Mar. 7, 1960), 60 (Dec. 12, 1960).
   Advances in Chemistry, "Saline Water Conversion," **No. 27**, Washington, D. C., American Chemical Society, 1960.
   (o) *Chem. Eng.*, **64**, 168 (1957).
   (p) *Chem. Eng. News*, **33**, 2206 (1955).
4. Attemann, J., "Über Losung und Hydratation des Anhydrites," p. 23, Berlin Akademie, Verlag Gmblt., 1950.

5. Atwood, G. E., and Bourne, D. J., *Mining Eng.* (Nov. 1953).
6. Autienrieth, H., Rieke, H., and Dust, H., *Chem. Ing. Technick*, **29**, 709 (1957).
7. Avrami, M., *J. Chem. Phys.*, **7**, 1103 (1939); **8**, 212 (1940); **9**, 177 (1941).
8. Badger, W. L., and Baker, E. M., "Inorganic Chemical Technology," p. 29, McGraw-Hill Book Co., 1928.
9. Bamforth, A. W., *Ind. Chemist*, **25**, 81 (1949).
10. Bannister, F. A., and Lonsdale, K., *Nature*, **151**, 334 (1943).
11. Barrer, R. M., *Nature*, **157**, 734 (1946).
12. Barth, T. F. W., "Theoretical Petrology," New York, John Wiley & Sons, 1952.
13. Basser, A., and Van Hook, A., 1958 (Colonial Sugar Refining Co., Sydney).
14. Bates, F. J., and Associates, "Polarimetry, Saccharimetry and the Sugars," p. 537, U.S. Bur. Standards, Washington, D.C. C 440, 1942.
15. Beardslee, K. R., *Carbide Eng.*, **9**, 5 (1957); *Chem. Eng. News*, p. 60 (Nov. 4, 1957).
16. Bekhedahl, N., *J. Res. Natl. Bur. Standards*, **13**, 11 (1934).
17. Bloch, M. R., Farkas, L., and Spiegler, K. S., *Ind. Eng. Chem.*, **43**, 1544 (1951).
18. Bielar, A., *Viertjschr. Naturt Ges. Zürich*, **97**, 1 (1952).
19. Bixler, G. H., and Sawyer D. L., *Ind. Eng. Chem.*, **49**, 442 (1957).
20. Bommel, H. E., Mason, W. P., and Warner, A. W., *Phys. Rev.*, **99**, 1894 (1955).
21. Booth, A. H., *Trans. Faraday Soc.*, **47**, 633 (1951).
22. Borchardt, H. J., *J. Am. Chem. Soc.*, **81**, 1529 (1959).
23. Borkovskii, M. A., *Sakharnaya Prom.*, **30**, 27 (1956).
24. Bottoni, G. F., *Ind. Sacc. Ital.*, **43**, 58 (1950).
25. Bowen, E. G.,
    (a) *Austral. J. Sci. Res.*, **A3**, 192 (1950).
    (b) *Weather*, **7**, 204 (1952).
26. Brain, L. R., *Proc. Queensl. Soc. Sugar Cane Tech.*, **17**, 177 (1951).
27. Brenner, S. S., *J. Appl. Phys.*, **27**, 1484 (1956).
28. Bridgman, P. W.
    (a) *Proc. Am. Acad. Arts and Sciences*, **60**, 303 (1925).
    (b) *J. Chem. Phys.*, **15**, 92 (1947).
    Sci. Am., **193**, 42 (1955).
29. Brillouin, L., *Am. Sci.*, **37**, 554 (1949).
30. Broughton, G., and Windebank, C., *Ind. Eng. Chem.*, **30**, 407 (1938).
31. Brown, F. C., *Phys. Rev.*, **2**, 85 (1914).
32. Brown, W. K., *Instr. Pract.*, p. 588 (1950).
33. Buflovak Equipment Co., Buffalo 11, New York.
34. Bundy, F. P., *et al.*, *Nature*, **176**, 51 (1955); **184**, 1094 (1959).
35. Bunn, C. W., "Fibres from Synthetic Polymers," Chap. 11, New York, Elsevier Publishing Co., 1953.
36. Burger, W. G., "Handbuch der Metallphysik," Vol. 3, Pt. 2, Berlin, Akad. Verlag, 1941.
37. Cahn, R. W., *Proc. Phys. Soc.*, **A63**, 323 (1950); *Acta Met.*, **4**, 449 (1958).
38. Caldwell, H. B., *Chem. and Met. Eng.*, **42**, 213 (1935).
39. Cartier, R. M.
    (a) *Am. Chem. Soc.*, Paper #150-37, Chicago, Ill. (1958), Univ. Microfilm #22652, 328 pp., Ann. Arbor, Michigan (1957).
    (b) with Pindzola, D., and Bruins, P. F., *Ind. Eng. Chem.*, **51**, 1409 (1959).

40. Chalmers, B., "Progress in Metal Physics," 6 vols., New York, Interscience Publishing Co., 1953.
41. Chatterji, A. C., and Rastogi, R. P., *J. Indian Chem. Soc.*, **28,** 599 (1951); *J Phys. Chem.*, **59,** 1 (1955).
42. Chatterji, A. C., and Singh, R. M., *J. Phys. Chem.*, **62,** 1408 (1958).
43. Choi, R. P., Tatter, C. W., and O'Malley, C. M., *Anal. Chem.*, **23,** 888 (1951).
44. Christensen, C. J., and Walker, A. C., *U.S. Pat.*, 2,459,869 (Jan. 25, 1949).
45. Cinnamon, C. A., and Martin, A. B., *J. Appl. Phys.*, **11,** 487 (1940).
46. Coble, R. L., *J. Am. Ceramic Soc.*, **41,** 55 (1958).
47. Conference, "Kinetics of High Temperature Processes," Dedham, Mass. (1958). *C.A.*, **54,** 6243.
48. Corwin, J. F., Swinnerton, A. C., *et al.*, A-37, p. 172; *J. Am. Chem. Soc.*, **73,** 3598 (1951); **75,** 158 (1953); *J. Chem. Ed.*, **37,** 11 (1960).
49. Cosgrove, J. F., Jr., M.S. Thesis, College of the Holy Cross, 1952.
50. Cottrell, A. H., "Theoretical Structural Metallurgy," New York, Longmans-Green Co., 1948.
51. "Cristallisation du Sucre," Bruxelles—Commision Internationale technique de Sucrerie, 1953.
52. Cunningham, W. A., Dunham, R. M., and Antes, L. L., *Ind. Eng. Chem.*, **44,** 2402 (1952).
53. Curtis, H. A., "Fixed Nitrogen," New York, Chemical Catalog Co., 1932.
54. Czyzak, S. J., Craig, D. J., and McCain, *J. Appl. Phys.*, **23,** 932 (1952); *Phys. Rev.*, **79,** 543 (1950).
55. Parken, L. S., and Gurry, R. W., "Physical Chemistry of Metals," New York, McGraw-Hill Book Co., 1953.
56. Dash, W. C., *J. Appl. Phys.*, **30,** 459 (1959).
57. Davey, W. P., "Crystal Structure and Applications," New York, McGraw-Hill Book Co., 1934.
58. Davis, L. G., *South African Min. and Eng. J.*, **61,** 91 (1955).
59. Davis, M., and Lever, R. F., *J. Appl. Phys.*, **27,** 835 (1956).
60. Dean, G. R., and Gottfried, J. B., in "Advances in Carbohydrate Chemistry," Vol. 5, p. 129, New York, Interscience Publishing Co., 1950.
61. Dedek, J.,
   (a) 10th Session, International Commission for Uniform Methods of Sugar Analysis, Washington, D. C., 1958.
   (b) British Sugar Corp., 6th Tech. Conf., 1953.
   (c) *Sugar*, **46,** 22 (1951).
62. De Vries, G. H.
   (a) *Sugar*, **52,** 27 (1957).
   (b) *Chem. Weekblad.*, **32,** 361 (1935).
63. de Whalley, H. C. S., *Int. Sugar J.*, June, July 1950.
64. Dobrzycki, J., *Gaz. Cukrovar*, **57,** 157 (1955).
65. Dolley, P. T., *Ind. Eng. Chem.*, **29,** 1101 (1937).
66. Drost, W., and Kebler, R. W., U. S. Pat. 2,852,890.
67. Dubourg, J., Saunier, R., and Lamaitre, A., *Sucre Franc.*, **93,** 121 (1952).
68. Dunning, W. J., and Albon, N., A-45, p. 446; *Nature*, **180,** 1348 (1957); *Acta Met.*, **12,** 219 (1959); **13,** 495 (1960).
69. Du Nouy, P. L., "Surface Equilibria," Chap. 10, New York, Chemical Catalog Co., 1926.

70. Egli, P., *Sci. Monthly*, **68,** 270 (1949).
71. Elmore, K. L., Mason, C. M., and Hatfield, J. D., *J. Am. Chem. Soc.*, **67,** 1449 (1945).
72. Elovich, J., *Tool. Eng.*, **42,** 209 (1959).
73. Eyring, H., and Eagle, F. W., *Z. Elecktrochem.*, **56,** 480 (1952).
74. Fehlner, F. C., *J. Chem. Ed.*, **33,** 449 (1956).
75. Flanders, C. A., private communication.
76. Flory, P. J., "Principles of Polymer Chemistry," Ithaca, New York, Cornell Univ. Press. (1953); *J. Polym. Sci.*, **18,** 592 (1955); *Science*, **124,** 53 (1953).
77. Frary, F. C., *Ind. Eng. Chem.*, **38,** 130 (1946).
78. Free, K. W., *Trans. Ind. Chem. Eng. (London)*, **36,** 115 (1958).
79. Freundlich, H., "Capillary Chemistry," p. 322, New York, Dutton Co., 1922.
80. Gale, W. A., *Ind. Eng. Chem.*, **30,** 867 (1938).
81. Gamannoto, S., *Japan Pat.*, #179, 1754 (July 26, 1949); *C.A.*, **45,** 9906; **49,** 13674.
82. Garner, W. E., "Chemistry of the Solid State," London, Butterworths, 1955.
83. Garrett, D. E., *Chem. Eng. Prog.*, **54,** 65 (1958)
84. Gee, E. A., *Ind. Eng. Cgem.*, **39,** 1178 (1947); **41,** 2242 (1949); **42,** 464 (1950).
85. General Electric Information Services, "Man Made Diamonds," p. 16, Schenectady, New York, March 1955.
86. Ghumakov, A. A., Silvestrova, I. M., and Aleksandrov, K. S., *Kristallographia*, **3,** 480 (1958); *C.A.*, **53,** 8756.
87. Gilliland, E. R., *Ind. Eng. Chem.*, **47,** 2417 (1955).
88. Gordon, L., Salutsky, M. L., and Willard, H. H., "Precipitation from Homogeneous Solutions," New York, John Wiley & Sons, 1959.
89. Grenville,-Wells, H. J., Lonsdale, K., *Nature*, **181,** 758 (1958).
90. Griostseva, E. A., and Golovin, P. V., *Trudy Tekhnol Ins. Pishchevoi Prom. im. A.I. Mikoyana*, **15,** 63 (1955); *C.A.*, **51,** 11744.
91. Grut, E., *Zucker*, **6,** 411 (1953).
92. Guebelin, E., *Diamant*, **2,** 14, 22 (1959).
93. Hale, D. R.
    (a) *Science*, **107,** 393 (1948); U. S. Pat. 2,675,303 (April 13, 1954).
    (b) A-42; Brush Strokes (Cleveland, Ohio) Dec. 1952.
    (c) Private communication.
94. Hall, J. M., and Green, S. J., *Trans. Am. Inst. Chem. Eng.*, **42,** 483 (1946)
95. Hannay, J. B., *Proc. Roy. Soc.*, **30,** 188 (1880).
96. Hermann, E., and Stipetic, *Z. anorg. Chem.*, **262,** 258 (1950).
97. Herring, C., *Bell Lab. Record*, **33,** 285 (1955).
98. Herrington, B. L., *J. Diary Sci.*, **17,** 501 (1934).
99. Hester, A. S., and Diamond, H. W., *Ind. Eng. Chem.*, **49,** 59A (1957); 672 (1955).
100. Hildebrand, J., and Scott, R. L., "Solubility," New York, Reinhold Publishing Corp., 1950.
101. Hightower, J. V., *Chem. Engr.*, **58,** 105 (1951).
102. Hoffman, J. D., Weeks, J. J., and Murphey, M. M., *J. Res. Nat'l. Bur. Stds.*, **63A,** 67 (1959).
103. Holden, A. N., U. S. Pat. 2,484,829 (1949).
104. Hollomon, J. H., and Fisher, J. C., *Science*, **111,** 489 (1950).
105. Honig, D., "Principles of Sugar Technology," Vol. 2, Amsterdam, Elsevier Publishing Co., 1959.

106. Honigmann, B.
(a) "Gleichgewichts und Wachstumsformen von Kristalle" Darmstadt, Steinkopt, 1958.
(b) *Z. Electrochem.*, **58,** 322 (1954).
107. Hudson, C. S., *J. Am. Chem. Soc.*, **26,** 1065 (1904).
108. Hudson, L. K., Private communication.
109. Humprey, W. J., "Rain Making and Other Weather Vagaries," Baltimore, 1926.
110. Hungerford, E. H., and Nees, A. R., *Ind. Eng. Chem.*, **26,** 462 (1934).
111. Ievins, A., and Osis, F., *Latvijas Valst. Univ. Kim. Fiz.*, **9,** 3 (1956); *C.A.*, **53,** 10905.
112. *Industrial Diamond Abstracts*, Industrial Diamond Information Bureau, London ECI.
113. Jeremiassen, F., and Svanoe, H., *Chem. and Met. Eng.*, **39,** #11 (1932).
114. Jono, W., Watanabe, T., and Ashida, M., *Koggo Zasshi*, **60,** 515 (1957); *C.A.*, **53,** 7707.
115. Kamewador, M., *Demkurr. Koggo Gakbaiski*, **2,** 21 (1954); **3,** 163 (1955/6); *C.A.*, **51,** 13427.
116. Kaufmann, D. W., "Sodium Chloride," New York, Reinhold Publishing Co., 1960.
117. Keepin, G. R., *J. Appl. Phys.*, **21,** 260 (1950).
118. Kennedy, J. D., *Am. Machinist*, **103,** 147 (1959).
119. Kerr, P. F., and Armstrong, E., *Bull. Geol. Soc. Amer.*, **54,** Supp. 1, 1 (1943).
120. Kersey, R. J., M.S. thesis. College of the Holy Cross (1959).
121. Khailenko, L. V., *Doklady Akad. Nauk. SSSR*, **115,** 1135 (1957).
122. Kingery, W. D., *J. Appl. Phys.*, **26,** 1203 (1955); **31,** 833–38 (1960).
123. Kirijama, R., *Kogja Kagaku Zasshi.*, **59,** 1231 (1956); *C.A.*, **52,** 15177.
124. Kirk, R. E., and Othmer, D., "Encyclopedia of Chemical Technology," Vol. 12, New York, Interscience Co., 1954.
125. Kistler, S., "Annual Review of Physical Chemistry," p. 40, Palo Alto, Cal., 1958.
126. Kittel, C., "Introduction to Solid State Physics," New York, John Wiley & Sons, 1953.
127. Koenig, J., "Methods of Producing Single Crystals of Nonmetallic Ferromagnetic Substances," Final Report, Contract A.F. -19-(609)-867 (1955).
128. Kohman, G. T., "Synthesis of Quartz and Crystal," Final Report, No. 242 74 D, Signal Corps' Project No. 142-B (1955); U. S. Pat. #2,895,812 (July 21, 1959).
129. Kopelman, B., and Gregg, C. C., *J. Phys. Chem.*, **55,** 557 (1951).
130. Krammer, H. P., and Rigby, M., *Meterolog. abstr.*, **1,** 174–205 (1950), *C.A.*, **46,** 9352.
131. Kraus, E. B., and Squires, P., *Nature*, **159,** 489 (1947).
132. Kremers, H. C., *Ind. Eng. Chem.*, **32,** 1478 (1940).
133. Kucharenko, J. A., *Planter Sugar Mfg.*, **53,** No. 19; **54,** No. 4 (1928).
134. Kuzcynski, G. C., "Kinetics of High Temperature Processes," New York, John Wiley & Sons, 1959.
135. Landt, E., *Central. Zuckerind.*, **44,** 910 (1935).
136. Langmuir, I., *Proc. Am. Phil. Soc.*, **92,** 168 (1948); *J. Meteorology*, **5,** 175 (1948).
137. Laudise, R. A., *J. Am. Chem. Soc.*, **80,** 2655 (1958); **81,** 562 (1959); A-45, p. 458.
138. Lebedev, N. V., Lubin, B. O., and Khai, D. M., *Zhur. Kirklad. Khim*, **23,** 739 (1950); *C.A.*, **48,** 9148.
139. Leontjewa, A., *Acta Physicochem. USSR*, **13,** 423 (1940); **16,** 97 (1942); *C.A.*, **54,** 20397.

140. Liander, H., *Am. Soc. Elect. Engr. J.*, **28,** 97 (1955); *Science*, **121,** 721 (1955).
141. Li Ch'iao-P'ing, "The Chemical Arts of Old China," Easton, Pa., Chemical Education Pbulications, 1951.
142. Lijempt, N. V., Ger. Pat. 929,600 (June 30, 1955).
143. Luyet, B. J., and Gehenio, P. M., "Life and Death at Low Temperatures," Normandy, Mo., Biodynamica, 1940.
144. Makower, B., and Dye, W. B., *Agr. and Food Chem.*, **4,** 72 (1956).
145. Malone, T. F., "Compendium of Meteorology," Boston, Mass., Am. Meteorol. Soc., 1951.
146. Mandelkern, L., *Chem. Rev.*, **56,** 903 (1956).
147. Marcic, S., and Markovic, I., *Z. anorg. Chem.*, **276,** 193 (1954).
148. Mason, B. J.
(a) *Nature*, **175,** 448 (1955); **181,** 382 (1958).
(b) Mason, B. J., and Ludlam, F. H., *Quart. J. R. met. Soc.*, **76,** 52 (1950).
(c) *Proc. Roy. Soc. (London)*, **A247,** 421 (1958).
(d) Sci. Monthly, **204,** 120 (1961).
149. Maurer, R. D., *J. Appl. Phys.*, **29,** 1 (1958).
150. McCartney, E. R., *J. Coll. Sci.*, **13,** 383 (1958).
151. McGinnis, Moore, S., and Alston, P. W., *Ind. Eng. Chem.*, **34,** 171 (1942).
152. Meade, G. P., A.C.S. meeting, Boston, 1959.
153. Mehl, R. F., "Growth of Metal Crystals," New York, Am. Inst. Min. Met. Engrs., 1951.
Mehl, R. F., with Johnson, W. A., *Trans. Am. Inst. Min. Met. Engrs.*, **135,** 416 (1939).
Mehl, R. F., with Anderson, W. A., *Ibid*, **161,** 140 (1945).
154. Melik-Gaikazgan, I. Ya., and Ermolaev, V. A., *Izvest. Vysshikh. Ucheb. Zavedeni. Fiz.*, **5,** 141 (1958).
155. Mellor, J. B., "Comprehensive Treatise on Inorganic and Theoretical Chemistry," New York, Longmans-Green Co., 1924.
156. Meryman, H. T., *Science*, **124,** 515 (1956), *Annals N. Y. Acad. Sci.*, **85,** #2, 501–735 (1960).
157. Meyers, D. M., and Bonython, C. W., *J. Appl. Chem.*, **8,** 219 (1958).
158. Michel, H., "Die Kunstliche Edelsteine," Leipzig, W. Diebener, 1926.
159. Miller, D. G., *J. Chem. Phys.*, **63,** 270 (1959).
160. Mokievskii, V. A., *Kristallgratiya*, **4,** 3 (1955).
161. Moller, C., *Int. Sugar, J.*, **49,** 182 (1947).
162. Monnickendam, A., "The Magic of Diamonds," 191 pp., London, Hammond, Hammond and Co., 1955.
163. Moriyama, T., and Yawataya, T., *Repts. Res. Lab. Asaki*, **4,** 42 (1954); *C.A.*, **50,** 4577.
164. Mosebach, R., *Sprechaal*, **90,** 247, 297 (1957).
165. Mossop, S. C., *Proc. Phys. Soc.*, **68B,** 193 (1955); **69B,** 165 (1956).
166. Mott, N. F., "Atomic Structure and the Strength of Materials," London, Pergamon Press, 1956.
167. Nacken, R., *Chem. Ztg.*, **74,** 745 (1950); *C.A.*, **45,** 411.
168. Nakhamanovich, M. I., Lyubin, B. O., and Khai, D. M., *J. Appl. Chem. USSR*, **23,** 1409 (1950); *C.A.*, **46,** 6417, 8399.
169. Neels, H., *Freiberger Forsch.*, **A123,** 119 (1959); *C.A.*, **54,** 7320.
170. Nees, A. R., and Hungerford, E. H., *Ind. Eng. Chem.*, **28,** 893 (1936).

171. Neuhaus, A.,
(a) *Angw. Chem.*, **66,** 532 (1954); 507 (Dec. 1954).
(b) *Angw. Chem.*, **69,** 551 (1955).
(c) *Chem. Ing. Technik.*, **155,** 300, 350 (1956).
172. Newkirk, W. B., *Ind. Eng. Chem.*, **16,** 1173 (1924), **31,** 18 (1939); U. S. Pat. 1,471,347 (Oct. 23, 1923); 1,508,569 (Sept. 16, 1924); 1,521,830 (Jan. 6, 1925); 1,571,212 (Feb. 2, 1926).
173. Nichik, M. S., *Sakhar Prom*, **27,** 19 (1953).
174. Nichols, J. B., *J. Appl. Phys.*, **25,** 840 (1954).
175. Nickerson, R. F., "Crystallinity of Cellulose," "Advances in Carbohydrate Chemistry," Vol. 5, New York, Academic Press, 1950.
176. Obukhovskii, E. A., "Production of Maltose Molasses," p. 153, Moscow, Gosudarst. Nuach. Tekh. Izdatel. Minister. Prom. Prodoval. Tovarov, 1959; *C.A.*, **54,** 23388.
177. Office of Technical Services, U. S. Dept. of Commerce, "Bibliography of Reports on Synthetic Crystals," CTR 367, 8, & 9 (Jan. 1959).
178. Ovsienka, D. E., *Akad. Nauk. Ukrain SSSR*, #4, 55 (1953); *C.A.*, **51,** 4803.
179. Palermo, J. A., Grove, C. S., Jr., and Schoen, H. M., *Ind. Eng. Chem.*, **49,** 470 (1957).
180. Palibin, P. A., and Froiman, A. I., *Z. Krist.*, **85,** 322 (1933).
181. Palmer, K. L., Dye, W. B., and Black, D., *Agr. and Food Chem.*, **1,** 72, 77 (1956).
182. Park, G. S., *Physics*, **5,** 193 (1934).
183. Parsons, W. A., and Heukelekian, H., *Ind. Eng. Chem.*, **46,** 1503 (1954).
184. Partington, J. R., "Treatise on Physical Chemistry," Vol. 3, p. 520, London, Longmans-Green Co., 1952.
185. Patti, J. J., M.S. Thesis, College of the Holy Cross, 1957.
186. Pauling, L., *Chem. Eng. News*, **24,** 1065 (1946).
187. Pernert, J. C., Private communication.
188. Perrie, D. W., "Cloud Physics," New York, John Wiley & Sons, 1951.
189. Perry, J. H., "Chemical Engineer's Handbook," New York, McGraw-Hill Book Co., 1941.
190. Pierce, J. B., *Chem. and Met.*, **44,** 718 (1937).
191. Powell, D. A., *Nature*, **178,** 428 (1956).
192. Powers, H. E. C.
(a) *Nature*, **178,** 139 (1956).
(b) *Ibid*, **188,** 289 (1960).
(c) *Int. Sugar J.*, **62,** 307 (1960).
(d) "Sucrose," London, Privately printed, 1958.
193. Pozin, M. E., and Muratova, M. I., *Zhur. Pricklad. Khem.*, **30,** 1378 (1957); *C.A.*, **52,** 3279.
194. Proskowtz, W., *Proc. Res. Soc. Japan Sugar Ref. Tech.*, **6,** 104 (1957).
195. Ramburg, R., "Origin of Metamorphic and Metasomatic Rocks," p. 317, U. Chicago Press, 1953.
196. Randall, M., and Doody, T. G., *J. Phys. Chem.*, **43,** 613 (1939).
197. Reese, K. M., and Cuniff, W. H., *Ind. Eng. Chem.*, **47,** 1672 (1955).
198. Report, *Ind. Eng. Chem.*, **44,** 1263 (1952).
199. Ridge, M. J., *Nature*, **184,** 47 (1959).
200. Robinson, S. P., U. S. Pat., #2,614,035 (Oct. 1, 1952).
201. Rogers, A., "Industrial Chemistry," 371, D. Van Nostrand Co., New York, 1942.

202. Rossini, F. D., "Chemical Thermodynamics," p. 435, New York, John Wiley & Sons, 1950.
203. Sadovgi, I. E., *J. Appl. Chem. USSR*, **26,** 875 (1953).
204. Saeman, W. C., *et al.*, *Ind. Eng. Chem.*, **44,** 1912 (1952); *Chem. Eng. Prog.*, **43,** 667 (1947); *J. Am. Inst. Chem. Eng.*, **2,** 107 (1956).
205. Saitcew, J., *Proc. 24th Conf. Asoc. Tec. Azuca Cuba*, 465 (1952).
206. Sakui, S., *Sci. Papers Inst. Phys. Chem. Res. (Tokyo)*, **34,** 1131 (1938).
207. Sangster, R. C., Maverick, E. F., and Croutch, M. L., *J. Electro. Chem. Soc.*, **104,** 317 (1957).
208. Sato, T., *J. Chem. Soc. Japan, Ind. Chem. Sect.*, **57,** 20 (1954); *C.A.*, **49,** 1412.
209. Scatchard, G., *J. Am. Chem. Soc.*, **43,** 2406 (1921).
210. Schaetter, V. J., *Chem. Rev.*, **44,** 29 (1949).
211. Schierholtz, O. S., *Can. J. Chem.*, **36,** 1057 (1958).
212. Schlichtkrull, J., *Acta Chem. Scan.*, **11,** 291 (1957); *C.A.*, **52,** 11512.
213. Schnerb, I., and Block, M. R., *Bull. Res. Council Israel*, **7A,** 179 (1958); *C.A.*, **52,** 19396.
214. Schoen, H. M., Grove, C. S., Jr., and Palermo, J. A., *J. Chem. Ed.*, **33,** 373 (1956).
215. Schrieber, G., *Wiss. Z. Humbolt Univ. Berlin*, **6,** 453 (1956/7); *C.A.*, **53,** 8756.
216. Schuur, G., "Crystallization of High Polymers," p. 82, Delft-Rubber Sticktung, 1955.
217. Sears, G. W., *J. Phys. Chem.*, **29,** 979 (1958); **30,** 1477 (1959).
218. Seitz, F., "Modern Theory of Solids," New York, McGraw-Hill Book Co., 1940.
219. Seitz, F., and Turnbull, D., "Solid State Physics," Vol. 3, New York, Academic Press, 1956.
220. Seymor, J. E., *Chemical Week*, p. 51 (Nov. 11, 1952).
221. Shaw, R. H., *Sugar J.*, **9,** 14 (1950).
222. Sheftal, N. N., *Compt. rend. Acad. Sci. URSS*, **31,** 33 (1941).
223. Sieman, A. K., in Kirk-Othmer, "Encyclopedia of Chemical Technology," Vol. 7, New York, Interscience Co., 1954.
224. Silin, P. M., "Physical Chemistry of the Sugar Industry," Moscow Pichepromizdat, 1941.
225. Simmonds, W. H. C., *Chem. Eng. Prog.*, **52,** 139 (1956).
226. Smith, A. U., "Biological Applications of Freezing and Drying," New York, Academic Press, 1954.
227. Smythe, B. M.
(a) Private communication.
(b) Proc. Xth Congress of International Soc. Sugar Cane Tech., Hawaii, 1959; D. Van Nostrand Co., 1960.
228. Snamenski, G. M., *Z. Zuckerind.*, **4,** 204 (1954).
229. Sofia, S. C., M.S. Thesis, College of the Holy Cross, 1959.
230. Spezia, G., *Acad. de Sci. de Torina*, **40,** 254 (1905); **41,** 58 (1908).
231. Sorgato, I., and Messa, F., *Ind. Sacc. Ital.*, **42,** 142 (1949).
232. Sproul, R. L., Dash, W. C., Tyler, W. W., and Moore, A. R., *Rev. Sci. Inst.*, **22,** 410 (1951).
233. Stanley, J. M., *J. Chem. Phys.*, **24,** 1279 (1956); *Ind. Eng. Chem.*, **46,** 1684 (1954).
234. Starodustev, S. V., and Timokhina, N. I., *Doklady Akad. Nauk. S.S.S.R.*, **62,** 619 (1948); *C.A.*, **43,** 1622.
235. Stober, F., *Z. Krist.*, **61,** 299 (1925).

236. Stookey, S. D.
(a) *J. Am. Ceram. Soc.*, **32,** 246 (1949); *Ind. Eng. Chem.*, **41,** 856 (1949); **45,** 115 (1953); **51,** 805 (1959).
(b) in Kingery's, "Ceramic Fabrication Processes," New York, John Wiley & Sons, 1958.
237. Straumanis, M.
(a) *Z. physik. Chem.*, **26,** 246 (1934); **53B,** 320 (1943).
(b) "Keimbildung, Kristallwachstum und Katalyse," Hanb. der Katalyse, IV, Wien, Springer, 1943.
238. Strong, J., *Phys. Rev.*, **36,** 1663 (1930).
239. Stuckenbruck, L. C., M.S. Thesis, U. Iowa, 1947.
240. Sugar Reference Book and Directory, New York, 1948.
241. Sugar Technicians Inc., 10th meeting, New York, 1950.
242. Svanoe, H., *J. Chem. Ed.*, **27,** 549 (1950).
243. Symposia
(a) "Phase Transformations in Solids," New York, Cornell U., New York, 1951, John Wiley & Sons.
"Changements de Phases," Paris 1952, Union Int. de Physique, Paris, 1952.
"Mechanism of Phase Transformations in Metals," London 1955, Inst. of Metals, London, 1955.
(b) "Dislocations and Mechanical Properties of Crystals," Lake Placid, New York, 1956, John Wiley & Sons, 1957.
(c) "Theoretical Aspects of Sintering," London, April 1959.
(d) "Clouds and Precipitation," Zürich, 1954; (Summary *Nature* **174,** 987 (1954).
"Physics of Water and Ice," London, 1957 (Summary *Nature*, **181,** 382 (1958).
"Condensation Nuclei," Dublin, 1955 (Summary *Nature*, **177,** 1008 (1956).
"Physics of Atmospheric Clouds," London, 1956 (Summary *Nature*, **178,** 320 (1956).
"Nuclei of Atmospheric Condensation," Basle and Locarno 1956 (Summary *Nature*, **178,** 1275 (1956).
"Recent Developments in Cloud Physics," Glasgow, 1957 (Summary *Nature*, **180,** 573 (1957).
(e) "Life at Low Temperature," *Nature*, **182,** 911 (1958).
244. Tammann, G., "States of Aggregation," New York, D. Van Nostrand Co., 1925.
245. Tannenbaum, M., in Hannay's, "Semi-Conductors," Chap. 3, New York, Reinhold Publishing Co., 1959.
246. Taylor, J. B., and Rowinson, J. S., *Trans. Faraday Soc.*, **51,** 1183 (1955).
247. Teeple, J. F., "The Industrial Development of Searles Lake Brines," New York, Chemical Catalog Co., 1939.
248. Telkes, M., *Ind. Eng. Chem.*, **44,** 1308 (1952).
249. Thompson, H. L., Mitler, P., Johnson, R. M., McCamy, I. W., and Hoffmeister, G., *Ind. Eng. Chem.*, **42,** 2176 (1950).
250. Tikhonov, V. A., and Borgnskaya, E. P., *Nauk. Zapiski L'vov Polit. Inst.*, **23,** 47 (1955); *C.A.*, **53,** 1883.
251. Tolansky, S., and Sunagawa, I., *Nature*, **184,** 1526 (1959).
252. Tomlinson, G. H., *Pulp and Paper Mag. Can.*, **45,** 817 (1944).

253. Turcotte, C. L., Private communication.
254. Turek, J., and Koran, V., *Ital. Pat.*, 462,152 Feb. 28, 1951.
255. Turnbull, D., *Acta Met.*, **1,** 689 (1953).
256. Turrentine, J. W., "Potash in America," New York, Reinhold Publishing Corp., 1943.
257. U. S. Bureau of Mines Yearbook, 1957.
258. Vahl, L., Private communication.
259. Vand, V., *J. Phys. Chem.*, **52,** 277 (1948).
260. Van Hook, *et al.*
(a) *Int. Sugar J.*, **61,** 167 (1959).
Proc. Xth Congr. Int. Sugar Cane Tech., Hawaii, 1959; D. Van Nostrand Co., 1960.
(b) *Ind. Eng. Chem.*, **40,** 85 (1948).
(c) *Ind. Sacc. Ital.*, **61,** 227 (1958).
(d) *Sugar J.* (Jan. 1952).
261. van't Hoff, J., "Zur Bildung der Ozeanischen Sabzblagerungen," Braunschweig, 1905.
262. Veksler, B. A., and Kravchenko, S. F., "Production of Molasses and Crystalline Glucose," p. 96, Morcow, Gosudarst, Nauch. Tekh. Izadatel. Minister. Prom. Prodoval. Torarov, 1960; *C.A.*, **54,** 2388, 16997.
263. Vener, R. F., and Thompson, A. R., *Ind. Eng. Chem.*, **42,** 171 (1950).
264. Verma, G. S., *J. Phys. Chem.*, **28,** 985 (1958).
265. Vesely, V., *Listy Cukrovar*, **74,** 159 (1958).
266. Volmer, M., and Schultze, W., *Z. Physik. Chem.*, **156,** 1 (1931).
267. Vonnegut, B., *Chem. Rev.*, **44,** 277 (1949).
268. Vrbaski, T., Ivekovic, H., and Pavlovic, *Can. J. Chem.*, **36,** 1410 (1958).
269. Waggaman, W. H., "Phosphoric Acid, Phosphates, and Fertilizers," p. 231, New York, Reinhold Publishing Corp., 1952.
270. Walker, A. C.
(a) *Ind. Eng. Chem.*, **42,** 1369 (1950); **46,** 1670 (1954).
J. Frank Inst., **250,** 481 (1950).
(b) *Bell Lab. Record*, **23,** 357 (1947).
(c) Private communication.
271. Waller, G., *Ind. Eng. Chem.*, **44,** 1328 (1952).
272. Waterman, H. L., and Gentil, A. J., *Chem. Weekblad.*, **23,** 345 (1926).
273. Webb, W. W., Dragsdorf, and Forgegs, W. D., *Phys. Rev.*, **108,** 498 (1957).
274. Webster, R., *Gemmologist*, **21,** 117 (1952); **27,** 124 (1958).
275. Wedepohl, H., *Kosmos*, **47,** 545 (1951).
276. Weichman, H. J., and Smith, W. J., "The Artificial Stimulation of Rain," p. 427, New York, Pergamon Press, 1957.
277. Weiser, H. B., *J. Phys. Chem.*, **36,** 1 (1932).
278. Werkspoor, N. V., Amsterdam
(a) Prospectus #78, p. 12, 1939.
(b) German Pat., 737,280, June 3, 1943.
Dutch Pat., 62,553, Feb. 15, 1949.
U. S. Pat., 2,587,293, Feb. 26, 1952.
279. West, P. W., *Chem. and Eng. News*, **22,** 717 (1944).
280. Weyl, W. A., *Econ. Geol.*, **48,** 288 (1959).
281. Whetstone, J., *Ind. Eng. Chem.*, **44,** 2663 (1952).

282. Whittier, E. O., and Gould, S. P., *Ind. Eng. Chem.*, **23,** 670 (1931).
283. Wilcox, N. G., *Sci. Monthly*, **70,** 157 (1950).
284. Willaime, French Pat., 621,797, Mar. 6, 1946.
285. Wise, W. S., *Int. Sugar J.*, **58,** 329 (1956).
286. Wood, L. A., and Bekhedahl, N., *J. Res. Nat'l. Bur. Standards*, **36,** 489 (1946).
287. Wooster, N., *et al.*, *Nature,* **167,** 940 (1951); *Mineral. Mag.*, **29,** 858 (1952); **157,** 247 (1946); A-37, p. 341.
288. World Meteorological Organization, "Artificial Control of Clouds and Hydrometeors," Tech. Note #13, 1955.
289. Young, F. E., and Jones, F. T., *J. Phys. Chem.*, **53,** 1334 (1949).
290. Zagrodski, S., *Wiadomosci Chem.*, **4,** (1942), 184 (1959).
291. Zapffe, O. A., and Worden, C. O., *Acta Cryst.*, **2,** 377 (1949).
292. Zerfoss, S., *Ceramic Age*, **56,** 20 (1950).
293. Zimonyi, G., *Acta Phys. Acad. Sci. Hung.*, **8,** 119 (1957).

APPENDIX

GENERAL REFERENCES ON CRYSTALLIZATION

Books

A-1 Buckley, H. E., "Crystal Growth," N. Y., John Wiley & Sons, 1951.

A-2 Cabrera, N., "Theory of Crystal Growth," "Solid State Physics," New York, Academic Press (to be published).

A-3 DeKeyser, W., and Amelinckx, S., "Les Dislocations et la Croissance des Cristaux," Paris, Masson et Cie, 1955.

A-4 Frenkel, J., "Kinetic Theory of Liquids," Oxford Press, 1946.

A-5 Holden, Alan and Singer, Phylis, "Crystals and Crystal Growing," Garden City, New York, Doubleday and Company, 1960.

A-6 Johnsen, A., "Wachstum und Auflosung der Kristalle," 27 p., Leipzig, 1910.

A-7 Kossel, W., "Die molekularen Vorgange beim Kristallwachstum," Leipzig, Hirzel, 1928. Summary in *Die Chemie*, **56,** 33–41 (1943).

A-8 Kutznetzov, V. D., "Crystals and Crystallization," (in Russian), 640 pp., 1953.

A-9 Landau, L. D. and Lifshitz, E. M., "Statistical Physics," Oxford Press, 1938.

A-10 Lawson, W. D., and Nielson, S., "Preparation of Single Crystals," New York, Academic Press, 1958.

A-11 Matz, G., "Die Kristallisation in der Verfahrenstechnik," Berlin, Springer, 1954.

A-12 Schoen, H. M., "Crystallization; The Unit Operation," Univ. Microfilm #20829, 243 pp., 1957, Ann Arbor, Michigan.

A-13 Schubnikov, A. V., "Crystals in Science and Technology," (in Russian), Izoguo Akad. Nauk. 48 pp., 1956.

A-14 Spangenberg, K., "Wachstum und Auflosen der Kristalle," Handb. der Naturwiss., X, 362 (1934), Jena, Fischer.

A-15 Straumanis, M., "Keimbildung, Kristallwachstum, und Katalysis," Handb. der Katalyze, Vol. IV, Heterogene Katalyze, Springer Verlag Wien, 1943.

A-16 Tertsch, H., "Trachten der Kristalle," Berlin, Springer, 1926.

A-17 Verma, A. R., "Crystal Growth and Dislocations," New York, Academic Press, 1953.

A-18 Volmer, M., "Kinetik der Phasenbildung," Dresden, Steinkopf, 1939.

Mullin, J. W., "Crystallizatun", Washington; D. C., Butterworth Inc., 1961.

Reviews

A-19 *Annual Reports, Chemical Society, London.*

Wells, A. F., 43, 62 (1946); also Chap. VII in Gomer, R. and Smith, C. S., "Properties of Solid Surfaces," U. Chicago Press, 1953.

Robertson, J. H., **49,** 343 (1952).

Tompkins, F. C., and Young, D. A., **50,** 70 (1953).

A-20 Annual Chemical Engineering Reviews—Crystallization, *Chem. and Process Eng.* (U.K).,

Bamforth, A. W., **30,** 258 (1949); **37,** 221 (1956); **38,** 324 (1957).

A-21 Annual Unit Operations Reviews—Crystallization. *Ind. Eng. Chem.*, McCabe, W. L., **38,** 18 (1946).
Grove, C. S., Jr., *et al.*, 1948 and on. Latest **52,** 173 (1960), **53,** 155 (1961).

A-22 Bennett, F. G.—"Crystal Growth; Comprehensive Bibliography," 1951–57. O.T.S., U. S. Dept. Commerce NAA-SR-2696 (1958).

A-23 Bradley, R. S., Nucleation in Phase Changes, *Quart. Rev.* (*London*) **V,** No. 4, 315–43 (1951); *J. Coll. Sci.*, **15,** 525 (1960).

A-24 Knacke, O., and Stranski, I. N., Die Theorie des Kristallwachstums, *Erg. Exakt. Naturw.*, **26,** 383–427 (1952).

A-25 Kossel, D., Crystals and Crystal Growth, *Naturorsch. u. Med. Deutschland*, **8,** No. 1, 15–42 (1947).

A-26 Leclerc, E., La Cristallisation Principes et Applications Industrielles. *Rev. Univ. des Mines*, **19,** No. 3, 12 pp., (1943).

A-27 Matthias, B. A., Solution and Crystallization; *Chem. Ztg.*, **65,** 92–5 (1941).

A-28 Matz, G., Kristallisatoren, *Chem. Ing. Tech.*, **27,** 18–22 (1955).

A-29 Neuhaus, A., Methoden und Ergebnisse der Modernen Einkristall-Zuchtung. *Chem. Ing. Tech.*, **28,** 155, 350 (1956).

A-30 Niggli, P., Growth of Crystals, *Vierteljahrsch. naturforsch. Ges. Zurich*, **97,** No. 3, 5–35 (1952).

A-31 Rideal, E., How Crystals Grow, *Nature*, **164,** 303 (1949).

A-32 Seifert, H., Das Problem der Kristalltracht und seine technische Bedeutung. *Chem. Ing. Tech.*, **27,** 135–42 (1955).

A-33 Short, M. A., Methods of Growing Crystals, *Ind. Chemist*, **33,** 3–8 (1957).

A-34 Thomson, G. P., Growth of Crystals, *Proc. Phys. Soc.*, **61,** 403–16 (1948).

A-35 Waeser, B., Progress in Heavy-chemical Plant Apparatus. VIII, Solution and Crystallization. *Chem. Tech.*, 17, 52 (1944); *C.A.*, **40,** 3941, 5605.

A-36 Wilke, K. Th., Crystal Growing since 1945. *Fortschr. Min.*, **34,** 85–150 (1956).

Symposia

A-37 The Faraday Society symposium on Crystal Growth at Bristol in 1949, Disc. No. 5.

A-38 The American Chemical Society symposium on Nucleation Phenomena, Chicago, 1951. *Ind. Eng. Chem.*, **44,** No. 6, 1269–1338 (1952).

A-39 Conference on Interfacial Tension and Nucleation in 1951 at Boston University. *Geophysical Research Paper* No. 37, 3 vol., (1955). Air Force Research Center, Cambridge, Mass.

A-40 Deutschen Bunsen Gesellschaft meeting on Crystal Surfaces, Berlin, 1952. *Zeit. Electrochem.*, **56,** No. 4, 263–428 (1952).

A-41 The First Conference on Crystal Growth of the Institute of Crystallography, Academy of Sciences USSR, 1956. 43 of the 83 papers presented are available in Vol. I, (1958) of *Growth of Crystals* by A. V. Shubnikov and N. N. Sheftal; while subsequent significant research is printed in Vol. II. (1959). Both are available from Consultants Bureau, Inc., 227 W 17 St., New York.

A-42 A section in Crystal Growth was included in the program of the 4th International Congress of the International Union of Crystallographers, Montreal, Canada, 1957.

A-43 Crystallization Division, Society of German Engineers, 1957, *Chem. Ing. Tech.*, **29,** 539 (1957).

A-44 The American Chemical Society and American Institute of Chemical Engineers held symposia on Crystal Growth at their fall meetings in 1958.

A-45 "Growth and Perfection of Crystals," International Conference on Crystal Growth, Edited by Doremus, R. D., Roberts, B. W., and Turnbull, D., Cooperstown, New York (1958), John Wiley & Sons, New York, 1958.

A-46 "Physical Chemistry of Aerosols," Faraday Society, Bristol, 1959. Summarized in *Nature*, **188,** 630 (1960).

AUTHOR INDEX

SUBJECT INDEX